Industrial Biotechnology:
A Training Manual

Moorpark College

May 2001

Sponsored by:
Amgen and The National Science Foundation

This project was supported, in part,
by the
National Science Foundation
Opinions expressed are those of the authors
and not necessarily those of the Foundation

CENGAGE
Learning™

Australia • Brazil • Japan • Korea • Mexico • Singapore • Spain • United Kingdom • United States

CENGAGE
Learning™

Industrial Biotechnology:
A Training Manual
Moorpark College
May 2001

Sponsored by:
Amgen and the National Science Foundation

Executive Editors:
 Michele Baird

 Maureen Staudt

 Michael Stranz

Project Development Manager:
 Linda deStefano

Senior Marketing Coordinators:
 Sara Mercurio

 Lindsay Shapiro

Production/Manufacturing Manager:
 Donna M. Brown

PreMedia Services Supervisor:
 Rebecca A. Walker

Rights & Permissions Specialist:
 Kalina Hintz

Cover Image:
 Getty Images*

For product information and technology assistance, contact us at
Cengage Learning Customer & Sales Support, 1-800-354-9706

For permission to use material from this text or product,
submit all requests online at **cengage.com/permissions**
Further permissions questions can be emailed to
permissionrequest@cengage.com

Library of Congress Control Number: 0000000000

ISBN-13: 978-0-7593-0514-4

ISBN-10: 0-7593-0514-5

Cengage Learning
5191 Natorp Boulevard
Mason, Ohio 45040
USA

Cengage Learning is a leading provider of customized learning solutions with office locations around the globe, including Singapore, the United Kingdom, Australia, Mexico, Brazil, and Japan. Locate your local office at:
international.cengage.com/region

Cengage Learning products are represented in Canada by Nelson Education, Ltd.

For your lifelong learning solutions, visit **custom.cengage.com**

Visit our corporate website at **cengage.com**

Printed in the United States of America

Acknowledgements

This training manual has been a cooperative effort that has benefited from the talents and expertise of a number of individuals. We would like to thank the Moorpark College Industrial Biotechnology Advisory Board for their initial guidance and support in determining the format and content of this manual. Numerous industry scientists volunteered to write chapters of this manual. We extend a tremendous thank you to all of them for their time and energy in providing a valuable resource to our students. The Operations Training Group at Amgen generously provided training documents that were written by their staff. The Amgen Manufacturing Team responsible for writing and assembling these documents are Laura Aguilera, Louise Perry and Todd Neslund. We would like to extend our sincere thanks to these individuals and also to Elisabeth Kaszas and Subhash Karkare for their assistance in providing these documents. We would also like to thank Hilda Ruiz, Daniel Nadalet, and Claudia Morgado for the clerical assistance they provided and Patti Ross, Kathryn Courtney, Linnea Fletcher, and Robert Bettis for critical reading of the manuscript.

Marie Panec
Maureen Harrigan

May 2001

Foreword

Many people have suggested over the last few years that we document the history of the design and development of the Biotechnology Program at Moorpark College. For we were told that the development of the project has valuable lessons and examples that would benefit others involved in similar undertakings. With this in mind, I will describe the impetus for creating the program, the development of the curriculum, and the unprecedented role of industry in this process.

In 1994, individuals from Baxter Healthcare Corporation's new production facility for Factor VIII approached Moorpark College with the idea for a Biotechnology Training program. The idea met with great enthusiasm at the College, however a new faculty member was needed to lead this project. I was hired in the fall of 1996 and with Floyd Martin, the Dean of Life/Physical Sciences, we began to assemble an Advisory Board. Eight department heads from Baxter volunteered to sit on the Board and were joined by numerous scientists from Amgen. In retrospect, the exceptional quality of our Biotechnology Program can be attributed to the blank slate we presented to the industry members of our Advisory Board. We presented them the opportunity to design and write our curriculum. They were incredulous, excited, and thrilled with the task. From the college catalog they selected existing mathematics, biology, chemistry, and computer courses for the core curriculum. At the same time, there were lengthy discussions about the biotechnology component of this program. All members of the Board agreed they wanted to design a "world-class" program that would give students an opportunity to experience the biotechnology workplace within a college setting. They agreed students should learn the skills, techniques, and information that is usually acquired only through on-the-job training. All believed that such a student would make an invaluable employee and decrease the time required for training within industry. The Biotechnology courses were designed so students are educated in all aspects of the industry with an emphasis on biomanufacturing. Students learn basic laboratory skills, equipment use, and an overview of biotechnology in an Introduction to Biotechnology course. Included in this course are such topics as Solution/Buffer Preparation, Safety, Documentation, Spectrophotometry, Centrifugation, Molecular Biology, Immunochemistry, Protein Purification and Analysis, and selected topics in Biotechnology. During the second semester of study, students take eight biomanufacturing modules, designed so the student experiences all of the operations within a biotechnology facility. The modules are Plant Design, Process Support, Cell Culture and Microbial Fermentation, Recovery and Purification, Formulation/Fill and Packaging, Environmental Monitoring, QC: Analytical Methods, and Validation. Each of the topics and laboratory activities for these modules were selected and designed by subject matter specialists within Amgen, Baxter, Millipore, and Flow Components. The content of these courses truly reflects what occurs within industry.

With the curriculum development well underway, the Advisory Board began to focus on the specific requirements for implementing this novel curriculum.

At one Advisory Board meeting an equipment list filled the white board. The discussion began about the cost of this enormous list, and then moved on to the more important question of where we would house all of the equipment. Robert Peyton, the academic planner for the newest campus of the California State University System was participating in our Advisory Board Meetings. It was his visionary suggestion and the generosity of the university that led to an 8,000 square feet Moorpark College Biotechnology Training Facility on the campus of California State University, Channel Islands. The industry involvement in both designing and equipping this facility were invaluable. The majority of the equipment, labware, and supplies were donated by Amgen and Baxter. In addition, the facility was set up to duplicate some of the industrial components of a biotechnology facility. The entrance is through a gowning room which leads to cell culture labs, purification areas, a QC lab, buffer/media prep and glassware wash and storage.

The industry involvement in the implementation of this biotechnology program extends beyond curriculum development and extensive donations. The biomanufacturing modules are all taught by industry volunteers. The vision for this program was that students to learn the concepts, skills, and hands-on techniques the same way it is done in the workplace. Therefore, students are taught by experts who have working knowledge of the topic and skills they are teaching. Approximately fifty industry scientists from eleven companies participate in the instruction of this program. The training is current, effective, and relevant. This is reflected in the 100% placement of students the program has experienced to date.

A grant from the National Science Foundation has enabled us to address the dearth of instructional materials suitable for use in a Biotechnology Program with a focus on manufacturing. This training manual is a result of a combined effort from many different participants. Our Advisory Board helped shape the content and format. The Operations Training Group at Amgen has been a mutual resource in sharing instructional materials and in providing many of the chapters in this manual. Many of the topics in this manual are written by the industry instructors in our program, again demonstrating the generosity and commitment of these individuals. I would like to thank all of them for their ongoing efforts and support of this project, for it is with their involvement and assistance that we continue to provide outstanding educational opportunities to our students.

Finally I would like to extend my sincere gratitude and appreciation to those individuals who were instrumental in launching the Biotechnology Program at Moorpark College. These are the individuals with the vision: Ernie Bognar, Robert Bettis, Lisa Severy, Mike Winter, Les Vincent, Saroj Angal, Mershid Alai, Adi Mohanty, Yong-Jick Kim, Bryan Kurata, Elisabeth Kaszas, Amnon Eylath and Mary Ackermann. They have indeed been successful in developing that "world class" program.

Maureen Harrigan, Ph.D.
May 2001

Table of Contents

Table of Contents

Table of Contents

Good Documentation Practices

Overview

Introduction

In a Good Manufacturing Practices (GMP) facility numerous types of documentation exist and serve a variety of functions. Examples of the functions of documentation include: providing a record of what was done, instructing an individual on how to perform tasks, defining specifications, ensuring traceability, and providing evidence that a product was made according to requirements. This document provides a conceptual overview of the minimum standards required when completing current Good Manufacturing Practices (cGMP) documentation.

Table of Contents

This document contains the following topics:

Good Documentation Practices

Objectives

1. Discuss a minimum of six specific functions of documentation.
2. Describe eight different types of laboratory documentation.
3. Explain the purpose of keeping a laboratory notebook.
4. Distinguish between an SOP and a protocol.
5. Describe the types of documentation that could be recorded in logbooks.
6. Discuss the use of labels in a manufacturing facility.
7. Describe the content of a laboratory label.
8. Demonstrate ability to design labels for specific uses.
9. Discuss the use of each of the following in the documentation of production for a biotechnology product: master batch record, batch record, SOPs, labels, forms and logs, training records, numbering system and product release certificate.
10. Explain Good Documentation Practices.
11. Explain the rules for writing in cGMP documents.
12. Explain the proper method for recording time in a cGMP document.
13. Explain the proper way to make corrections.
14. Discuss the correct handling of raw data.
15. Explain the practice of verification signatures.
16. Explain the use of SOPs and master batch records.
17. Describe the guidelines for entries in laboratory notebooks.
18. Describe the components of an SOP.
19. Demonstrate ability to write an SOP.
20. Explain potential SOP problems.
21. Describe the essential components of a batch record.
22. Explain what a deviation is and the necessary actions required.
23. Explain what an investigation is and the objectives involved.
24. Explain when an investigation is conducted.
25. Explain why an investigation is documented.

Background

Why Document?
The rules set forth in this document should apply to all personnel in a biotechnology company involved in the holding, transportation, manufacture, testing, support, or packaging of clinical and commercial drugs, whether temporary or regular staff. Biotechnology companies are regulated by the Food and Drug Administration as well as by foreign regulatory agencies. Strict documentation rules are set to ensure compliance with all regulatory agencies. By placing your signature on a cGMP document, you have proven that you have completed a step in the view of the FDA. cGMP documents and records include, but are not limited to the following: Standard Operating Procedures (SOPs), Manufacturing Procedures (MPs), Specifications, Analytical Methods, Validation Documents, Batch Records, Product and Sample Labels. All cGMP documents may be reviewed by the FDA or other regulatory agencies.

Documentation Rules

Do
When writing in cGMP documents do:
- Use only black, indelible, ball-point ink
- Make all entries legible (readable)
- Initial and date all entries (unless a signature is required)
- Document each step before moving to the next
- N/A, initial, and date spaces if it is not appropriate to fill them in
- Record numbers less than one with a zero before the decimal point

Do Not
When writing in cGMP documents do not:
- Overwrite
- Use liquid correction fluid
- Backdate
- Record data before the action or event has occurred
- Use ditto marks
- Leave required data spaces blank
- Approve, verify, or review your own performance

Documentation Rules

Initial / Date

All entries to a cGMP document must be accompanied by the identity of the person (initials or signature) and the date that the entry was made. This is required by the Code of Federal Regulations (CFRs) and serves as a tracking method to determine that a task was indeed performed and who did the work.

Initials are the accepted standard method of identification. However, some operations require a signature. For example, an "Approved By" space must be filled with a signature, not initials.

Recording Time

Military time: two (2) digits to indicate the hour (00 to 23) followed by two (2) digits to indicate the minutes (00 to 59).
    Example: 0850
                 1750

Meridian time: One or two digits to indicate the hour (1 to 12) followed by two digits to indicate the minutes (00 to 59), then the morning (AM) or afternoon (PM) designation.
    Example: 8:50 AM
                 5:50 PM

Note: Either method mentioned above is acceptable for recording time.

Corrections

No handwritten changes or corrections shall be made to the printed text of an approved cGMP document. Consult with your supervisor if you discover an error. Any changes required to an approved cGMP document shall be implemented through the established quality system.

When making a correction to a manually recorded entry on a controlled document perform the following steps:
- Place a single line through the incorrect entry
- Initial and date adjacent to the cross-out
- Enter the correct data near the original entry
- The mistake must still be legible through the cross-out.
- Date of correction is the date the correction was made, not the date the error was made

Continued on next page

Documentation Rules

Performed By   Performance of a step must be documented at the time of completing the step and prior to moving on to the next step. Do not execute a step if the manufacturing procedure is not available for documenting necessary data at the time of execution. The following personnel may initial and date the "Performed By" space:

- Personnel already proficient in the task performed

  OR

- Personnel who are in training under the supervision of their qualified trainer

Recorded By   The "Recorded By" space is used if the operator performing the operation is unable to initial and date immediately, due to working in a confined or restricted space, such as a laminar air flow hood. This situation is the only exception to the "Performed By" rule. Data must then be recorded by another person watching the operation. The person recording data must initial and date the "Recorded By" space prior to moving on to the next step.

Verified By   Verification shall be performed prior to moving on to the next step. Operators executing a task cannot verify their own action. At least one other person must review documentation for accuracy. Personnel may initial or sign and date the "Verified By" space if:

- They witnessed that a task, operation, or procedure was performed per written instructions and accurately documented

  AND

- They are already proficient in the task performed

Deviations   If you deviate from a written procedure, you must:
- Notify your supervisor
- Document the deviation using the appropriate quality system

Missing Data   If information is not entered at the time of completing the step, the blank entry shall be marked by an asterisk or similar notation. The use of each notation is limited to one per page. Comments explaining the reason information is missing, along with the proper information (e.g., date event actually occurred), shall be documented on the same page of the record. The explanation shall be initialed and dated at the time of recording.

Continued on next page

Documentation Rules

Voiding Records

On occasion, errors are made in the execution of making an in-process material such as a buffer and all the proper documentation was completed. However, because of the error, the decision is made to scrap the material and start all over with new in-process material. The original document would need to be voided and attached to the document replacing it. The documents are voided to prevent confusion or mix-ups with the correct document. When voiding a document do the following:

- Get supervisor and Quality Assurance (QA) approval
- Write "Void" across the front of the document and include initials and date

Recreating and Rewriting Records

Recreating or rewriting records should be avoided; however, it is sometimes necessary. Supervisor and QA approval is required when recreating records. It is important to identify the recreated document as "Rewrite" and to reference the sources of the information. Records can be recreated only when:

- Record is illegible
- Incorrect form or document was used
- Record is irreparable

Rounding Off Rules

The following rules apply to rounding off:

- In a series of calculations, carry the extra digits through to the final result, then round off.
- If the digit to be removed <5, the preceding digit stays the same. For example, 1.84 rounds to 1.8.
- If the digit to be removed ≥5, the preceding digit is increased by 1. For example, 1.85 rounds to 1.9.

Glossary

Approved By	Signature of a qualified individual (supervisor or designee) indicating that the information documented is complete, accurate, and acceptable.
Backdating	Backdating is the practice of going back to a previously completed task that has not been properly initialed and dated and placing the date that the task was completed on the date line, as though filling in the date had been done in a timely fashion. This practice is <u>not allowed</u> in any cGMP document.
Batch Production Record	Collection of records associated with the manufacture of a specific lot of product.
Comment	Any written additions to a document for informational purposes. All comments must be initialed and dated by the person writing the addition and may require a verification.
Controlled Documents	Written approved documents used in association with cGMP-related activities to ensure compliance with U.S. and international regulations, as well as Amgen standards.
Cross-out	A cross-out indicates a correction has been made. This is accomplished by drawing a single straight ink line through information which has been entered inadvertently or incorrectly. All cross-outs must be initialed and dated.
Data	The values and information generated by processing, calculating or transcribing from the raw data. This may include computer printouts.
Date	The date is the actual day on which information is entered or printed on a document.
Document	A written or printed form which is used to furnish information or provide instructions.

Continued on next page

Glossary

Identifiers
Information that serves to identify or describe something, such as effective dates, lot number, line number, equipment number, manufacturing or task date, product description, container numbers, specification number, run number. Identifiers can usually be retrieved from another source or document.

Initials
Consist of the first letter of both the first name and the last name (surname). Use of the middle initial is optional.

NA or N/A
Abbreviation for the phrase "Not Applicable." It is used to indicate that the entering of data into a space provided is not appropriate in that particular case.

Overwriting
Overwriting refers to writing over previously recorded information to make a change. Overwriting is never allowed on any cGMP document.

Performed By
Initials or signature of the person executing an operation or task (usually the "operator" or "analyst").

Quarantine
The default status for raw materials and packaging components upon receipt from the supplier and for drug products upon completion of processing while awaiting evaluation against identified release criteria.

Raw Data
The actual information obtained from an observation, test, measurement or activity. This may include computer or instrument printouts.

Recorded By
Initials or signature of a person documenting information, results, or readings of an operation (may be the "operator").

Reviewed By
Initials or signature of the person examining a task, document or record in order to confirm its accuracy and completeness, including checking calculations.

Signature
Consists of at least the initial of the first name and the complete last name.

References

Video	Corporate Quality Concepts: cGMP Documentation Practices
Q002	Corporate Quality Policy: cGMP Documentation Practices

Documentation, Quality Systems and GMP

Laboratory

Introduction   Students will practice good documentation and cGMPs in two laboratory activities designed to introduce them to manufacturing.

Materials and Supplies

Bread	Utensils
Peanut Butter	Aluminum Foil
Jelly	Balances

Activities at a Glance   Students will work in groups to develop a company that will manufacture peanut butter sandwiches. Each group will develop the following:

Day One

Part A
1. Name of Firm
2. Quality Policy and Mission Statement
3. Organizational Chart

Part B
1. Specifications for sandwiches
2. Raw materials needed for sandwiches
3. Equipment requirements
4. Process controls

Day Two

Part A
1. Each company creates a batch record for the manufacture of their product.

Part B
1. Each group gives their batch record to another company for production of their product.
2. Each contract group manufactures the product and evaluates the batch record during the process.

Part C
1. Each group reviews the quality of their product with those who performed the manufacturing.
2. Discuss the quality of the batch record and modifications.

Facility Design and Environmental Controls

Overview

It is important for a biotechnology company to control the environment in which its products are manufactured. By keeping the temperature and pressure of the manufacturing areas constant, it is possible to avoid contamination of the product and comply with the Code of Federal Regulations (CFRs). The way a building is designed and built can also reduce the potential for contamination of the product.

The Code of Federal Regulations Subpart C-Buildings and Facilities require that manufacturing facilities meet specific guidelines for the production of drugs. The following CFR regulations are specific to Facility Design and Environmental Control:

- 211.42(a,b,c) Design and construction features
- 211.46(a,b,c) Ventilation, air filtration, air heating and cooling

Table of Contents

This document contains the following topics:

Facility Design and Environmental Controls

Objectives

1. What is a flow diagram?
2. Identify the different types of flow that need to be considered in a manufacturing plant.
3. Explain what is meant by process flow.
4. Explain what is meant by personnel flow.
5. Draw a flow diagram.
6. Explain the role of a Building Management System.
7. Describe the utilities needed to run a manufacturing plant.
8. Explain the differences between plant steam and clean steam.
9. Explain HVAC and its significance/importance to a manufacturing plant.
10. Explain the function of air handler units.
11. Describe the different parameters the HVAC system controls.
12. Explain HEPA filtration and its significance/importance to a manufacturing plant.
13. Give a definition of a cleanroom and explain its function in manufacturing.
14. Explain the room classifications for aseptic areas.
15. Describe the design of walls, ceilings, floors, and surfaces in a manufacturing facility.
16. Explain the use and importance of pressure differentials in clean areas.
17. Describe a smoke challenge and the reason for using it.
18. Describe an air lock and its function.

Facility Design

Size, Space, and Segregation

Manufacturing facilities are built to be of suitable size, construction, and location to facilitate cleaning, maintenance, and proper operations. They have adequate space for the orderly placement of equipment and materials to prevent mix-ups between different components, drug product containers, closures, labeling, in-process materials, or drug products. The flow of components, drug product containers, closures, labeling, in-process materials, and drug products through the building is also designed to prevent contamination. Operations are performed within specifically defined areas of adequate size.

Wall and Ceiling Surfaces

The CFRs require that floors, walls, and ceilings be made with smooth, hard surfaces that are easily cleanable. Surface contamination can spread through a processing area, eventually working its way into the product. Specialized epoxy paint is used on the ceilings and walls to prevent flaking and to maintain crevice-free surfaces to inhibit biological growth.

Floors

The floors in processing areas are often wet and subject to mildew and bacterial growth. The floors are sloped to promote draining and to prevent bacterial growth in wet areas. The floors are covered with a specialized aggregate epoxy coating that can be sanitized easily and will stand up to heavy traffic and heavy use of chemical cleaning agents.

Nooks and Crannies

Nooks and crannies in the production area can also trap moisture and promote bacterial growth. Molding around doors, windows, and cabinets is designed to fit tight and is caulked to prevent voids where contamination can start.

Facility Environmental Controls - Ventilation

HVAC System   The Heating Ventilating Air Conditioning (HVAC) system controls room temperature as well as other environmental parameters. The following table outlines the environmental control parameters of the HVAC system:

HVAC Control Parameter	Method of Control
Room Particulates	Air Handler Unit (AHU) pre-filters and terminal HEPA filters capture particulates
Room Differential Pressure	Air velocity/pressure and volume of air exchanges per hour
Temperature	Air supply from each zone is cooled and then re-heated with a hot water system as necessary for each zone.
Relative Humidity	Modulated steam system - based on return air humidity

Air Handlers   Adequate ventilation is provided by the air handler units. The air handlers are designed to recirculate the majority of the air and have 10% to 20% air make-up from the outside. Air is sent through ducts to each individual room. Terminal High Efficiency Particulate Arresting (HEPA) filters are mounted in the ceiling to catch particulates $\geq 0.3 \mu m$ in size. The air returns to the air handler units through air return ducts typically mounted low on the walls. Local exhaust fans serve individual equipment items such as autoclaves and glasswashers. Air handler boundaries are designed to minimize recirculation of air from different functional areas.

HEPA Filter   A HEPA filter is the basic safety barrier used in all biological safety cabinets and laminar flow clean benches. A HEPA filter consists of a thin pleated sheet of boron silicate microfibers. Corrugated aluminum separators are placed between the pleats to direct the air through the filter. A HEPA filter removes airborne particles and microorganisms. Gases pass through it freely. HEPA filters remove over 99.95% of particles 0.3 micrometers or larger in diameter. A HEPA filter typically lasts three to five years, depending on hours of operation, cleanliness of the laboratory, and type of work being performed. The annual certification of biological safety cabinets and laminar flow clean benches tests for the function status of the HEPA filters among other things.

Continued on next page

Facility Environmental Controls - Ventilation

Room Pressurization

The areas of the manufacturing facility have different room pressures. Air and particulate flow from high-pressure areas to low-pressure areas. Controlling the air differential pressure creates air flow in a direction from the most clean to the least clean area to help reduce contamination in the process areas.

Specialized Rooms-Cold and Warm

Some manufacturing processes require that certain operations be performed in rooms that require temperature ranges other than ambient temperature. Cold rooms and warm rooms are controlled in a similar way as the other rooms in the manufacturing facility, except at a narrow temperature range. Deviations from the set temperature range can have irreparable effects on the process and product. It is very important to minimize traffic through such tightly controlled rooms, because simply opening the door can cause temperature fluctuations. If the door is held open for a long time or is opened many times in a short period, the fluctuation may be large enough to cause an excursion, potentially jeopardizing production.

Building Management System

The Building Management System (BMS) is the environmental control system that records and monitors the temperature, pressure, and relative humidity in the rooms of the manufacturing facility in relation to the HVAC systems. Alarms will sound if a room's parameters go out of specification. Every effort should be made to maintain the environmental parameters of the manufacturing facility. The following is a list of things operators should be aware of in order to maintain the environmental control of the facility:

- Do not place equipment or any other items in front of the air return ducts. This will block the flow of air back to the air handler unit causing an increase in pressure. An alarm will be activated if the pressure increases past an acceptable level.
- Do not hold a door open for an extended period of time. This will cause the pressure to fluctuate depending on the classification of the area.
- Minimize opening and closing of doors to cold rooms and warm rooms. Excessive use of the doors could cause temperature fluctuations wide enough to cause an excursion, potentially jeopardizing production.

Facility Environmental Controls - Air Classification

Air Classifications

Room classifications are based on the number of 0.5μm particles allowed per cubic foot. The following table lists air classifications from least to most clean.

Air Classification	Typical Area	Standard Met
95% ASHRAE*	Office and Support areas	Filtered air
Class 100,000	Fermentation and Support areas	Less than 100,000 0.5μm particles per cubic foot - terminal HEPA filters employed
Class 10,000	Purification and Cell Culture areas	Less than 10,000 0.5μm particles per cubit foot - terminal HEPA filters employed
Class 100	Fill/Finish and Roller Bottle areas	Less than 100 0.5μm particles per cubic foot, usually achieved in a laminar flow environment - terminal HEPA filters employed

*ASHRAE: American Society of Heating, Refrigerating and Air-conditioning Engineers

Processing Areas

Processing areas have at least Class 100,000 air quality and maintain positive pressure with respect to outer support areas. The support areas operate at 95% ASHRAE or Class 100,000, as appropriate for the operation. A pressure differential exists between areas of different air classifications, as well as between adjacent processing areas within the same air classification, as appropriate.

Glossary

95% ASHRAE   Standard upheld by the American Society of Heating, Refrigerating. and Air-conditioning Engineers defined as prefiltered air with no terminal HEPA filters.

Class 100,000   Prefilters and terminal HEPA filters with a defined number of air changes per hour such that the maximum particle count is 100,000 particles/minute.

Class 10,000   Prefilters and terminal HEPA filters with a defined number of air changes per hour such that the maximum particle count is 10,000 particles/minute.

Class 100   Prefilters and terminal HEPA filters with constant laminar flow such that the maximum particle count is 100 particles/minute.

HEPA Filters   High Efficiency Particulate Arresting filters are designed to remove 99.95 percent of all particles $\geq 0.3\mu m$ in size. This reduces the number of airborne particles in the processing area and lessens the chance for contamination. HEPA filters need to be certified and maintained on a regular basis.

Reference

Hutton, Robert   <u>Amgen Colorado Longmont Project Update</u> 1998.

Facility Design

Laboratory

Introduction

The purpose of this exercise is to familiarize students with the basic concepts involved in the layout and design of a biomanufacturing facility.

Materials and Supplies

Clip boards
Pens
Paper
Rulers

Activities at a Glance

1. Students will make a block drawing of the laboratory facilities.

2. Using the block diagram, students must establish flows (using arrows) for the following:
   a. Process
   b. Personnel
   c. Environment

3. For all of the flows outlined in step 2, students should provide their reasoning and justifications.

4. Students will assign room classifications to all areas of the facility, providing reasoning and justifications.

Facility Design: A Case Study

Overview

Introduction   The Bulk Commercial Manufacturing facility for a major biopharmaceutical product provides an example of the layout used to segregate the different phases in the production of a therapeutic protein. An overview of the operational areas, process support, access, safety, and flows for personnel, product, and material are provided.

Table of Contents   This document contains the following topics:

Background

Building 6	Building 6, a Bulk Commercial Manufacturing facility, provides the first three levels of the commercial manufacture of a therapeutic protein: Cell Culture, Purification, and Formulation. It is approximately 21,000 square feet in size and consists of eight operational areas which are organized with respect to production and functional responsibilities: Inoculum Preparation, Cell Culture Production, Purification, Formulation/Fill, Material Handling, Utility and Maintenance, Administrative and Laboratory, and General Access Areas. Approximately 12,000 square feet are dedicated to processing areas, while clean utilities, shipping/receiving, and general support occupy the remaining area of the plant.
Facility Design	The design basis for B6 provides for segregation of the significant phases of manufacturing. Manufacturing areas, where product is handled, are provided with HEPA filtered air at Class 10,000. Passageways and nonproduct handling areas are supplied with Class 100,000 air. There are various Class 100 hoods scattered throughout the plant dedicated to specific process areas. Two of these areas require additional gowning and therefore are accessed through separate gowning suites.
Inoculum Preparation	The B6 Cell Culture Inoculation area is accessed through an airlock. The recombinant cell line for production is stored and cultivated here for scale-up in production.

- The preparation of sterile media for the Inoculation Area occurs in the media prep room. It contains a Class 100 hood for dispensing the prepared media into bottles for storage.
- Frozen ampules of Chinese Hamster Ovary (CHO) cells are thawed and cultured in the inoculation room. This room contains two Class 100 hoods to provide an aseptic environment while handling the cell cultures.
- Primary and secondary cell cultures are incubated in an area adjacent to the inoculation room. This room contains roller racks for attached cultures and spinner plates for suspension cultures.
- Raw materials for the Inoculum and Cell Culture Areas are stored in cold rooms. Contained in there cold rooms is a locked, segregated area for storage of the Master Working Cell Bank (MWCB).
- Suspended cultures of CHO cells are sent to the fermentor room and are then inoculated into any of three 450-Liter Biolafitte fermentors. These cell cultures are then sent to the Cell Culture Area for roller bottle processing.

Operational Areas

Cell Culture   The production of the protein in roller bottles is performed in Cell Culture and consists of the following areas: sterile media preparation, roller bottle handling and storage, media harvest, and an in-process storage freezer.

- Media preparation for the Cell Culture area and fermentor room is performed in a separate room and contains equipment for sterile media preparation, storage, and transfer for use in the roller bottle and fermentor processes. It also contains an automated Clean-In-Place skid that services most of the equipment in the Cell Culture department.
- The roller bottle area is first accessed through an air lock. The roller bottle area consists of facilities for an automated roller bottle handling machine and a warm room for roller bottle storage. The roller bottle area is a Class 1000 clean room, however Class 100 conditions are maintained under the curtained areas and are accessed through an air lock in the adjoining room.
- The Media Harvest Area contains equipment for the clarification, concentration, and diafiltration of conditioned media harvested from roller bottles. It also contains a Class 100 hood for the dispensation of Diafiltered Media (DFM) into bottles for freezing.
  - An additional area houses the in-process freezer that stores bottled DFM at minus 40 degrees Celsius.

Continued on next page

Operational Areas

Purification

The Purification area receives DFM from the Cell Culture area and purifies the protein using a four-column chromatography process. It consists of a DFM thaw room, two buffer preparation rooms, and three chromatography cold rooms.

- **DFM Thaw Room**. This room contains roller racks to thaw the frozen DFM received from the Cell Culture area.
- **Buffer Preparation Rooms**. Two rooms are used to prepare and store all buffers used throughout the purification process. The first room contains dedicated tanks to supply buffer to columns 1 and 3, as well as an automated Clean-In-Place skid which services all areas of the department. The second room contains tanks to prepare and store buffers used in Column 4 and formulation operations.
- **Purification Cold Rooms**. Three cold rooms are used for chromatography operations. One contains chromatography skids for columns 1 and 3. A laminar air flow hood is also located in this room for pooling DFM. This is performed at the start of the purification process. The second cold room contains a chromatography skid for column 2 as well as buffer tanks to support column 2 operations. It also contains ethanol buffers for column 2 operations and is maintained as a Class 1, Division 1 rated environment. The final cold room contains a chromatography skid for column 4.

Formulation/ Fill

The Formulation/Fill Area receives purified bulk from the Purification Area which is then sterile-filtered, formulated, and filled into shipping containers for transport to the final finishing facility. It contains a Class 100 hood for sterile processing and is accessed through an air lock in the adjoining room.

Continued on next page

Operational Areas

**Process
Support Areas**

- **Equipment Washroom.** This room is used for washing portable equipment and various stainless steel parts used throughout the plant. The glassware washroom contains two automated autoclaves, an automated sonicator, and a glassware washer and dryer.
- **Dirty Glassware Storage.** This room is used to stage all dirty labware and equipment generated throughout the plant.
- **Clean/Sterile Labware Storage.** This room contains pass-through doors from the autoclaves located in the equipment washroom and serves as a storage area for autoclaved and cleaned equipment and labware parts.
- **Warehouse.** The warehouse is used to receive and stage all raw materials involved in production. Material entering the plant must pass through the air lock in the adjoining room.
- **Instrument Shop.** There is an instrument shop located in the facility. It is used as a in-plant work area for the instrumentation group.
- **Filter Integrity Test Room.** This room is used to integrity test all filters used throughout the plant.
- **Manufacturing Analytical Lab.** The B6 Manufacturing Analytical Services (MAS) lab is used to test buffers and media made throughout the plant. It also processes, receives, and transports in-process samples to the QC labs in Building 25 for testing. There is also a pass-through air lock used to transfer paperwork and samples between the MAS lab and the plant core.

Personnel Flow

Facility Access

Entry into the building is made though the break room located on the northwest corner of the building. Access to the building is restricted to authorized personnel using magnetic card keys. Access to the interior manufacturing core is made by entering into either of the two gowning rooms. Access to these rooms is also controlled by magnetic card key. Access to the facility is obtained by completing safety training, gowning training, and approval by the area Production Manager. These forms are available from Security, Access Level Managers, or the Building Access Coordinator.

There is also an entrance on the south side of the building that can be used to gain access to the B6 MAS lab. This door is also controlled using magnetic card keys.

Personnel Flow

Entry for all personnel into the manufacturing core must be made through one of the two gowning rooms. Both rooms enter into the passageway that leads to the final doorway of the plant. From there, one main passageway, runs the length of the plant and leads to all operational areas.

- **Inoculum Prep**. Personnel wishing to access this area must enter through an air lock.
- **Roller Bottle.** To enter the roller bottle area personnel must enter an air lock room.
- **Harvest Area**. Access to the harvest area can be made through the Roller Bottle area or directly from the main passageway.
- **Purification**. Entry into any of the purification rooms can be made directly through the main passageway.
- **Formulation**. Entry into the Formulation Room must be made through an air lock.

Equipment Flow

Equipment

All equipment entering the Building 6 manufacturing area is wiped down with secondary disinfectant prior to entering or while within the air lock. Racks and carts used to bring equipment into the Building 6 manufacturing area are not allowed to leave the building.

Soiled Labware

Dirty equipment generated throughout the plant is staged in the Dirty Labware Storage Room. All dirty equipment is then transferred for cleaning into the equipment washroom and is then stored in the Clean Storage area. The equipment washroom also contains two autoclaves. Equipment to be autoclaved is loaded here and passed through directly to the Clean Storage upon completion of the cycle.

Purification Flow

Dirty or expired portable tanks and purification columns are cleaned in the Tank Washroom and stored in the clean storage room. Dirty equipment from the processing suites that are not cleaned in place are moved to the Dirty Equipment Storage areas.

Material Flow

Raw Materials

Raw materials are received and inspected in the warehouse air lock. All containers are wiped down with the appropriate secondary disinfectant prior to transfer into the plant. Materials received here are then transported to the designated storage area for the respective production group. The materials are then segregated by lot and stored in area cages or a cold box until ready for use in production. All GMP materials are segregated using appropriately labeled shelves or racks. Materials will be wiped down as they are transferred into the plant.

Product Flow

All product intermediates and products waiting further processing are stored and segregated appropriately. In-process samples are in closed containers. All products transported out of B6 must be in a closed, sealed, and appropriately labeled container which ensures adequate protection.

Continued on next page

Material Flow

Waste Disposal   Within each processing area, small disposable containers and refuse are placed in the waste receptacles. B6 maintains a recycling program for paper and cardboard only. (Note that the cardboard is not brought into the plant core.)

Permitted disposal – Water-soluble non-hazardous waste in the pH range of 2 to 12.5 or neutralized to this range is disposed directly to drain.

Prohibited disposal – Water soluble hazardous materials including:
- Acetone
- Ethanol
- Formaldehyde
- Phenols

Disposal of these materials varies with the material, volume, and concentration. Organic wastes that are not miscible are collected in hazardous waste containers approved by the safety office, and are safely stored until disposal.

Wipe Down   Wipe down or outer bag removal for double-bagged items takes place for every container as it passes into the plant. This is done in order to minimize particulates and keep potential contamination from entering the processing areas. All materials and components are wiped down with secondary disinfectant prior to entering the B6 manufacturing area within any of the access air locks.

Restricted Materials   Material that has a high instance of shedding particulate is prohibited from the processing areas. Some examples are:
- Cardboard
- Wood
- Excessive amounts of paper

Continued on next page

Material Flow

Allowed Materials

Material that has a smooth, cleanable, nonshedding surface is allowed. Some examples are:
- Nonshedding wipes
- Glass
- Plastic
- Stainless Steel

Emergency and Safety Equipment and Alarm Systems

Emergency and safety equipment for B6 is generally located next to the building exit doors. These include:
- Fire extinguishers
- Fire alarm manual pull stations
- Safety showers
- Eye wash stations
- Steam emergency shutoff switches

Area Safety Representatives

The area safety representative should be notified of safety problems or concerns in their respective areas. An updated list of area representatives is located on the manufacturing server.

Safety

Staff Responsibility

It is the responsibility of all staff members to:
- Report and resolve any unsafe conditions
- Complete all required safety training
- Work in a safe manner at all times

Glossary

Operational Areas	Areas within B6 where product processing steps take place.
Released Raw Materials	Ingredients used in the manufacture of drug products that have met all written specification testing.
Unidirectional Flow	Movement through the manufacturing facility is in one direction to enhance cleanliness.
Wipe Down	To wipe the entire exterior surface of an object with approved secondary disinfectant.

Control Systems

Overview

Introduction

Automation control systems are used in many commercial manufacturing processes including biotechnology. Control systems use computer systems to automatically monitor, control, and/or archive data related to the manufacturing process.

Examples

- Home thermostat
- Traffic light intersection
- Power plant control
- Various biotechnology systems – bioreactors, chromatography, cleaning equipment (COP, CIP), autoclaves

Table of Contents

This document contains the following topics:

Control Systems

Objectives

1. Give a brief explanation of a Control System.
2. Give several examples of Control Systems.
3. Distinguish between a Distributed Control System (DCS) and a Programmable Logic Controller (PLC).
4. Give a brief explanation of a Supervisory Control and Data Acquisition (SCADA).
5. Explain the function of a Human Machine Interface (HMI).
6. Give an explanation of a Building Management System (BMS).
7. Discuss why Control Systems are used.
8. Give a brief history of the PLC.
9. Give a brief history of the DCS.
10. List the components of a control system.
11. Explain the function of an Engineering Station.
12. Distinguish between ladder logic and function charts.
13. Explain the function and use of an Operator Station.
14. Explain the function and use of a Historian.
15. Explain the function and use of a Controller.
16. Give a specific example when a Controller is used.
17. Explain proportional-integral-derivative (PID) control.
18. Explain the function and use of an Input/Output Block.
19. Explain the function and use of Instruments/Sensors with specific examples.
20. Distinguish between Digital and Analog.
21. Explain the function and use of a Communication Network.
22. Explain the information provided by a Process and Instrumentation Drawing (P&ID).
23. Explain how 21.CFR.11 applies to Control Systems.
24. Give examples of what 21.CFR.11 requires of Control Systems.
25. Demonstrate ability to identify an HMI.
26. Demonstrate ability to identify a Controller.
27. Explain what is meant by a 4 to 20 amp standard and its application.
28. Explain the use of ladder logic in Control Systems.
29. Demonstrate ability to identify a Communication Network.
30. Demonstrate ability to identify a P&ID.

Equipment Overview

Introduction

This section describes the components used to build a process control system. The key features of a typical control system are:
- Instruments
- Input/Output Block (I/O)
- Controller
- Operator Station
- Engineering Station
- Historian
- Communication Network

Each is described below and illustrated on the diagram on the following page.

Instruments

Instruments are field devices which monitor or control equipment. They are characterized in four types: Digital Input (switch), Digital Output (pump start/stop, valve open/close), Analog Input (temperature, pressure, pH), Analog Output (agitator speed, control valve position).

Input/Output Blocks

Input/Output Blocks (I/O) are the location where instruments are wired. They can be either digital or analog and input or output blocks.

Controller

The Controller is the computer device that runs logic to watch and control desired results.

Operator Station

The Operator Station allows the operator to graphically view or control the process. It also displays process alarms and system diagnostics.

Engineering Station

The Engineering Station allows the creation of logic which runs in the controller. There are various programming types including ladder logic, function chart logic, and structured language (similar to Fortran, Pascal, etc).

Historian

The Historian is a computer station which stores and archives process related information. It also can produce process reports.

Continued on next page

Equipment Overview

Communication Network

The Communication Network is the means by which all the other components communicate. Depending on the system, this can be ethernet, coax, serial cable, etc.

Typical Control System

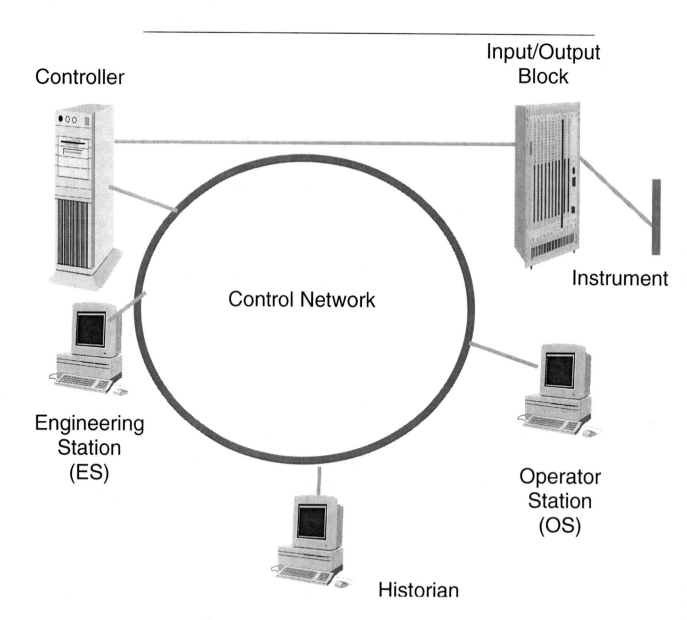

Industry/Process Applications

Overview   There are various types of control systems. These include PLCs, DCSs, SCADA, HMIs, and BMSs. Each is discussed below.

Building Management System   Building Management System (BMS) is an application of any control system that is used to control building environment systems. This includes room temperature, pressure, and humidity. These applications can use either a DCS or a PLC with SCADA/HMI operator interface.

Distributed Control System   Distributed Control System (DCS) is an integrated control system that can be used to control an entire facility. These single systems combine the functions of a PLC and SCADA into a single system. They were also developed in the late 1960s for batch automation processes.

Human Machine Interface   Human Machine Interface (HMI) computer systems allow process monitoring and provide operator control to the process. They do not store any archive data.

Programmable Logic Controller   Programmable Logic Controllers (PLC) are generally used to control a single system. They can be networked together to control an entire manufacturing area. They were developed in the late 1960s to replace electrical relay logic in the automotive industry.

Supervisory Control and Data Acquisition   Supervisory Control and Data Acquisition (SCADA) computer systems allow process monitoring and provide operator control to the process. They are linked to a PLC via a communications network. The Data Acquisition aspect means these systems will store process data in an archive file.

Control Methods

Introduction

This section describes some common control methods:
- PID control
- Dead band control
- Interlock logic

PID Control

A proportional-integral-derivative or "PID" controller looks at the current value of the error, the integral of the error over a recent time interval, and the current derivative of the error signal to determine not only how much of a correction to apply, but for how long. Those three quantities are each multiplied by a tuning constant and added together to produce the current controller output 'u' according to the equation:

$$u = K_P e + K_I \int e \, dt + K_D \frac{de}{dt}$$

In this equation, K_P is the proportional tuning constant, K_I is the integral tuning constant, K_D is the derivative tuning constant, and e(t) is the error between the setpoint SP(t) and the process variable PV(t) at time t.

$$e(t) = SP(t) - PV(t)$$

If the current error is large, has been sustained for some time, or is changing rapidly, the controller will attempt to make a large correction by generating a large output. Conversely, if the process variable has matched the setpoint for some time, the controller will leave well enough alone.

Dead-Band Control

Dead-band control is a simple method to control a process parameter. The control system will determine if the process variable is beyond a 'dead-band' above or below a setpoint, and make a control action if this dead-band is exceeded. An example of this is a home thermostat. During heating, when the temperature falls below the setpoint (greater than dead-band), the heater turns on until the temperature rises to a dead-band above the setpoint. It can be seen that PID control provides closer control to a setpoint.

Interlock Logic

Interlock logic control is used to either protect the process, operator, or the facility. Interlocks will override operator commands to prevent an unsafe condition. An example is a tank fill valve that cannot be opened if the level is greater that 99%.

21.CFR Part 11

Introduction   This section describes the requirements of 21.CFR Part 11.

21.CFR Part 11 is a FDA requirement for electronic records and electronic signatures which became effective on August 20, 1997. The scope of the rule covers the creation and maintenance of electronic records that support all regulated activities surrounding the drug development/manufacturing process.

Requirements   Below are some of the key items of Part 11 compliance.

Goal	Description
Security of Records	Procedures or systems to deter falsification by mishap or casual misdeed, and to help detect such alterations when they occur. This may include physical security, system software security, and user access procedures.
Accountability of Users	Procedures must exist to include policies that hold individuals accountable and responsible for actions initiated under their electronic signature in order to deter record and signature falsification.
Education and Training	Procedures or systems must exist to determine that persons who use electronic record/signature systems have the education, training, and experience to perform these tasks.
Data Archive	Procedures or systems must exist to ensure availability of electronic data throughout record retention period.
Computer Generated Audit Trails	Computer systems that allow data to be created, modified, or deleted must provide automatic audit trails to not obscure previous data and to link user, date, and time to this action.

Control Systems

Laboratory

Introduction Students will gain familiarity with the different components and key features of an automated control system. This includes instruments, controllers and operator interface.

Materials and Supplies Control system for temperature measurement

---

Activities at a Glance This activity and demonstration uses the following components for instruction on automated control systems:

- **Instruments**.
  3-way switch to simulate discrete inputs
  RTD temperature element
  Light to simulate discrete output

- **Controller**. Allen Bradley PLC Controller with various Input/Output Cards. The PLC has logic to monitor the various instruments and perform simple calculations which can be displayed on the operator interface.

- **Operator interface**. Computer with Intellution application. Intellution is a SCADA software which communicates with controller to display process equipment conditions and allow operator control. The SCADA system also archives process data.

- **Panelview operator interface**. Panelview is a simple operator interface which displays process equipment conditions and allows operator control.

Gowning

Overview

Introduction

Gowning requirements for operational areas are set appropriately for the activities that occur within those areas. Appropriate gowning will minimize the number of particulates shed by each operator. This helps a facility maintain the appropriate air classification in each area, which in turn protects the product from potential contamination.

Table of Contents

This document contains the following topics:

Gowning

Objectives

1. Explain the differences between aseptic processing versus terminal sterilization.
2. Explain Sterility Assurance Level (SAL) and its role in aseptic processing and terminal sterilization.
3. Explain why the FDA allows aseptic processing.
4. Describe the conditions required for aseptic processing.
5. Explain the term bioburden.
6. Define a micron.
7. Describe the sources of contamination in a clean room.
8. Explain the requirements for a Class 100 clean room.
9. What are the concerns regarding smokers entering clean rooms and how are these concerns addressed?
10. What is a shedder?
11. Explain laminar airflow.
12. Name a dozen prohibited personnel actions in a clean room.
13. Describe the relationship between personnel movement and contamination indices.
14. Describe preventive measures that can be taken to protect the clean room from personnel.
15. Explain the importance of unidirectional flow of personnel in a critical aseptic area.
16. How can an excessive talker be identified after work in a clean room?
17. Describe six items that have been found to produce contamination and are prohibited in the clean room.
18. Explain why air from the waist down is considered dirty.
19. Describe the proper procedure for retrieving an item dropped in a clean room.
20. Explain the proper way to enter/exit a critical aseptic area.
21. Describe a media fill and explain its use in manufacturing.
22. Explain the importance of aseptic technique while gowning for a clean room.
23. List the proper gowning sequence.
24. Demonstrate proper gowning/gloving technique.
25. Explain how the technique of an individual undergoing gowning qualification is tested.
26. Explain the proper way to dispose of trash accumulated while gowning.
27. Explain why one needs to protect the clean room.

Background

Gowning	Gowning is the donning of cleanroom garments to protect the low particle counts required in the processing areas. Different levels of gowning are required, depending upon the operations being performed.
Code of Federal Regulations	21.CFR Part 211.28 (a) states: " Personnel engaged in the manufacture, processing, packing, or holding of a drug product shall wear clean clothing appropriate for the duties they perform. Protective apparel, such as head, face, hand, and arm coverings, shall be worn as necessary to protect drug products from contamination."
In General	General gowning points include the following: • Gowning will take place in gowning air locks. • Each gowning room will have the maximum number of individuals allowed to gown at one time clearly posted. • Choose a gown that is large enough to allow unrestricted movement, but not so large as to interfere with movement.
Disposable or Reusable?	In some areas, disposable gowns will be used instead of reusable garments. Disposable gowns should be placed in trash receptacles upon degowning. Reusable garments should be placed in laundry bins upon degowning.
Permitted Items	The following items are permitted in gowning level 0-3 areas: • Earrings • Rings • Watches
Prohibited Items	The following items are not permitted in the manufacturing facility at any time: • Cosmetics that could shed particles • Excessive jewelry that cannot be covered by gowning (example: dangling earrings)

Gowning Concepts

Key Concepts

The following points are <u>key</u> concepts:

- In the locker rooms, prior to entering the circulation corridor, shoes should be inspected for mud and debris. If necessary, replace soiled shoes with clean shoes.
- Tacky mats are present near all gowning room doors. Whenever moving through a gowning room, always step on the tacky mat to remove debris from the bottom of your shoes.
- Prior to donning appropriate level gowning, hands must be sanitized. Hand sanitization stations are available in each gowning room.
- Safety glasses must be donned prior to entering the production areas. Safety glasses are required and can be sanitized with ethanol prior to wearing. Safety glasses may be removed for short periods to perform close-up work, such as viewing though a microscope or examining roller bottles. Safety glasses are not required in nonprocessing rooms within the production area.
- If any gowning garment is found to be defective, it should be tied in a knot for easy identification and placed in the soiled garment bin.
- While gowning, every effort should be made to minimize garment contact with floor, wall, or equipment.
- When gowning, all zippers and snaps should be completely fastened. If they are not, the gown will not perform as it is designed.
- At various points in or around the gowning area there are lines of demarcation on the floor. These demarcation lines separate the clean side from the dirty side of the gowning room. Shoe covers and knee-high boots are donned as you step across the line of demarcation from the dirty side to the clean side.
- To degown, reverse the appropriate level gowning sequence. For areas in which single-use garments are worn, operators may step over the line of demarcation to a lower gown level to remove gown garments.
- Only one activity (e.g., gowning, degowning, material transfer, environmental monitoring, cleaning, etc.) may occur in a gown or degown room at a time.
- For mechanical space that is accessed from GMP process areas, personnel may be required to don additional gown garments (as posted) and remove those garments upon reentry into a process area.

Gowning Levels 0-3

Introduction   Appropriate gowning requirements are determined for any given biomanufacturing facility. Gowning levels 0-3 are presented as an example of gowning for a manufacturing facility. However, they are not a universal industry standard.

Gowning Levels 0 Through 3   The following are the minimum requirements for gowning levels 0 through 3:

- Level 0 gowning consists of street clothes (clean pants, shirts with sleeves, and clean, close-toed shoes) or plant uniforms and safety glasses.

- Level 1 gowning consists of items in gowning level 0 plus shoe covers.

- Level 2 gowning consists of items in gowning level 1 plus a frock, hair cover, and facial hair cover (when appropriate).

- Level 3 gowning consists of items in gowning level 0 plus knee-high boots, hair cover, facial hair cover (when appropriate), and a coverall.

Level 0   Gown for Level 0 in the following sequence:

Action	Rationale
Inspect shoes for mud and debris. Replace with clean shoes if necessary.	Depositing debris in the circulation corridor increases the chance of contaminating the processing areas.
Sanitize safety glasses with secondary disinfectant or pre-wetted wipes.	Removes bacteria and debris that may be carried into the manufacturing areas.
Ensure that legs and shoulders are covered; facility scrubs are available, if necessary.	This is necessary to minimize particulate shedding within the facility.

Level 0 Applicability   Refer to the applicable facility gowning Standard Operating Procedure for level 0 gowning applicability.

Continued on next page

Gowning Levels 0-3

Level 1 Gown for Level 1 in the following sequence:

Action	Rationale
Sanitize hands with Alcare or equivalent.	Clean gowning should be handled with clean hands.
Sanitize safety glasses with secondary disinfectant or pre-wetted wipes.	Removes bacteria and debris that may be carried into the manufacturing areas.
Don shoe covers while stepping across the line of demarcation from the dirty to the clean side of the gowning room.	This action ensures that the clean side of the gowning room remains clean.

Level 1 Applicability Refer to the applicable facility gowning Standard Operating Procedure for Level 1 gowning applicability.

Level 2 Gown for Level 2 in the following sequence:

Action	Rationale
Sanitize hands with Alcare or equivalent.	Clean gowning should be handled with clean hands.
Sanitize safety glasses with secondary disinfectant or pre-wetted wipes.	Removes bacteria and debris that may be carried into the manufacturing areas.
Don hair cover and tuck in all hair.	Hair covers keep hair from shedding.
Don facial hair cover (if applicable).	Hair covers keep hair from shedding.
Don shoe covers while stepping across the line of demarcation from the dirty to the clean side of the gowning room.	This action ensures that the clean side of the gowning room remains clean.
Don appropriately sized frock and ensure that all zippers and snaps are completely closed.	Gown will not do its job properly if it is not completely closed.

Level 2 Applicability Refer to the applicable facility gowning Standard Operating Procedure for Level 2 gowning applicability.

Continued on next page

Gowning Levels 0-3

Level 3   Gown for Level 3 in the following sequence:

Action	Rationale
Sanitize hands with Alcare or equivalent.	Clean gowning should be handled with clean hands.
Sanitize safety glasses with secondary disinfectant or pre-wetted wipes.	Removes bacteria and debris that may be carried into the manufacturing areas.
Don hair cover and tuck in all hair.	Hair covers keep hair from shedding.
Don facial hair cover (if applicable).	Hair covers keep hair from shedding.
Don knee-high boots while stepping across the line of demarcation from the dirty to the clean side of the gowning room.	This action ensures that the clean side of the gowning room remains clean. Donning boots first keeps the inside of the coverall clean.
Don appropriately sized coverall and tuck legs into knee-high boots.	Tucking ensures that gown legs will not touch the floor and become soiled and keeps particulates from escaping down the gown leg onto the floors.

Level 3 Applicability

Refer to the applicable facility gowning Standard Operating Procedure for Level 3 gowning applicability. Level 3 gowning is required in areas where processing occurs, with the addition of a mask and gloves when appropriate. It is considered good practice to wear gloves at all times within the processing areas, but gloves are not required for minimum Level 3 gowning. Gloves, however, must be worn whenever equipment is handled within the production areas. If at any time gowning becomes visibly soiled, personnel must move to a degowning room, remove soiled gown, and re-enter the area through the gowning room, donning appropriate clean gowning material. Once inside the processing area, personnel may not unzip their coverall or degown in any way, except in case of emergency. Personnel must move to a gowning room to access pagers, radios, etc. within gown.

Continued on next page

Gowning Levels 0-3

Masks and Gloves

When performing certain operations, a mask and/or gloves must be worn in addition to Level 3 gowning.

When	Then
Handling clean/sanitized labware or product processing components	Wear clean gloves.
Product or processing materials are exposed to the environment	All individuals in the lab must wear masks and clean gloves.
Taking a sample of in-process product	Individual taking the sample must wear a mask and clean gloves.
Making aseptic product contact connections	Individual making the connections must wear a mask and clean gloves.

Gowning

Laboratory

Introduction

Students will learn the concepts and skills involved in gowning for an aseptic area (Class 100). Each student will don complete gowning attire in an aseptic manner and be plated to demonstrate successful acquisition of the skills. Video taping of students as they gown will enable students to evaluate themselves and receive positive critiques.

Materials and Supplies

Gowns
Overboots
Hoods
Gloves
Masks
Beard covers
Shoe covers
Bouffant caps
RODAC plates
Video Camera

Activities at a Glance

1. The laboratory activity will begin with a demonstration of gowning and gloving techniques by the industry instructor.

2. Students will perform the gowning sequence under the supervision of instructors. Students should be divided up into small groups, each with a qualified individual to lead gowning sequence.

3. One individual from each group will be plated in 13 locations to determine effectiveness of gowning techniques.

4. If feasible, gowning practice can be videotaped and students can view and critique performance.

Environmental Process Monitoring

Overview

Introduction

The Environmental Monitoring program is designed to monitor manufacturing areas to determine the load of viable organisms, total particulates in the air, and bioburden on equipment and facility surfaces. The data gathered from environmental monitoring provides a means of determining whether a manufacturing area is in a state of control. Maintaining environmental control in a manufacturing area is essential for preventing microbial contamination of product.

Table of Contents

This document contains the following topics:

Environmental Process Monitoring

Objectives

1. Explain aseptic technique and its importance to biomanufacturing.
2. Identify three behaviors to be followed while practicing aseptic technique.
3. Explain the role of Federal Standard 209E in relation to cleanrooms and their classification.
4. Explain Environmental Monitoring (EM).
5. State the particulate specifications for Environmental Monitoring.
6. Describe the selection of media used and the type of organism each detects.
7. Describe the time, incubations, and temperatures given in the United States Pharmacopia for the growth of yeast/molds and bacteria.
8. Explain the importance of out-of-specification responses.
9. Explain the difference between an alert level and an action level.
10. Explain how one sets alert or action levels.
11. Explain static and dynamic monitoring and what each accomplishes.
12. Describe the use of a Met-One particle counter in an EM program.
13. Explain the theory behind the operation of a Met-One.
14. Demonstrate use of the Met-One.
15. State the components of a facility where quantification of microbes is desired.
16. Explain three types of microbial quantification methods used in EM.
17. Explain what the term RODAC represents.
18. Demonstrate/explain the use of RODAC plates.
19. Demonstrate/explain the use/assembly of an RCS.
20. Demonstrate/explain the use of fallout plates.
21. Demonstrate/explain swabbing techniques.

Background

Sources of Contamination

There are several sources for environmental microbial contamination. These include:

- Water
- Soil
- Dust
- Air
- People

Of the sources listed above, people are the greatest source of contamination because they shed a large number of particles (skin flakes, hair fragments, moisture droplets, cosmetics etc.). These particles carry an array of different microbes.

Responsibility

The staff's responsibilities in ensuring the environment is maintained in a state of control include:

- Follow procedures which govern gowning and flows (personnel, equipment, and material)
- Report any unusual circumstances (i.e. wall, ceiling, floor damage, leaks, etc.) immediately
- Maintain clean and organized workstations
- Report or clean up spills as soon as possible

Environmental Monitoring

Sampling Methods

In order to assess the environmental load of viable organisms (microbial) and nonviable particles in manufacturing areas, air and surfaces are sampled on a routine basis. Routine monitoring is performed during production (dynamic) as well as during nonproduction (static) EM conditions. In addition to routine environmental monitoring, EM is also performed during periods when product is directly exposed to the environment.

Continued on next page

Environmental Monitoring

Air Sampling Air is sampled routinely during production and during nonproduction conditions.

- Nonviable particles are detected in air samples using laser particle counting instruments. Particle counting instruments sample the air and quantify the particles within a specified size range in the sample.
- Viable organisms are detected in the air by utilizing Slit-to-Agar (STA) instruments. STA instruments impinge airborne organisms on an agar media plate. The agar media plates are incubated for a period of time to allow organisms that may have been captured during sampling an opportunity to grow. Quantification and potential identification follow.
- Viable organisms in the air can also be detected using the Reuter Centrifugal Sampler (RCS). This instrument is mostly used in explosion rated rooms. The RCS is a battery operated air sampler that uses an impeller blade to draw air into the sampler. Agar strips are inserted into the sampler and surround the impeller blade. When the sampler is turned on, the force of the rotating blade draws air in and airborne viable particles are forced onto the agar strip. The strip is incubated (like an STA) and the microbial load of air sampled is calculated based on the time of the exposure.

Surface Sampling Surfaces are also sampled routinely during production and during non-production conditions. Replicate Organism Detection and Counting (RODAC) plates are used to quantify bioburden on environmental surfaces. RODAC plates contain an agar medium that is slightly raised above the surface of the plate. The lid is removed and the plate is contacted directly to the surface being sampled exposing agar media to predetermined sites (floors, walls, and equipment) in the manufacturing area. The agar media plates are incubated for a period of time, allowing organisms that may have been captured during sampling to grow, be counted, and potentially identified.

Continued on next page

Environmental Monitoring

Alert and Action Levels

If the results from air or surface samples exceed established levels, they will be classified as either Alert or Action level excursions.

- Alert levels indicate a <u>potential</u> departure from normal environmental conditions. An investigation may occur to determine the cause of the high results.
- Action levels indicate a <u>definite</u> departure from normal environmental conditions. An investigation is <u>required</u> along with a corrective action to prevent recurrence of the excursion.

Environmental Monitoring Grades

Alert and action levels are assigned to rooms based on the room's established Environmental Monitoring grade. Additionally, alert levels are based on the individual building's historical data, but action levels are a combination of industry standards or site wide historical data. EM grades are categorized from the least controlled, Grade 1 (entry areas, access control vestibules etc.), to the most controlled, Grade 7 (Class 100 rooms, walls, and hoods used for sterile filtration). The grade classifications are based on the following:

- Design of room
- Room functions/stage of processing/criticality
- Room design adjacencies/pressure differentials

Alert/action levels are evaluated annually and revised, if necessary.

Process Monitoring

Manufacturing Requirements

Environmental monitoring must be performed by manufacturing staff during aseptic operations in a hood or other Class 100 area or when directed by a Manufacturing Procedure (MP). Sampling takes place at these times because CFRs require demonstration that the area is in a state of environmental control during open process operations. The air sampled must be that which immediately surrounds the open process operation. Immediate surroundings is defined as:

- Within three feet of the process operation, unless it interferes with safety or processing.

This is true for both the STA and particulate counter probes.

STA Operations

Preparation

Prior to open process operations, the STA sampler must be prepared for use.
- First, disinfect the sampler and its surroundings with a secondary disinfectant and allow it to dry as directed by the appropriate SOP.
- Attach sample tubing and power supply cable as directed in the appropriate SOP.
- Initiate power and perform a Ground Fault Current Interrupt (GFCI) Test.
- Set the air flow rate to 60 Standard Cubic Feet/Hour (SCFH) and purge the unit.
- Ensure that the turntable is rotated fully clockwise.
- Ensure that the plate is adjusted to the proper height.
- Ensure that the dome is placed securely.

Note: When setting the plate height, it is important to rotate the turn table adjustment knob clockwise or counterclockwise until the red anodized portions of the distance indicator are not visible at the top or side relief of the distance indicator mount.

Label the Plate

Prior to placing the plate on the turntable, label it with the following information:
- Sample start line (from center to edge of plate)
- Sample start time
- Initials of operator and date
- Sample site number or description
- Metrology control number of the sampling assembly
- Product description, lot number, and step number

Sampling

Aseptically place the plate on the turntable, remove the cover, and place the dome such that the slit lines up with the start line. Turn on the sampler. When the time is up or the operation is complete, turn off the sampler (if necessary), lift the dome, cover the plate, and remove it from the sampler. If the process operations are continuing, place another labeled plate on the sampler, set the timer, and resume sampling within five minutes.

Finishing the Plate

Secure the cover to the plate with tape. Label the plate with the time sampling ended. To ensure that sampling was actually performed, the agar plate should be visually inspected for impingement marks. If impingement marks are not apparent or if the marks do not correspond to the time sampled, the sample will be considered invalid. In this case, if possible, retake the sample.

Total Air Particulate

Preparation   Program the appropriate unit or initiate the appropriate recipe. Programming of a Climet or similar particle counter will include setting the following:
- Sample volume
- Delay time (delay time before first sample is taken)
- Interval time (time between samples)
- Time of day
- Date
- Alarm (room classification dependent – Class 100 room alarm level =100)

Sampling   Connect an appropriately cleaned/sanitized sampling probe as close to the operation as possible, without interfering with processing. Press Start to begin sampling. The first sample taken will be a "purge" sample and data will not be used. During open processing operations, samples shall be taken during the entire processing period as required by the Manufacturing Procedure. The number of samples taken shall be set to infinite so as to continually take samples until the particle counter is manually stopped at the end of processing. If an excursion should occur during processing, it shall be appropriately documented on the appropriate EM submission at the time when it occurs. At the end of processing, turn off the counter and complete all appropriate documentation.

Documentation

Environmental Monitoring Submission Form   At the completion of sampling, an EM submission form must be completely and accurately filled out, signed, dated, and turned in to QC along with:
- Appropriately labeled STA plates
- Appropriately labeled Total Air Particulate documentation

Glossary

EM	Environmental Monitoring. Method used to ensure that the manufacturing environment is within a state of control.
Nonviable Particulate	Nonliving particles above a certain size that may contaminate an open process.
STA	Slit-To-Agar. A device used to sample the air for viable organisms.
TSA	Trypticase Soy Agar. The type of agar plate used with an STA.
Viable Particulate	Living organisms that pose a threat to the sterility of the process.

Environmental Monitoring

Laboratory

Introduction   Environmental monitoring within a biomanufacturing facility utilizes several different types of equipment. Students will learn the use and applications of the MET-One and the RCS. In addition, students will learn swabbing techniques and the use and application of settling plates. A variety of locations within the laboratory will be monitored, including the laminar flow hoods (Class 100). Students will be required to analyze the data collected and demonstrate proficiency with the equipment.

Equipment   RCS
Met-One
LAF Hoods

Materials and Supplies   TSA plates
SDA plates
Biotest strips for RCS
RODAC plates
Sterile swabs
WFI or diluent in vial
Alcohol wipes
Supplies for cleaning hood: 70% ethanol, lint-free sterile wipes
Video: "Behavior in the Cleanroom"

Laboratory

**Activities
at a Glance**

1. Students will perform environmental monitoring of an LAF hood or BSC.

2. Students will be divided into groups. Each group will be responsible for monitoring one of the LAF hoods. The hoods will be cleaned prior to testing.

3. Each group will perform the following tests to determine the effectiveness of the cleaning and to evaluate the performance of the HEPA filters in the hoods.
   a. RCS

   Load Biotest strips into RCS and perform air sampling test for eight minutes.
   b. FALLOUT OR SETTLING PLATES

   Use fallout plates placed in different locations within LAF hood. A minimum of 4 plates/hood should be used with a 30 minute exposure.
      i.   TSA plates: one at left side, one at right side
      ii. SDA plates: one at left side, one at right side
   c. MET-ONE TEST

   Use the Met-One to monitor the total particulates in the hood. Students should correlate results with the classification of the hood.
   d. SWABBING

   Surfaces of the hood will be tested using sterile swabs and sterile water and swabbing onto TSA and SDA plates.

4. Incubate plates and RCS strips at 25°C and 37°C for seven days.

5. Each group will select a location within the laboratories and repeat both the RCS and Met-One tests for this location.

Laser Particle Counters

Overview

Introduction

This document provides a conceptual overview of the information needed to perform total air particulate monitoring during processing in a manufacturing facility.

Table of Contents

This document contains the following topics:

Laser Particle Counters

Objectives

1. Explain the importance of monitoring total air particulates in a facility.
2. Explain the basic principles in the operation of a laser particle counter.
3. Demonstrate the ability to set up a laser particle counter such as the Met-One or Climet units.
4. Demonstrate the ability to program a laser particle counter.
5. Explain the significance of particle size in monitoring total air particulates.
6. Explain the role of alarm limits in monitoring.
7. Identify the alarm limits for the different room classifications in a facility.
8. Explain the importance of Unit Identification numbers for monitoring equipment.
9. Identify and describe some of the sample parameters that should be programmed into a laser particle counter.
10. Demonstrate proper placement of the isokinetic probe of a laser particle counter.
11. Demonstrate proper labeling of the printout from the instrument.
12. Describe some of the appropriate personnel practices while performing sampling.
13. Explain the course of action if counts exceed alarm limits during sampling.

Background

Environmental Monitoring- Total Air Particulate

The monitoring of manufacturing areas for Total Air Particulate (TAP) is essential in ensuring product quality. TAP can be either viable or nonviable and, if not kept in control, could cause loss of product due to contamination. The data, gathered from total air particulate environmental monitoring, provides a means of determining whether a manufacturing area is in a state of control. Maintaining environmental control in a manufacturing area is essential for preventing contamination of product.

Sources of Contamination

There are several sources for particulate contamination, including:
- Soil
- Dust
- Air
- People

Of the sources listed above, people are the greatest source of contamination because they shed a large number of particles (skin flakes, hair fragments, moisture droplets, cosmetics etc.).

Manufacturing Requirements

TAP monitoring must be performed by trained manufacturing staff during aseptic operations in a hood or other Class 100 area, or when directed by a manufacturing procedure. Sampling takes place at these times because CFRs require demonstration that the area is in a state of environmental control during open process operations.

Laser Particle Counter Principle

The air pump pulls sample air into the sensor through the inlet nozzle. Particles suspended in air are introduced in the view volume of the sensor along the centerline of the laser where they are impacted by the laser light. A wide-angle elliptical mirror collection system reflects light from the particles and focuses the scattered light to a solid-state photodetector. The detector responds to the scattered light and converts it to electrical signals whose amplitude increases with particle size. Since the detector sees the light from a wide angle, variations in response due to particle shape and refractive index are minimized. The overall response to particle size is linear. The microprocessor and associated circuitry sort and count these pulses. The output is displayed as particles per cubic foot on a digital display and is provided as a hard copy printout. Particle counts are also stored in memory to be retrieved later, if required.

Equipment Set-Up

Equipment Set-up

The following is a list of steps that should be performed during set-up for taking total air particulate samples during in-process monitoring.

- Ensure that the metrology control calibration status sticker is current and, if applicable, that the unit's laser sensor function indicator is showing that the sensor is within range. If any of these calibration indicators are not acceptable and can not be adjusted, the unit should not be used for sampling.
- The laser counter should be plugged in at a location that is as close as possible to the point of monitoring without obstructing the processing operation or posing a safety hazard.
- Ensure that the isokinetic probe is attached to the air inlet port and turn on the power to the unit.

Laser Counter Functions and Programming

Laser Counter Functions and Programming

Program the appropriate unit per the appropriate laser particle counter SOP. Programming a Met-One, Climet CI-500 or similar particle counter will include setting or enabling the following functions:

- Particle size
- Printer
- Alarm limits
- Audible alarm
- Date and time
- Count mode
- Unit ID
- Sample parameters: sample volume/sample time, initial delay time (Delay time before first sample is taken), interval time/hold time (time between samples), number of samples, concentration

Continued on next page

Laser Counter Functions and Programming

Particle Size
Most particle counters will count particles of varying sizes from 0.3µm to 10µm, or greater. However, the particle sizes that concern manufacturing quality are particles 0.5µm and larger. Particulates, in general, is not a product-threatening concern during bulk biopharmaceutical processing. However, bacterial contamination is a product-threatening concern. This particle size (0.5µm) is important because it is the minimum size of bacteria. By controlling the particulate level for particles ≥0.5µm in the manufacturing plants, we are protecting the product from microbial contamination, as well as from total particulate contamination. Set the particle counter to display particles ≥0.5µm.

Printer
The printer must be enabled prior to sampling and should be in the print mode. Always check that there is enough paper in the printer to perform/complete the necessary monitoring. Install paper per the appropriate unit operating SOP as necessary to ensure that sampling is documented. The particle counter will display the results of the sample on the printout. This is important because this printout provides the necessary documentation for collection of the sample data. Most particle counters have the ability to store information from a specific number of previous samples in their memory databanks. If for any reason the printout was not delivered after sampling, and the processing operation has been completed, attempt to retrieve the data from the particle counter's memory.

Continued on next page

Laser Counter Functions and Programming

Alarm Limits   The particle counter alarm limit should be set per the appropriate site environmental monitoring SOP. Alarm limits depend on the total air particulate classification of the area that is being sampled and are usually set at the area Action limits. TAP classifications are designated as having less than a specific number of total air particulate $\geq 0.5\mu m$ /cubic foot of air. If an area or room is designated Class 100,000, it means that in one cubic foot of air there should be less than 100,000 particles $\geq 0.5\mu m$ in that area or room. Therefore the action level for TAPs in this area is <100,000 total air particulate $\geq 0.5\mu m$/cubic foot of air. The alarm limit should be set for 100,000. The only exception to this is in Class 100 areas. In Class 100 areas the alarm limit is set to the area alert level, which is <50 total air particulate $\geq 0.5\mu m$/cubic foot of air. The alarm limits should only be set for particles $\geq 0.5\mu m$. All other particle sizes should have the alarm limit set to "0" or "OFF". The following is a list of room classifications and alarm limits:

- Class 100,000 = Alarm limit is 100,000 (action level)
- Class 10,000 = Alarm limit is 10,000 (action level)
- Class 100 = Alarm limit is 50 (alert level)

Audible Alarm   The audible alarm must be activated in order for the operators to know if any samples taken during processing have exceeded the programmed levels.

Date and Time   The date and time should be accurately set. The format for the date should be MM/DD/YY and the format for the time should be in military time. For example: 1:00 P.M. = 1300.

Continued on next page

Laser Counter Functions and Programming

Count Mode　　The count mode on the laser particle counters should always be set to cumulative/total. Some particle counters will display and count the particles sampled in cumulative/total or differential count modes. Cumulative/total count mode means that the counter counts and totals all of the particles in a given sample at and above a specific particle size. Differential count mode means that the particle counter will count and total all of the particles in a given sample greater than one particle size and smaller than the next particle size. In order to record the data as total air particulate ≥0.5μm/cubic foot of air, the counter must be in cumulative/total count mode.

Unit ID　　Many particle counters are used by biotechnology companies and the Unit ID number is a way to identify each one. The particle counters are tracked by their equipment number and by the group responsible for the unit. The suggested ID for each unit is the equipment number of the unit and reference to the group responsible for the instrument (e.g., # 2000/B-7 Ferm.) This ID number will be printed on each sample printout and documented on the sample submission form. It is important to identify each unit, so appropriate data trending can be performed. For instance, if an area is having problems meeting the TAP levels, and it is noticed that the same particle counter was used for each sample, it would be a good idea to have the unit checked to verify that it is working properly.

Sample Parameters

Sample Parameters　　The following sample parameters must be programmed per the appropriate laser counter operating SOP:
- Sample volume/sample time
- Initial delay time (delay time before first sample is taken)
- Interval time/hold time (time between samples)
- Number of samples
- Concentration (per cubic meter or per cubic foot)

Continued on next page

Sample Parameters

Sample Volume/ Sample Time

Laser particle counters need to be programmed to sample an air flow rate of one cubic foot of air per one minute. Sample volume can be set to one cubic foot/minute by entering the value at the "Sample Volume" screen (Climet CI-500), or it can be set by adjusting the air flow rate until the air flow display middle Light-Emitting Diode (LED) is illuminated (Met-One 200L). Once the sample volume has been set, the sample time can be set. Since the requirement for results is in TAPs ≥0.5µm/cubic foot of air, and the sample volume has been set to one cubic foot/minute, the sample time should be set for one minute.

Initial Delay Time

The initial delay allows the user time to vacate the area before the unit begins to sample and allows the pump to reach the proper air flow. This initial delay is usually used for routine monitoring and is not required during in-process monitoring, since in-process monitoring is performed during the manufacturing operations when operators are present.

Interval Time/ Hold Time

The interval/hold time determines how much time will elapse between samples. The time between samples needs to be set so that at least five (5) one minute samples can be taken during the process in which the product is exposed. If the processing time is such that total product exposure is less than fifteen minutes, the interval/hold time should be set for one minute. However, if the processing time is such that total product exposure is expected to be greater than fifteen minutes, the interval/hold time may be set for four minutes. However, ensure that at least five one minute samples are taken. It is perfectly acceptable to have the interval/hold time set for one minute for all sampling. These interval/hold times were chosen to ensure that a representative number of samples (at least 5) are taken during the processing operation.

Number of Samples

Laser particle counters can be programmed to take a specified number of samples or an unlimited number of samples. Routine particulate monitoring requires that only five samples be taken per sampling site. However, during in-process monitoring, samples must be taken for the duration in which the product is exposed to the environment with a minimum of at least five samples taken. Therefore, the particle counter must be programmed to perform continuous sampling once started. When the "Number of Samples" display is reached, enter "INF" (Infinite) for the Climet CI-500 or enter "0" for the Met-One 200L. This will cause the unit to continuously take sample after sample until it is manually stopped.

Continued on next page

Sample Parameters

Concentration As mentioned earlier, the sampling requirements are for total air particulate ≥0.5μm/cubic foot of air. Therefore, ensure that the particle counter is set to measure in cubic feet and not in cubic meters.

Sampling

Isokinetic Probe Placement The isokinetic probe draws air from the direction in which it is pointing. For in-process TAP sampling, orient the probe toward the production activity and place it as close to the production process as is possible (within 3 feet) without obstructing operations or creating a safety hazard.

Label the Printout Press the paper feed pad on the particle counter to release enough paper to clearly label the particle counter printout with the appropriate information:

- **Site Number.** This is denoted on the sample submission form and usually consists of the building number, room number, and sampling site number (i.e. 07-123-01 for building 7, room 123, site number 1
- **Product.** The name of the product that is being processed
- **Lot Number.** The lot number of the product being processed
- **Specification Number.** The specification number of the product being processed
- **Manufacturing Procedure Number.** The number for the manufacturing procedure requiring sampling to be performed
- **Step Number.** The step number from the manufacturing procedure requiring sampling to be performed
- **Operator's Name.** First initial and last name of the operator performing the sampling
- **Sampling Date.** Date that the sample is being taken

Begin Sampling Once processing begins, press the "START" or "RUN" button to begin sampling. The first sample taken will be a "purge" sample and this data will not be used. During open processing operations, samples shall be taken during the entire processing period as required by the Manufacturing Procedure. While monitoring is being performed, check the particle counter to assure it is functioning properly (i.e., printer is functioning, unit is counting).

Continued on next page

Sampling

Personnel Practices

It is important for personnel performing the manufacturing operation and sampling to adhere to the following practices while sampling total air particulates:

- Keep your movements slow and deliberate. Any excessive movement around the particle counter can cause excess particles to shed from the operator and would be detected by the particle counter. This may cause the particulate levels for the area to be exceeded.
- Do not spray any liquids (i.e. alcohol) in the vicinity of the probe while the air pump is on as this will damage the sensor and may cause inaccurate results.

Counts Exceeding Alarm Limits

Operators are very busy during a manufacturing operation. This is why it is very important to have the audible alarm turned on, which will signal high particulate counts reached during TAP sampling. When the audible alarm sounds, the operator hearing the alarm can survey the environment to determine possible causes for the alarm. If an excursion, other than the purge, should occur during processing, acknowledge the audible alarm and document on the alarmed sample printout any activity occurring in the area that could have caused the high particulate count along with the operator's name and date. If the cause is unknown, document "cause unknown" and operator's name and date. Monitor the next sample to ensure that the counts are back within the area alarm limits. If two consecutive samples are still exceeding the alarm limits, immediately notify the area supervisor. If three consecutive samples exceed alarm limits during a filtration or filling operation, processing must be stopped, and the supervisor must be immediately notified. Processing may not resume until the TAP counts are within alarm limits.

Sampling Completion

At the end of processing, press "STOP" to cease counting. Ensure that the unit's air pump is off, then shut off the power to the unit. Review the printout to ensure that it was properly labeled and that the counts on the printout are within alert/action levels. Ensure that any counts above alert/action levels have an appropriately documented explanation on the printout.

Documentation

Environmental Monitoring Submission Form

At the completion of sampling, an Environmental Monitoring (EM) submission form must be completely and accurately filled out, signed, dated, and turned in along with the TAP printout to QC on the day of sampling or no later than noon the next day.

Troubleshooting

Trouble Shooting

The following are some troubleshooting techniques that can be useful when sampling problems arise:

- If the printer does not deliver a printout after each sample, check to see if the printer is enabled.
- If the printer delivers paper after each sample but no print is present on the paper, the roll may be installed upside down. The paper will only print on the outside surface of the roll.
- If the printer has jammed, the instrument may need to be turned off and then turned back on in order to reset the printer.
- A faulty or loose power cord may cause power surges. Check power cord attachment at unit A/C receptacle and at A/C power source.
- If the unit alarm goes off, but counts for 0.5 µm have not exceeded set alarm limits, check to see if alarms have been set for other particle sizes. Also check for air flow being out of range and adjust if necessary.
- Consult the appropriate particle counters owner's manual for additional troubleshooting instructions.

Manual Labware Cleaning

Overview

Introduction

Clean equipment and labware are critical to the biomanufacturing process. Equipment is cleaned to prevent malfunction or contamination that would alter the safety, identity, strength, quality, or purity of the drug product.

Table of Contents

This document contains the following topics:

Manual Labware Cleaning

Objectives

1. Explain the significance/importance of parts cleaning to biomanufacturing.
2. Describe the role of validation in parts cleaning.
3. Name four tests for validation of cleaning.
4. Name three daily tests used to determine labware/parts cleanliness.
5. Explain the significance of Total Organic Carbon in parts cleanliness.
6. Explain the importance of shelf-life in labware cleaning
7. Distinguish between clean and sterile.
8. Explain the role of training in labware cleaning.
9. Demonstrate/explain use of labels in labware cleaning.
10. Describe the use of two different labware cleaners.
11. Describe the different cleaning utensils and when each should be used.
12. Perform calculations for preparation of needed amount of cleaning agent.
13. Prepare coffin of cleaning agent.
14. Demonstrate preparation of parts for cleaning.
15. Explain appropriate soak times for lab items.
16. Demonstrate proper cleaning of valves and valve assemblies.
17. Explain/demonstrate proper cleaning of tubing/hoses less than three feet in length.
18. Explain/demonstrate proper cleaning of tubing/hoses greater than three feet in length.
19. Perform proper labeling of dried clean parts/labware.
20. Demonstrate proper storage of clean parts/labware.
21. Design necessary labels for labware cleaning procedures.
22. Explain the use of storage bins and expiration dates.
23. Explain the importance of proper flow of clean and dirty parts in a facility.
24. Describe the attire for labware cleaning.

Equipment Staging

Introduction

"Soiled" or "to be cleaned" equipment should be rinsed, labeled, and staged until cleaning can be performed. The equipment can be held for a specified amount of time before it has to be cleaned. The appropriate area SOP should be checked, as the hold times vary from one area to another. The soiled items that cannot be moved, such as tanks, are broken down and the parts removed for hand wash, Clean-Out-of-Place (COP), or the lab washer. They are then staged by being rinsed and labeled with their status until cleaning can be performed.

Importance of Equipment Staging

Equipment staging is necessary for the following reasons:
- To segregate dirty from clean equipment reducing potential cross-contamination.
- Prerinses are performed as part of staging to prevent process material from drying and adhering to the equipment.
- If equipment cannot be cleaned immediately, it is staged in a designated staging area to keep it segregated from clean equipment. In some cases, rinses are the first steps of cleaning.
- Cleaning is necessary to remove organic and inorganic residue from equipment. All nondisposable equipment used in processing requires cleaning.

Manual Cleaning Concepts

Definition

Manual cleaning is the act of cleaning equipment by hand, as if doing dishes.

What Does Manual Cleaning Accomplish?

Hand washing of equipment and labware results in the following desirable outcomes:
- Reduction of microbial contamination
- Reduction of endotoxins
- Removal of cleaning agent residuals

Cleaning Solution and Concentrations

What kinds of cleaning solutions and concentrations can be used for hand wash cleaning?
- The most common is Linbro 7X using a 5% concentration.
- It is critical to check the area SOP for approved cleaning solutions and concentrations.
- Scrub pads (i.e., S.O.S. pads) are not acceptable due to possible damage to stainless steel parts.

Requirements for Manual Cleaning

What are the requirements to manual cleaning?
- Prerinse
- Detergent wash
- Thorough Water For Injection (WFI) rinse
- Visual inspection
- Labeling
- Drying

Continued on next page

Manual Cleaning Concepts

Regulatory Issues

The regulatory reasons for cleaning equipment used in manufacturing are:
- To remove or obliterate previous batch components
- To prevent contamination that would alter the safety, identity, strength, quality, or purity of the drug product.

Determination of Cleaned Equipment or Labware

How can you tell if something has been cleaned?
- Items that have been cleaned using a validated method are labeled clean.
- Wrapping is required for items that will be autoclaved.

Storage of Clean Equipment

The proper storage of clean equipment and labware includes the following:
- Items should be placed in sealed pouches
- Items should be kept in parts drawer
- Open ports on portable tanks and glassware should be covered with Bioshield

Equipment Preparation

The following steps should be taken to properly prepare equipment for hand wash:
- Disassemble all equipment to be hand washed.
- Discard tubing, small filters, and nonreusable items. Keep in mind that some items need to be retained, such as large filters to be saved for postintegrity testing.
- Inactivate contents if vessel contains product. Check your area SOP on biohazard waste inactivation.

Continued on next page

Performing Manual Cleaning

Performing Manual Cleaning

When performing manual cleaning it is important to keep in mind the following:

- Always refer to area specific SOP for complete instructions.
- Water systems are delicate and easily contaminated. Exercise good technique when drawing water to prevent contamination of the drop and/or system.
- Detergents such as Linbro 7X are typically used for manual cleaning.
- The formula used to determine the proper amount of cleaning agent for a given quantity of cleaning solution is:

$$(\text{concentration 1}) \ X \ (\text{volume 1}) = (\text{concentration 2}) \ X \ (\text{volume 2})$$

- Check the area specific SOP to determine the appropriate detergent and concentration to use for manual cleaning.
- Scrub the equipment or labware with the cleaning brush until no residue is visible.
- Do not use scrub pads due to possible damage to stainless steel parts.
- If glassware is being cleaned, use caution to prevent breakage.
- Rinse the equipment thoroughly with WFI (3 full volume rinses) while visually inspecting the equipment for cleanliness.

Manual Labware Cleaning

Laboratory

Introduction Labware and equipment cleaning is a skill that is essential for any employee within the biotechnology industry, whether in a research laboratory or within manufacturing. The strict requirements for a biomanufacturing facility will be taught as the standard in this laboratory. Knowledge of cleaning agents, equipment, and process will be gained through hands-on practice.

Equipment Large tubs (coffins) for washing/storage of dirty parts

Spinners

Stainless steel parts for washing (tee's, clamps, endcaps etc.)
Equipment to be washed

Materials and Supplies

7X Linbro	WFI water hoses
Glassware for washing	Gloves
Nalgene bottles/caps	Labels
Drying rack/area	Tape
Graduated cylinders and scoops	Markers
Nylon brushes	Stapler
Deionized water	

Activities at a Glance

1. Examine coffins in Glassware Prep room and make determinations of amount of cleaning solution each will require.

2. Perform calculations for preparation of required volumes of 7X Linbro cleaning solution.

3. Set-up soak of dirty glassware/labware including spinner flask parts, clamps, stainless steel fitting, shake flasks, etc.. The instructor will help students determine their clean glassware and equipment needs for future labs. Students are responsible for cleaning, wrapping, and autoclaving all required items.

4. Make temporary labels for steps of cleaning.

5. Following soak time, perform cleaning of glassware/labware. Air dry.

Equipment Preparation and Assembly

Overview

Introduction

Equipment preparation is the cleaning of equipment followed by sanitization or sterilization. Improper equipment preparation could result in cross-contamination from product to product, cross-contamination from lot to lot of the same product, or failed runs.

Table of Contents

This document contains the following topics:

Equipment Preparation and Assembly

Objectives

1. Explain the difference between tubing and pipe.
2. Identify one inch tubing and one inch pipe.
3. Explain the reasons for use of tubing in biomanufacturing.
4. Describe the two types of tubing and how they are made.
5. Explain the measurement of tubing walls.
6. Explain why the inner diameter (ID) of one inch tubing may vary.
7. Explain the use of a profilometer and the information it provides regarding tubing.
8. Explain the significance of RA in these measurements.
9. Explain why the finish of tubing is important to biomanufacturing.
10. Describe the uses/outcomes of electropolishing on tubing.
11. Identify an electropolished tube among untreated samples.
12. Identify the following fittings: elbows, tees, concentric reducer, eccentric reducer.
13. Distinguish between auto-weld and clamp-end fittings.
14. Identify gaskets used to attach tubing.
15. Describe the United States Pharmacopoeia Class 6 testing on elastomeres for gaskets, hoses, and seals.
16. Name three different gasket materials.
17. Explain the use of diaphragm valves.
18. Describe the three parts of diaphragm valves.
19. Discuss the advantages of using diaphragm valves.
20. Describe the materials used for diaphragms.
21. Distinguish between two types of bonnets.
22. Explain the uses/operation of centrifugal pumps.
23. Explain the uses/operation of positive displacement pumps.
24. Discuss the problem of cavitation.
25. Explain the use/operation of double diaphragm pumps.
26. Explain the use/operation of peristaltic pumps.
27. Identify a centrifugal pump, a positive displacement pump, and a double diaphragm pump.
28. Explain the use of hoses.
29. Identify and describe the different types of hoses.
30. Distinguish hoses/tubing/piping.

Equipment Cleaning

Introduction

The purpose of equipment cleaning is to remove or obliterate previous batch components and to prevent contamination that would alter the safety, identity, strength, quality, or purity of the drug product. More specifically, cleaning:

- Reduces microbial contamination
- Reduces endotoxin level
- Removes cleaning agent residuals

Methods for Cleaning Equipment

There are four ways to clean equipment:

- **Manual Cleaning**. This involves hand scrubbing equipment with a nylon brush and detergent, and then rinsing with WFI or purified water.
- **Glassware Washer**. Using this method involves loading equipment into a washer and subjecting the equipment to a cleaning cycle.
- **Clean-Out-Place Bath**. Equipment is loaded into a COP washer and subjected to a cleaning cycle.
- **Clean-In-Place**. A CIP skid is attached to the equipment requiring cleaning, and a cleaning cycle is executed by circulating cleaning solution and rinse water through the equipment.

Cleaning Validation

Cleaning validation studies are performed on all cleaning methods and cycles to demonstrate that cleaning procedures are effective, reproducible, and under control. If soiled equipment were cleaned using a method that had not been validated, one could not be sure the equipment was clean. In general, manufacturing areas clean equipment using the methods described above. However, some areas are moving toward validating WFI rinses as a form of tank cleaning between same buffer batching steps.

Equipment Preparation and Assembly

Sanitary Versus Nonsanitary Fittings

A sanitary connection is a connection with a smooth inner bore that will not hold up residual liquid that could act as a growth medium for bacteria. Some examples of sanitary connections are tri-clamp connections on tanks, process lines, and clean steam utility drops.

A non-sanitary connection is a connection with a rough bore such as threaded pipe or Swagelock fitting that could potentially hold up liquids and provide a growth medium for bacteria. Examples of nonsanitary connections include standard pipe thread such as glycol supply lines and plant steam lines.

In order to prepare equipment properly, one needs to consider the sanitary state of fittings used to transport required utilities.

Continued on next page

Equipment Preparation and Assembly

Notes on Selected Equipment

Material of Construction. Only parts made out of stainless steel, Viton, Teflon, or silicon can be used if parts come in contact with product. These materials are inert and will not react with the product. Stainless steel parts should be inspected for roughing, corrosion, scratches, and visible debris prior to installation.

Tri-Clamp Connections. Select the gasket with the right Inner Diameter (ID); the gasket must match the largest ID in the connection. Ensure the gasket is centered and the two fittings are square. Tri-clamp connections need only be hand tightened to be effective.

Fittings with O-rings. Ensure the o-ring is not damaged and that it is the right size. To facilitate installation, lubricate the o-ring with purified water, WFI, or ethanol.

Hose Barb Fittings. Select tubing so that it fits snuggly around the barb, ensuring that tubing completely covers all of the barb threads. Use cable ties to secure the tubing on the barb.

Diaphragm Valve. Ensure the diaphragm is not worn or damaged. Align the weir mark with the valve, tighten screws crosswise and ensure the valve is open when tightening.

Filters. Filters are used to remove particles in liquid or gaseous solutions. They are used to filter product or in-process materials that come in contact with product (i.e., buffers, media, or gases). Filters must be installed on equipment in the correct orientation to be effective. Hydrophobic filters will not allow water to pass through them and are usually used as tank vents. Hydrophilic filters are for solutions and will let liquids pass through them.

Steam Traps. The purpose of a steam trap is to maintain steam pressure in the vessel while evacuating all the steam condensate. Steam traps must be installed on equipment in the correct orientation to be effective.

Check Valves. Check valves permit the flow of fluid in one direction only and must be installed in the proper orientation to work correctly. Check valves are typically used to prevent back flow.

Equipment Preparation and Assembly

Laboratory

Introduction

Students will learn to identify various process equipment, pumps, fittings, tubing, clamps, and valves. Examples of all common items encountered in a facility will be available.

Equipment needs for future process activities will be discussed and delineated. Students will primarily prepare and assemble items required for cell culture and purification. Such items should have been cleaned in previous classes and are ready for assembly.

Equipment

Pumps, diaphragm, centrifugal, and peristaltic
Tubing, variety of material, ID, and OD
Valves, diaphragm, ball
Fittings, variety
Clamps
Hoses, variety
Spinner flasks and parts
Bioreactors, probes, filters, and tubing
Chromatography columns, analytical and preparative

Activities at a Glance

1. Students will learn assembly of spinner flasks following an SOP.

2. Students will assemble the bioreactors with appropriate probes, filter, and tubing so that they are ready for the autoclave.

3. Students will assemble chromatography columns with required pumps, monitors, and chart recorders. Students will learn how to make sanitary connections with appropriate fittings and tri-clamps.

Autoclave and Labware Handling

Overview

Introduction

Autoclaves are large pieces of equipment that are widely used in the biotechnology industry. They contain large compartments capable of sterilizing a wide variety of equipment and labware used in the production process. While disinfectants are used in the sanitization of floors, walls, tabletops, and other surfaces, the autoclave is the means by which labware and other pieces of equipment are sterilized for use in sterile application. The autoclave is capable of sterilizing many pieces of equipment in a relatively short period of time. Equipment and labware are cleaned prior to autoclaving and the autoclave is used to sterilize the equipment. At $121.1^{\circ}C$ for a specified length of time, microorganisms and their spores are no longer viable. The autoclave, through the injection of clean steam, raises the pressure and temperature of its interior, and therefore its contents, to at least this level. Equipment or labware can be considered sterile and ready for use once it has been sustained at this temperature for the required period of time.

Table of Contents

This document contains the following topics:

Autoclave and Labware Handling

Objectives

1. Explain the reasons and importance of labware preparation.
2. Distinguish between sterile parts and clean parts.
3. Explain what items require sterility in a biomanufacturing facility.
4. Identify different components of spinner flasks.
5. Demonstrate assembly of spinner flasks.
6. Demonstrate proper function of spinner flask on stir plate.
7. Explain/demonstrate use/placement of autoclave tape.
8. Explain/demonstrate use of autoclave bags/sterilization pouches.
9. Demonstrate/explain the proper placement of items into autoclave bags/sterilization pouches.
10. Explain use of labels and importance of expiration dates for clean and sterile labware.
11. Demonstrate appropriate label use for labware.
12. Describe the course of action taken with unlabeled items.
13. Demonstrate the use of BioShield/Biowrap and explain the reasons for using it.
14. Demonstrate/explain the use of autoclave tape.
15. Demonstrate inspection of parts for cleanliness/integrity and explain reasons for such inspections.
16. Determine daily needs for labware preparation and usage.
17. Explain how you would determine whether an item can be autoclaved..
18. Explain how a steam sterilizer kills microorganisms.
19. Distinguish between SIP, autoclave, and a depyrogenation oven.
20. Explain how temperature and pressure are related to kill time.
21. Give the four major phases of steam sterilization.
22. Describe what occurs during each of the above phases.
23. Explain why is it essential for air to be removed from within the autoclave chamber.
24. Give the different cycle choices for the autoclave in the laboratory and explain the differences between them.
25. Explain what type of documentation is needed for autoclave use.
26. Describe the information that is recorded on a log sheet for autoclave use.
27. Describe how you would validate your choice of expiration time for autoclaved items.

Continued on next page

Objectives

28. Explain the purpose of minimum and maximum load to validation.
29. Demonstrate the use of an autoclave.
30. Demonstrate the use of a chart recorder.
31. Explain safety considerations when using an autoclave.
32. Explain the course of action you would take during an autoclave run if the temperature drops below the required setting.
33. Describe the appropriate wrapping procedure for an item that will be transported through three rooms with different classifications.
34. Give the fundamental equation used in sterilization theory.
35. Explain decimal reduction time and its relation to sterilization.
36. Explain F and its relation to sterilization.
37. Explain the use of *Bacillus stearothermophilus* or other biological indicators in sterilization.
38. Identify four factors affecting steam sterilization.

Wrapping Labware

Introduction

Wrapping the labware is the first step in proper autoclaving. It is crucial that all items and openings are properly wrapped so that the openings are completely covered. In this way the labware surface that comes in contact with product will not be exposed to contaminants once they are removed from the autoclave.

Materials for Labware Wrapping

The following materials are commonly used for wrapping labware prior to sterilization in an autoclave:

- **Bioshield or Biowrap**
  Bioshield is used to cover all openings on labware and equipment.
- **Autoclave rubber bands**
  Autoclaveable rubber bands are used to seal the equipment or labware once it has been completely wrapped with Bioshield.
- **Autoclave pouches**
  Autoclave pouches are used when the entire piece of equipment or piece of labware that is going in to the autoclave needs to be sterilized. A dot on the package turns black at the completion of a successful autoclave cycle.
- **Autoclave tape**
  Autoclave tape is used as an indicator or sometimes to seal the equipment or labware once it has been completely wrapped with Bioshield. The stripes on the tape will turn to black once the appropriate temperature has been reached and then sustained for the specified length of time.

Continued on next page

Wrapping Labware

Considerations for Labware Wrapping

- Prior to autoclaving, all labware must be properly wrapped with appropriate autoclavable wrap (e.g., Bioshield) or autoclaveable pouches. This step will ensure that equipment and labware remain in a sterile state after they are removed from the autoclave.
- Overstuffing the pouches could cause them to open during autoclaving and result in ineffective sterilization.
- When preparing equipment for use in Class 100 environments, it is especially important to apply two layers of Bioshield on all openings of valves, bottles, etc. and to double wrap items in autoclave pouches. Additionally, it is important to place all caps facing down towards the paper side of the autoclave pouch as they are placed in the pouch.
- When wrapping items such as transfer flasks, be sure that all valve ports have the appropriate sized gaskets prior to wrapping the ports with Bioshield.
- It is important to completely seal the Bioshield or pouch. This will ensure the equipment is not exposed to microorganisms when it is removed from the autoclave chamber.
- All valves and bleeders must be in the open position. This allows the clean steam to contact all surface areas, ensuring thorough sterilization. Also, all valve ports should be sealed with Bioshield to prevent contamination after autoclaving.
- Complete all necessary documentation, which will typically consist of a status label or card for individual items or Equipment Use Records (EUR) for major equipment and autoclave logs. You must always refer to the SOP to determine the specific required documentation.

Preparation for Autoclave Operation

Introduction After completion of proper labware wrapping, the next step is to prepare for autoclave operation. There are numerous brands and models of autoclaves, and differences exist between the various autoclaves. Before running an autoclave cycle, always check the appropriate SOPs located near each machine.

Autoclave Inspection The following points need to be considered when performing an inspection of an autoclave prior to operation:

- Check the drain screen for debris.

  The temperature control of the chamber is based on the coldest point in the autoclave, which is typically the chamber's drain. If there is a blockage in the drain, this will prevent the condensate from draining and create a cold spot. This could make it difficult to reach the required temperature and the cycle may abort. Items that possibly could be found in a drain include: rubber bands, zip ties, Bioshield, or wipes. If any blockage is noticed clean out debris. Notify a supervisor, if the blockage is extensive.

- For an autoclave to function properly, all of its system instruments must be calibrated to ensure that they are working at peak performance. The temperature gauges, pressure gauges, and chart recorders will all have calibration stickers that detail the current status of these systems.

- If the autoclave is experiencing a problem or is being serviced, tags will be posted on the control panel. When an autoclave that has a "Work in Progress" tag and/or is in "Lockout Tagout," inform a supervisor that the autoclave is unavailable.

Note: Lockout Tagout is the term used to describe a system that is physically locked out due to mechanical/safety issues. A "Work in Progress" tag is used to take a system out-of-service for maintenance or repair work. If either situation exists, the system should not be used.

Continued on next page

Preparation for Autoclave Operation

Verification of Utilities

When verifying utilities it is important to be aware of the following:

- Always ensure that the power supply is on.
- Clean steam is the most important utility used in autoclaving. Clean steam is injected into the main compartment, raising the internal temperature to at least 121.1°C. Always check the on/off orientation of the steam supply valve to make sure it is in the "on" position.
- There is a compartment between the internal autoclaving compartment and the outside environment. This area is called the jacket. When needed, plant steam is automatically injected into the jacket. This acts as an insulator, helping to regulate the temperature of the internal compartment.

Inspection of Equipment and Labware

When inspecting equipment and labware the following points are important to consider:

- Make certain the clean steam is able to contact and sterilize all surface areas of the equipment. All labware valves should be open. All caps on bottles should be loosened. This will allow the steam to penetrate the interior of the labware.
- Load the rack correctly prior to running the autoclave cycle. If objects are placed too close to each other on the rack, the clean steam might not contact all surface areas. Also, the SOPs must be checked prior to autoclaving. The SOPs will illustrate any special load configurations that should be employed for that particular cycle.

Documentation

The following documentation sources are critical to preparing for an autoclave cycle:

- Determine run number by checking the log.
- Determine and verify cycle load by checking the SOP.
- Document the information into the autoclave log.
- Complete status stickers and place them on all items or complete logs and status cards for all major equipment.
- Refer to area SOP for specific information on documentation completion.

Autoclave Operation

Activate System The RTD is the main temperature sensor for the autoclave. There may be several in a chamber, but the one in the drain is most critical. When the steam condenses and returns to a liquid state, it must travel down the drain. Therefore, the liquid in the drain is the coldest point for the equipment being autoclaved. When the temperature in the drain reaches 121.1°C, it can be assumed that the temperature in the rest of the compartment is at least 121.1°C.

Different types of equipment will require a different duration of time at the kill point of 121.1°C to be considered sterile. For certain items this duration has been precalculated and the parameters have been entered into the autoclave. These "programs" may be accessed (per SOPs) and utilized during the autoclave process. Always refer to your area SOP to determine which cycle to run.

The final step before activating the system is to check the chart recorder. This instrument records the vital information during autoclaving such as temperature, pressure, and duration. It should be determined if the recorder has enough paper to complete the documentation for the run. If it does not, a fresh supply of paper should be installed and aligned correctly.

At this point the system start switch can be activated.

Monitor Autoclave Operation While the autoclave is running, one should be ready to respond should an alarm sound. Refer to your SOP for an explanation of the different alarms on your model of autoclave.

If an alarm does sound, a supervisor should be contacted immediately.

Continued on next page

Autoclave Operation

Postoperation Procedures

1. Once the autoclave has completed its cycle, the recorder should be checked to ensure that all of the parameters outlined in the SOP were met. If the required temperature, pressure, or autoclaving duration standards were not met, the run cannot be considered valid and must be rerun to ensure sterility. It may be necessary to investigate the cause of the failure, so appropriate repairs can be made.

2. Inspect the equipment after autoclaving to ensure the run was a success:
   - The autoclave tape should have turned black, indicating the appropriate temperature was met.
   - The Bioshield and pouches should still be intact. Specifically, one should ensure that there are no rips in the pouches and that all items are completely dry.
   - All valves must be closed after the equipment is unloaded to prevent contamination of the equipment in the event the Bioshield comes off.

3. All equipment, labware, media, and liquids will be very hot and should be handled with care. Safety gloves should always be worn when handling hot equipment.

4. Stage equipment. Once a packaged autoclaved item is opened it will no longer be considered sterile. It is considered clean and sterile as long as the clean expiration date has not expired.

Autoclave and Labware Handling

Laboratory

Introduction

In this laboratory students will learn how to prepare a variety of labware and equipment for sterilization in the autoclave. Students will gain experience in the loading and operation of an autoclave. This will include safety issues, minimum and maximum load determinations, use of a chart recorder, log sheets, cycle choices, and validation procedures.

Equipment

Autoclave
Equipment to be autoclaved

Materials and Supplies

Chart recorder paper
Bioshield/Biowrap
Autoclave pouches
Autoclave rubber bands
Autoclave tape
Autoclave log book
Labware to be autoclaved

Activities at a Glance

1. A variety of equipment glassware, small parts (bioreactor, shake flasks, spinner flasks, housings, stainless steel funnels, etc.) should be available for autoclaving.
2. Students will first practice proper wrapping using pouches, Bioshield, rubber bands, and autoclave tape.
3. Students should determine proper load configurations for the autoclave cart and practice loading the cart into the autoclave.
4. Each student will demonstrate knowledge of the components of the autoclave, especially the chart recorder, gauges, buttons, cycle selections, and other controls involved in the operation of the unit.
5. Each student will practice use of the autoclave through the duration of the course.

Clean Room Conduct and Aseptic Technique

Overview

Introduction

Humans are the major source of contamination during the manufacture of therapeutic proteins in a biotechnology facility. This contamination can be controlled through proper behavior and the use of aseptic technique. The safety, quality, and purity of the product depend upon the application of the precise behavioral guidelines discussed in this document.

Table of Contents

This document contains the following topics:

Clean Room Conduct and Aseptic Technique

Objectives

1. Give a definition for aseptic contaminants and sterilization.
2. Describe the steps to follow for work in a Laminar Air Flow (LAF) hood and Biosafety Cabinet (BSC).
3. Demonstrate proper cleaning of an LAF hood/BSC prior to use.
4. Explain the role of a runner and why work in an LAF hood/BSC is done in pairs.
5. Describe/demonstrate appropriate personnel behaviors while working within and around an LAF hood or BSC.
6. Describe the appropriate placement of labware/materials in an LAF hood/BSC.
7. Demonstrate organization of laboratory materials in an LAF hood/BSC.
8. Explain how placement of items in vertical or horizontal LAF would differ.
9. Demonstrate aseptic procedure for putting on sterile gloves and sleeves.
10. Demonstrate proper cleaning of hands with 70% ethanol.
11. Demonstrate proper positioning of arms and hands for aseptic hood work.
12. Demonstrate aseptic removal of caps in an LAF hood/BSC.
13. Demonstrate two ways to open individually wrapped pipettes in an LAF hood.
14. Demonstrate aseptic pouring of sterile liquids in an LAF hood/BSC.
15. Demonstrate aseptic pipetting of sterile liquids in an LAF hood/BSC.
16. Perform proper cleaning of an LAF hood/BSC following use.
17. Perform appropriate documentation of equipment use on log sheet.

Clean Room Conduct

Introduction

Clean room conduct involves applying common sense techniques to general behavior in order to prevent the spread of contamination in production facilities. Clean room conduct must be followed at all times when in a facility.

Importance of Clean Room Conduct

Many biotechnology companies are in the business of producing drugs that benefit human health. Great care needs to be taken to protect the product from contamination that could be harmful to patients. Many of the biotechnology drugs are injected. When a pill is taken orally, the body's defenses can fight contaminants that may be present. When a drug is injected, it bypasses several of the body's defenses. There is a very real potential for patient sickness and death if the drug is contaminated.

Humans as a Source of Contaminants

The human body is the source of over 80% of all contaminants found in processing areas in a facility. The human body is constantly shedding skin cells and hair, even when an individual is seated. Much greater numbers are shed when walking or running around. The simple act of scratching your head will dislodge skin flakes and hair and deposit them into the clean environment. Any contamination on the head could be transferred to the hands, to equipment, and ultimately to the product. The shoes of employees carry dirt particles and many forms of microorganisms into the processing area. Bare hands and dirty gloves transmit bacteria to the environment and, more critically, to labware and potentially to the product. Coughs and sneezing expel particles at a high rate of speed and over a large distance, easily contaminating the environment and potentially the product. Clean room conduct requires applying basic common sense to techniques that help prevent the spread of contaminants in the environment, thereby protecting the product.

Continued on next page

Clean Room Conduct

Clean Room Conduct and Workplace Behaviors

In the workplace, there are specific behaviors that should be observed while working in the cleanroom. The following guidelines apply:

- Follow all gowning procedures for an area per SOP.
- Wear gloves whenever handling equipment. Sanitize gloves with secondary disinfectant and replace gloves as soon as they become damaged or soiled. This procedure helps to minimize the spread of bacteria and other contaminants.
- Use tacky mats whenever possible to minimize the spread of dirt and contaminants. Change mats when they have become excessively soiled.
- Assume the floor and anything that touches it are dirty.
- Avoid touching exposed skin. Also avoid any unnecessary touching of your gown with your gloves, objects, etc.
- Walk slowly to avoid stirring up particulates.
- Avoid socialization in clean rooms, particularly in Class 100 rooms.
- Do not walk too close or too quickly near the air monitoring equipment. Dust particles will be stirred up, causing an alarm to sound and potentially exposing the product to contaminating particles.

Related Behaviors at Home

In addition to appropriate workplace behaviors for working in the clean rooms, there are additional considerations to be given attention in the home. The following should be addressed prior to coming to the workplace:

- Shower before coming to work and use lotion on dry skin. This reduces shedding.
- Reduce the amount of make up worn or eliminate it entirely based on the classifications of rooms you will enter.
- Reduce the amount of jewelry worn to prevent its exposure in the clean room, or eliminate it entirely based on the classifications of rooms you will enter.
- If you are sick, stay at home. If you must come in to work, wear a mask.

Aseptic Technique

Definition

Aseptic technique is the handling of sterile objects so as to maintain their sterility. Aseptic technique is related to Clean Room Conduct in that it prevents the spread of contamination, but it involves more precise behavioral guidelines.

Maintaining Sterile Conditions

Microorganisms exist in much of the environment in, around, and on us. Given appropriate conditions and nutrients, most microorganisms have the potential for prolific growth. If introduced into the process during the manufacture of a biopharmaceutical product, microorganisms could cause any one of the following:

- Utilization of nutrients intended for the desired culture
- Alteration of growth conditions and inhibition of the desired culture
- Production of a toxic substance that
    - inhibits growth of the desired culture
    - could harm the patient
- Production of a substance that reacts with or degrades the desired product

In order to control microbial growth and prevent its occurrence in sterile or clean environments, it is imperative that personnel strictly adhere to the principles of aseptic technique.

Continued on next page

Aseptic Technique

General Principles of Aseptic Technique

In order to ensure that a growing culture contains only the desired organism, everything that contacts the culture must be sterile (i.e., free of all forms of life). This includes all equipment, media, water, air, etc. Methods of sterilization are discussed elsewhere in this manual. Suffice it to say that incomplete or inadequate sterilization of anything used in the culture process invites contamination.

Following sterilization great care must be taken to avoid contamination. Anything that comes in contact with sterile materials must itself be sterile. Media, other nutrients, and the culture itself must be introduced into a vessel in such a manner as not to inadvertently introduce other microorganisms as well.

Guidelines

The following guidelines will serve to ensure aseptic technique:

- The growth medium and its container must be sterilized as soon as media is prepared.
- Keep vessels covered as much as possible. Covers should not be placed on other surfaces, which might harbor contaminants.
- When exposing the culture to the environment, do so in an area with little turbulence and as free from other microorganism as possible.
- All personnel working with or near the growing culture should be appropriately gowned, for their own protection as well as that of the culture.
- Avoid excessive movement or talking while transferring cultures.
- Do not mouth pipette cultures.
- Avoid contact with sterile equipment, surfaces, instruments, etc.

Clean Room Conduct and Aseptic Technique

Laboratory

Introduction The laminar air flow hoods and biosafety cabinets are critical pieces of equipment used in cell culture. This laboratory exercise is designed to train students in the proper organization of the work space within the hood. Students will learn the procedures for donning sterile apparel and the basics of aseptic technique while performing manipulations within the hood.

Equipment LAF hoods or BSC
Incubators, 37° C

Materials and Supplies

Sterile media (i.e., LB)   70% ethanol
50 ml Falcon tubes, sterile   Spray bottles
15 ml Falcon tubes, sterile   Sterile pipettes
Pipet-aids   Sterile sleeves
Lint–free sterile wipes   Sterile gloves

Activities at a Glance

1. Each student will clean the LAF hood or BSC prior to use, following the appropriate SOP. Post-use cleaning will be done by the next student as their pre-use cleaning. Final student in each hood will perform post-use cleaning.
2. Students will be instructed on the proper methods for donning sterile sleeves and sterile gloves. All students are required to wear these items in addition to other gowning requirements.
3. Each student will set-up and organize materials for work in LAF hood/BSC. An instructor will verify proper organization.
4. Each student will practice aseptic manipulations and transfer of media by pouring and pipetting under the observation of an instructor:
   a. Pipette 40 mls from media bottle to 50 ml tube
   b. Pour 10 mls from 50 ml tube into 15 ml tube
   c. Repeat b with a pipette
   d. Pour 15 mls from 50 ml tube into 15 ml tube
   e. Pipette 15 mls from 15 ml tube into 50 ml tube
5. Incubate all tubes at 37°C to determine success of aseptic technique.

Lot Track Trace

Overview

Introduction   Lot Track Trace is the ability to track and trace the specific amount and lot number of each component used in each lot of product. By following the Lot Track Trace concept and procedures, biotechnology companies comply with the CFRs, ensure that the manufacturing processes are consistent and reliable, and can correct problems in case of a component recall.

Table of Contents   This document contains the following topics:

Lot Track Trace

Objectives

1. Explain why raw material logistics are so important to the manufacture of biotherapeutic drugs.
2. Explain how a tracking system for raw materials works within a facility
3. Describe the role of Manufacturing Resource Planning.
4. Explain the importance of having backup stock for each raw material.
5. Explain the role of quarantines for raw materials.
6. Describe the tagging of raw materials.
7. Describe how raw materials are stored in a facility.
8. Explain material flow through a facility.
9. Explain how materials are requisitioned within a facility.
10. Explain the handling of unused raw materials.
11. Explain the role of an operating system in Lot Track Trace.
12. Explain the concept of lot reconciliation.

Lot Track Trace

CFR 211.101(b) Charge-in of Components

CFR 211.101(b) states, "Components for drug product manufacturing shall be weighed, measured, or subdivided as appropriate. If a component is removed from the original container to another, the new container shall be identified with the following information: (1) Component name or item code, (2) Receiving or control number, (3) Weight or measure in new container, (4) Batch for which component was dispensed, including its product name, strength, and lot number." Biotechnology companies comply with this CFR through a system of Lot Track Trace.

Operating System

All Lot Track Trace activities, including inventory, are controlled by an Operating System (OS). Trained manufacturing personnel use the system to open work orders for material dispensing and input product inventory at the end of the production run. Although the system is computerized, the manufacturing operators are ultimately the ones who add and document which components, and how much of the components, are used to make the products or in-process components. Errors in Lot Track Trace should be caught and corrected by production personnel as they occur on the production floor prior to entering data into the OS.

Material Supply Requisition

Materials will be requisitioned into the process using a Material Supply Requisition (MSR). This form lists the item specification and quantity to be dispensed, as well as the product and lot number that the released raw materials will be charged in to. One copy of this form is kept with the production batch record, while the other is sent to Production Planning and Inventory Control (PPIC) in order to track the amount of each specific material on hand.

Continued on next page

Lot Track Trace

Material Supply Return

Unused unit items may be returned to material storage from the processing areas if the outer wrapping is intact. This is tracked by the use of a Material Supply (MS) Return form. This form returns the item to inventory and makes it available to another process, thus reducing waste. The same form is also used to track the disposal or scrapping of opened excess raw materials.

Material Movement Form

A third material form is used for movement of intermediate product from one place to another. This is called a Material Movement Form (MMF). If, for instance, DFM was moved from one storage freezer to another, an MMF would be completed. One copy of the form would stay with the DFM Log, while the other would be sent to PPIC in order to track the precise whereabouts and quantity of the intermediate product.

Lot Reconciliation

Lot reconciliation is performed following the completion of a production run. All raw materials and components used for production are verified to ensure that the proper components and amounts were used to make the product. The disposal or scrapping of opened excess raw materials or components not used during the production run must be accounted for. The most accurate way to accomplish this is to weigh out or count all scrap components, then double check that amount against what was documented as used in the manufacturing procedure.

Glossary

Lot Track Trace

The process of knowing how much of each lot of each raw material is used in each finished product lot.

MMF

Material Movement Form is a form used to move intermediate product from one place to another.

MS Return

Material Supply Return is a form used to return items to inventory or to waste.

MSR

Material Supply Requisition is a form used to request raw material be dispensed for a particular product lot.

Lot Track Trace

Laboratory

Introduction   Students will design and set up an inventory system of the laboratory. All reagents, raw materials, and disposable items will be placed into the inventory system and become part of the Lot Track Trace system for the laboratory.

Materials and Supplies

Clipboards
Pens
Excel
Automatic label machine

Activities at a Glance

1. Students will design an inventory system for the laboratory.

2. Students will organize themselves into teams for the inventory.

3. All cabinets and drawers in the laboratory facility should be labeled so the contents are known.

4. Students will perform the inventory and enter the information onto an Excel spreadsheet.

Buffer and Media Batching

Overview

Introduction

Media and buffers are critical components of the biomanufacturing process. Each are used at different stages during production. Proficiency and knowledge in the preparation of media and buffers are essential to operators in the manufacturing facility.

Table of Contents

This document contains the following topics:

Buffer and Media Batching

Objectives

1. Define media.
2. Explain how the correct media is chosen for any given application.
3. Explain what is used as a buffer in DMEM.
4. Explain why phenol red is added to media.
5. Explain why the following parameters need to be considered with respect to media choice: buffer, temperature, osmolality, viscosity, surface tension, foam.
6. Describe what a Manufacturing Formulation Record (MFR) is.
7. Identify the type of information that would be recorded on an MFR.
8. Explain why serum is often added to media.
9. Explain why the biotechnology industry prefers serum-free media.
10. Perform calculations for preparation of DMEM with sodium bicarbonate.
11. Perform calculations for addition of serum to media at final concentration of 10%.
12. Demonstrate ability to prepare media.
13. Demonstrate use of a pH meter.
14. Demonstrate use of balances.
15. Perform aseptic filtration of media in an LAF hood.
16. Demonstrate use of vacuum pump and filtration units.
17. Demonstrate use of an analytical balance.

Background

Role of Media in the Process

Media is used in mammalian cell culture and microbial fermentation. Media contains the nutrients for mammalian or bacterial cells during growth and product producing phases. Media is designed to contain the necessary components that cells need to grow, multiply, and produce product. If the media is lacking any of the components, the cells would either begin to die or not produce the product effectively, resulting in a failed run.

Role of Buffers in the Process

Buffers are extensively made and used in purification areas; however, some recovery unit operations that occur in fermentation and/or cell culture areas require buffers as well. Each buffer has a specific purpose in the process. Examples of these include:

- To adjust the pH of a product solution
- To change the ionic charge of the product solution prior to a chromatography step
- To provide the components for oxidation and solubilization reactions to occur
- To dilute the product to a desired concentration
- To formulate the product

Buffer Preparation Process

Introduction

The techniques for both media and buffer preparation are very similar. In this discussion, buffer batching will be used as an example to demonstrate the concepts of each.

Prebuffer Preparation

The following steps should be taken before beginning the buffer preparation process:

- Get an official copy of the Manufacturing Procedure (MP).
- Ensure all the necessary ingredients have been ordered and are available.
- Clean and sanitize/sterilize all equipment that will be used in making the buffer.
- Review the MP to ensure you have everything you need to make the buffer.

Continued on next page

Buffer Preparation Process

Significant Figures

Always document data in the MP with the correct number of significant figures. When performing calculations, the answer should have the same number of significant figures as the least precise measurement used in the calculation. For example: $4.56 \times 1.4 = 6.384$ is incorrect. The correct way to write the answer is 6.4 because 1.4 is the least precise measurement.

Buffer Preparation Process

After receiving the required materials and preparing equipment, operators should follow the relevant MP for making the particular buffer that is needed. Although the procedure will vary from buffer to buffer, some generalized steps in buffer preparation are listed below:

1. Perform a visual inspection of the tank and check the tank Equipment Use Record (EUR) to ensure the tank is ready for use.

2. Install appropriate instruments such as conductivity probe, pH, temperature probe, etc.

3. Put an "In Process" status card on the tank prior to adding contents.

4. Verify raw materials by checking them for lot number, expiration date, specification, and quantity.

5. Accurately calculate the amount needed of each material and write the answers in the MP.

6. Assign a buffer lot number according to the SOP and record it in the MP. An example of how lot numbers may be assigned is given here.

BB	G	MMDDY	A
Building Code	Mfg Group Code	Date	Multiple Lot in Day
Bldg 4	A = Cell Culture		A is 2nd lot of day
= 04	B = Fermentation		B is 3rd lot of day
	C = Purification		
	D = Formulation		
	E = Filling		

   For example, the lot number for the first buffer made in the Fermentation area of Building 4 on September 11, 2000, would be 04B091100.

7. If using a scale to determine volume, place tank on scale and properly tare the scale.

Continued on next page

Buffer Preparation Process

8. Add the proper amount of components to the tank in sequence.
9. Follow proper Point of Use Water (PUW) procedures when adding WFI.
10. Mix the buffer for the required time.
11. Determine the final net amount of buffer and record in the MP.
12. Affix a "To Be Tested" label on the "In Process" label on the tank.
13. Store the buffer at the right conditions, as indicated in the MP.
14. Sample the buffer, adhering to proper technique, and label sample.
15. Test the sample and record results.
16. If sample meets testing criteria, approve buffer and affix "Approved for Use" label on the status card of the 04B091100 tank.
17. Adhere to proper clean room conduct procedures at all times.
18. Adhere to all other aspects of the particular MP.
19. If necessary, prepare unused materials for return to inventory.
20. Deface labels and dispose of empty containers appropriately.

Buffer Sampling

Buffers are tested to ensure they are made properly.

- A buffer is sampled and tested to determine if it meets established testing criteria as specified in the MP.
- Test results from assays such as conductivity and pH are critical for approving a buffer for use.
- Favorable test results indicate that procedures were followed properly, while an unfavorable result indicates the opposite.
- If test results indicate that the buffer does not meet acceptance criteria, the operator should contact a supervisor.

Potential Problems and Consequences

Potential Problem	Consequence/Result
Failure to make visual inspection of tank and log	Tank may not be properly prepared. Expiration of CIP or SIP on equipment may be missed. Buffer must be dumped.
No pH probe installed	Instrument is critical, if titration is required it cannot be done.
Equipment or buffer not labeled correctly	Mix-ups will occur.
Failure to check lot number, expiration date, specification number, etc. on raw materials	May use incorrect materials in insufficient quantity. May use up materials designated for another purpose or that have expired.
Calculations for significant figures not done properly. Did not use correct significant figures given in the MP	Buffer or media will not prepared correctly.
No lot number assigned	Cannot identify where the buffer came from, what raw materials were used to make the buffer, and what product lot made use of the buffer. Therefore, the buffer must be dumped.
Forget to tare the scale	Errors made in determining the amount of buffer that was made. If you do not know the amount, you cannot tell if the concentration is correct.
"Recipe" in the MP not followed correctly and the wrong amount of components were used.	You may have soup instead of pudding. The buffer or media will not meet acceptance criteria.

Continued on next page

Potential Problems and Consequences

Potential Problem	Consequence/Result
Point of Use Water procedures were not followed.	The water drop may become contaminated. This could contaminate the buffer, or in the worst case, the entire system in the building.
Buffer not mixed properly	Samples will have uneven concentrations of ingredients. This will affect the pH and conductivity of the samples.
Buffer not stored properly	Buffer could degrade and become unusable.
Proper aseptic technique was not used in taking sample.	Sample could be contaminated.
Labels were not defaced on empty containers. Empty containers not disposed of properly.	Personnel could be exposed to dangerous substances.
Adhere to all aspects of a particular MP.	Failure to document any part of the process can invite FDA scrutiny.

Buffer and Media Batching

Laboratory

Introduction   Preparation of media required for use in mammalian cell culture will be performed by each student. Students will be required to make assessments of media requirements for the course and plan and prepare all needed amounts. Students will be required to perform calculations, acquire proficiency in the use of equipment, and perform preparation, and filtration of all the required buffers and media.

Equipment   Assorted glassware
pH meters
Balance
Stir plates
LAF hoods
Vacuum pump

Materials and Supplies   DMEM powder
Fetal calf serum
$0.2\mu m$ filter units
Sodium bicarbonate
pH standard buffers
Stir bars

Activities at a Glance   Students will prepare media for use during the culture of mammalian cells. Each student will prepare and be responsible for their own media. The following steps will be followed:

1. Perform calculations for preparing desired volume of media from powder.
2. Make media.
3. Determine pH of media and adjust to desired pH with acid/base.
4. Add fetal calf serum, if appropriate.
5. Filter sterilize media using proper aseptic technique.
6. Label media appropriately.

Clean-In-Place

Overview

Introduction

Clean-In-Place (CIP) refers to the act of cleaning a piece of equipment that is too large to clean by manual cleaning methods. Tanks, fermentors, liquid transfer lines, and series of hoses are some of the items that are cleaned with a CIP skid.

Table of Contents

This document contains the following topics:

Clean-In-Place

Objectives

1. Describe the physical appearance of a transfer panel, what it is used for, and where you may encounter one.
2. Explain the role of a transfer panel in CIP.
3. Explain the function of a proximity switch on a transfer panel.
4. Define the term "jumper" and explain its function.
5. Explain what a CIP skid is and describe the components.
6. Explain the purpose of using WFI during CIP.
7. Explain the role of the human-machine interface in CIP.
8. Describe the path of a solution during CIP from beginning to end.
9. Following completion of your connections for CIP, describe the course of action should the computer tell you "path unavailable."
10. Describe the role of each of the following in CIP: PLC, temperature indicators, flow rate, PSI gauge, and conductivity meter.
11. Explain the function of a spray ball.
12. Describe how ports, valves, and J tubes are cleaned during CIP.
13. Explain the function of the bypass on a bioreactor.
14. Explain why the set-up of a bioreactor for CIP is different than for culturing cells.
15. Explain how CIP procedures are validated.
16. Explain the function of a biological indicator.
17. Explain why monitoring is critical during a CIP cycle.
18. Propose a scenario during a CIP cycle that would require troubleshooting on the part of the operator.

Background

Why Clean?   Cleaning is performed to remove or obliterate previous batch components. It is used to remove in-process residues, control bioburden, and reduce endotoxin levels within processing equipment and systems. Residue removal is accomplished during CIP with a combination of heat, chemical action, and turbulent flow. The Code of Federal Regulations (CFR) 211.67(a) states "Equipment and utensils shall be cleaned, maintained, and sanitized at appropriate intervals to prevent malfunctions or contamination that would alter the safety, identity, strength, quality, or purity of the drug product beyond the official or other established requirements."

Repeatability   Repeatable, reliable, and effective cleaning is of the utmost importance in a biopharmaceutical manufacturing facility. Adequate cleaning of all process equipment must be demonstrated and validated. Cleaning procedures are validated to demonstrate that they are effective, reproducible, and under control. Procedures must be carefully followed to ensure that validated procedures are used at all times. In order to adequately clean processing equipment:
- The equipment must be designed with smooth stainless steel surfaces and interconnecting piping that has cleanable joints.
- The chemical properties of the cleaning agents must properly interact with the chemical and physical properties of the residues being removed.

Cleaning Agents   Appropriate cleaning agents must be selected that will ensure proper interaction with the residue to be removed. It is also important to recognize the interactions between the residues and the surfaces to which they may be adhered. Processing equipment made of different types of material may require different types of cleaning to remove the same residue.

Cleaning Agents

Sodium Hydroxide

Sodium hydroxide (NaOH) is used as the caustic (alkaline) cleaning agent. Sodium hydroxide has good dissolving, saponifying, and peptizing power, as well as being highly germicidal and relatively inexpensive. On the negative side, NaOH is not free rinsing and is very corrosive to many nonstainless steel metals.

CIP 100, Potassium Hydroxide

CIP 100 Potassium hydroxide (KOH) is also used as a caustic (alkaline) cleaning agent. CIP 100 Alkaline Process & Research Cleaner is a high performance, phosphate-free, alkaline detergent system for use in manual, immersion, and recirculating spray equipment including clean-in-place systems. It is effective in hard water and efficiently removes a wide variety of soils typically found in pharmaceutical, biotechnology, cosmetic, and food and beverage processes. The product is designed to be extremely free-rinsing. CIP 100 is very corrosive to many nonstainless steel metals.

Phosphoric Acid

Phosphoric acid is used as the acidic cleaning agent. Phosphoric acid has good dissolving and peptizing ability. It is able to dissolve mineral precipitates that caustic cleaners may leave behind and remove heat precipitated proteinaceous residues. Acidic cleaners often follow caustic cleaners because the caustic is often not free-rinsing; therefore, the acid helps to neutralize the alkaline and rinses clean.

Clean-In-Place

CIP Equipment	The equipment required to perform CIP includes:

- **CIP Skid**. A CIP skid is a system used to clean equipment in a consistent and reliable manner and can be either portable or built-in. The CIP skid is made up of a solution holding tank, pumps, automatic valves, a heat exchanger, a computer to control the flow and temperature of cleaning solutions, and instrumentation to monitor and record operations.
- **Cleaning Agents.** Sodium hydroxide (NaOH) is used as the caustic (alkaline) cleaning agent. Phosphoric acid is used as the acidic cleaning agent.
- **Clean Air Hose.** Clean air is needed to activate the pneumatic valves on the CIP skid, as well as to perform the blow down cycles of the CIP circuit.
- **Reinforced PUR/WFI Hose.** PUR or WFI water is used for rinsing and to make up the cleaning solution. Whenever connections to either PUR or WFI drops are made, clean parts, or better yet, steam sanitized/sterilized parts should be used.
- **Plant Steam Hose.** Plant steam is used to heat the solutions via a heat exchanger on the CIP skid. Plant steam is hot and will produce serious burns if used improperly.
- **Electricity.** Electricity provides power for the Programmable Logic Controller (PLC), the level probe, the chart recorder, and the other instruments on the CIP skid. Care must be taken when using electricity in a wet area.
- **Spray Ball.** A spray ball is a cleaning aid designed to spray cleaning solution on the entire inside surface of a tank. Using a spray ball ensures that the residue on the interior surfaces of the tank is removed. Spray balls are specifically designed to aid in removing residue in the hard to reach areas of a tank.

Preparation	When processing equipment has become soiled and is ready to be cleaned the following steps will take place:

- Ensure all processing operations associated with the system are complete.
- Label equipment "To Be Cleaned."
- Ensure that the equipment is not pressurized.
- If cleaning a tank, ensure that the appropriate spray ball is installed.
- Drain equipment or the prerinse will not be effective.
- Connect equipment to the CIP skid. Note: Hoses can be cleaned in series which means that the hoses are connected one after the other and then to the CIP. Tanks, however, can not be cleaned in series. There is not enough pressure coming from the drain of one tank to get enough flow through the next tank's spray balls. Tanks can be cleaned in parallel but not in series.
- Begin CIP cycle.

Continued on next page

Clean-In-Place

CIP Cycle   During a CIP cycle, the control unit will execute the following operations, in order:

1. Pre-rinse with PUR/WFI. This is performed to wet the interior surface of the tank and to remove residue. It also provides a nonchemical pressure test of the CIP flow path.
2. Caustic wash with 0.1M sodium hydroxide. The caustic wash removes bacterial cell debris.
3. Acid wash with 0.1M phosphoric acid. The acid wash is used to remove mineral precipitates and proteinaceous residues.
4. Final rinse with PUR/WFI. The purpose of this rinse is to flush out residual cleaning agents.
5. Final air blow. The final air blow cycle is used to remove moisture remaining after the CIP cycle.

Critical Parameters   The following critical parameters must be met and remain within the specification for the duration of the cycle. If the specification is not reached or maintained, cleaning will not be ensured and will have to be repeated. The critical parameters of a CIP cycle include:

- Temperature
- Flow rate
- Chemical concentration
- Chemical contact time
- Final rinse conductivity

Continued on next page

Clean-In-Place

Trouble-shooting

A CIP cycle is a complex orchestration of events. At times, alarms will become active and the operator will have to discern the next best step.

Always consult an area supervisor if CIP circuit integrity is called into question.

When troubleshooting, it is best to think of the obvious things first. For instance:

If	Then
Chemical solution does not reach proper temperature	Ensure the temperature control system is active.
There is a cycle return failure	Ensure the solution flow path valves are open.
Chemical concentration is too low	Ensure the steam trap valve is closed.
Final rinse water remains in a tank	Ensure the final rinse has reached effective completion.
Pneumatic valves not operating and air blow down failure	Ensure that clean air is supplied to the CIP skid.
Cleaning solutions leaking (Note that this condition could cause equipment damage or personal injury.)	Ensure that all hose connections are tight.

CIP Completion

In order for a CIP cycle to reach effective completion:
- The conductivity must be within specification. Equipment is considered clean when the conductivity of the final rinse solution drops to the value of the water being used.
- There should be no final rinse water remaining in the vessel, unless it is to be immediately followed by SIP. Moisture remaining in the tank will promote microbial growth.
- The Equipment Use record must be completed.
- The Equipment Status Card must be completed. The equipment is considered "CLEAN" when the equipment has been cleaned per the appropriate SOP. If the SOP was not properly followed during cleaning, the equipment may not have been cleaned effectively and the use of it may compromise product. This would require that the equipment be recleaned.

14.7

Glossary

Aqueous   Solution made primarily of water.

CIP   Clean-In-Place. The automatic cleaning of processing equipment, vessels, piping, and in-line devices with minimal manual set-up and shut-down, and little or no operator intervention during cleaning.

CIP Skid   A skid composed of tanks, pumps, cleaning agents, valves, and instrumentation that circulates cleaning fluid and water to the equipment being CIP'd.

Denaturation   A process by which the structure of a protein is altered from its active state. Denaturation may change the physical properties of the protein.

Hydrophilic   A substance is termed hydrophilic if it is readily soluble in water. Literally means water-loving.

Hydrophobic   A substance is termed hydrophobic if it is not readily soluble in water. Literally means water-fearing.

Proteinaceous   Consisting primarily of protein in some form.

Clean-In-Place
Laboratory

Introduction   CIP and SIP are difficult procedures to set up in an instructional laboratory. The classroom exercise will enable students to acquire a familiarity with the equipment. A tour of the manufacturing facility will enable students to see the active use of these components.

Equipment   Bioreactors
HMI
Media prep area
Media tanks
Transfer panels
Jumpers
Balances
Autoclave
Spray balls

Activities at a Glance

1. Utilizing the bioreactor in the laboratory as an example, students will receive training on each of the components involved in CIP and SIP. Samples of the various components used in CIP and SIP will be provided. Such items include jumpers, five-valve clusters, spray balls, and an HMI.

2. The ideal way for students to gain a working understanding of the CIP and SIP procedures is to tour a manufacturing facility. Prior instruction in the equipment is essential for them to benefit from the tour.

Steam-In-Place

Overview

Introduction Steam-In-Place (SIP) is a method of sanitizing or sterilizing equipment that is too large to be autoclaved. SIP can be used to sanitize or sterilize empty stainless steel vessels or it can be used to sterilize batches of media for microbial fermentation. The main point is to reduce or eliminate microbes from the equipment and/or media. This is vital in lowering the risk for contamination during a production run, which could cause loss of product. SIP is performed after a piece of equipment has been cleaned and inspected, as a method of preparation for processing operations.

Table of Contents This document contains the following topics:

Steam-In-Place

Objectives

___

1.   Explain the basic concept of SIP.
2.   Explain the critical parameters monitored during SIP.
3.   Explain how SIP procedures are validated.
4   Explain the function of a biological indicator.
5.   Explain why monitoring is critical during an SIP cycle.
6.   Explain how cold spots can be identified during an SIP cycle.
7.   Describe the role of steam traps during SIP.
8.   Describe how high points are handled during an SIP cycle.
9.   Propose a scenario during an SIP cycle that would require troubleshooting on the part of the operator.
10.   Explain the role of a pressure test.
11.   Explain why air overpressure is used after SIP.
12.   Describe several possible causes of an ineffective SIP.
13.   Draw/describe an example of a five valve cluster.
14.   Explain the purpose of a five valve cluster.
15.   Define sterile barrier and explain where and why it would be used.
16.   Describe a procedure for creating a sterile barrier.
17.   Explain where you would remove a sample from a bioreactor.
18.   Describe the procedure for aseptically taking a sample from a bioreactor.

___

Background

How Does SIP Work?

During empty vessel SIP, clean steam is sent in through the top most port, and condensate is drained through the bottom most port, usually the bottom valve. The steam gives up its heat to the stainless steel as it condenses from the vapor phase to the liquid phase. Superheating (≥121.1°C) the stainless steel for a defined period of time kills the microbes present. Sanitization is a reduction of microbes, while sterilization is the elimination of microbes and requires a longer cycle time.

Empty Vessel

When an empty vessel is SIP'd, the steam heats the stainless steel directly, that is, it sets up a conductive temperature gradient through the metal. The temperature of the stainless steel vessel is the monitored parameter.

Liquid Filled Vessel

When liquid is heated within a vessel, the steam heats the stainless steel jacket surrounding the vessel. The liquid is moved by an agitator within the vessel creating a convective current. That is, heat is transferred from the jacket wall to the liquid as it makes contact. That heat is then carried into the remaining liquid by the convective current created by mixing. In this case it is the temperature of the liquid that is the monitored parameter.

Critical Parameters

Critical Parameters

Three critical parameters are monitored during SIP:
- Steam temperature
- Steam pressure
- Exposure time

Temperature

There is a direct relationship between temperature and sterilization. Prolonged exposure to high temperatures kills microbes including bacterial cells and spores. Saturated steam has a higher kill power than dry heat at similar temperatures because heat transfer is more readily accomplished.

Continued on next page

Critical Parameters

Pressure
The pressure that the system achieves will vary depending upon the type of system being SIP'd. An empty vessel will usually reach between 17 to 20 psig at 121.1°C. The pressure of a liquid filled vessel will usually reach about the same pressure, but variance is dependent upon the available head space above the fluid and the vapor temperature or boiling point of the liquid being sterilized.

Time
The amount of time that the target temperature is maintained on the system is directly related to whether or not sterilization is achieved. In order to achieve validated sterilization, a sufficient number of F_0's must be accumulated.

Validation

Validation
Validation is a quality control mechanism used to prove that a system accomplishes what it is designed to do in a reliable, consistent manner. For SIP, validation consists of testing for reduction in bioburden related to exposure to steam at a set pressure and temperature for a set period of time. This is measured by accumulation of F_0 (theoretical calculation) and biological indicator testing (data to support theoretical calculations).

F_0
F_0 is a theoretical calculation of the <u>heat equivalent minutes</u> necessary to achieve sterilization. Sterilization can be accomplished at temperatures much lower than 121.1°C, but it would take a very long time. The temperature 121.1°C is the accepted standard temperature for sterilization. F_0 is accumulated over time at a given temperature. The accepted value for sanitization is $F_0 \geq 6$; this is usually accomplished by maintaining 121.1°C for at least 6 minutes. The accepted value for sterilization is $F_0 \geq 12$; this is usually accomplished by maintaining 121.1°C for at least twenty minutes.

Sanitized
To say that something is sanitized is to say that a three log reduction in bioburden has been achieved. That is, most, but not necessarily all, viable micro-organisms have been killed. An F_0 accumulation of ≥ 6 is usually adequate for sanitization. F_0 is measured using a piece of equipment called a Digistrip.

Continued on next page

Validation

Sterilized   To say that something is sterilized is to say that a twelve log reduction in bioburden has been achieved. This indicates that all viable microorganisms have been killed. An F_0 accumulation of ≥ 12 is usually adequate for sterilization. In addition to measurement of F_0, a biological indicator test must be performed.

Biological Indicator Test   This test consists of placing a known quantity of viable microorganisms inside the vessel to be sterilized. At the end of sterilization, the micro-organisms are plated and allowed to incubate for a specified period of time. The viable microorganisms are then counted. For a cycle to be validated as a sterilization cycle, all microorganisms must be killed. The test yields raw data to support the theoretical calculation of the kill rate.

Cold Spots   During a validation study, a vessel is equipped with temperature probes and the temperature is measured throughout the vessel. The coldest spots are usually at the bottom of the vessel by the steam traps. A cold spot can be an area that doesn't meet a specific temperature or it can be a spot in the vessel that exceeds the temperature but is the coldest temperature overall. While an SIP is in progress, a temperature indicating Tempilstik can be used as a method of manually checking for cold spots.

Equipment Design Concerns

Heat Resistance   Any equipment that must be sanitized or sterilized repeatedly with steam must be able to withstand high temperatures and moisture without warping, oxidizing, or otherwise being destroyed. Stainless steel is often the material of choice due to its easy cleanability, oxidation resistance, and high heat capacity.

Linked Cycles   When large systems must be SIP'd, sometimes several cycles are linked together to ensure that the entire system reaches the appropriate temperature for the appropriate time with no cold spots. This is done by placing valves such that an overlap occurs between each section of the linked cycles.

Continued on next page

Equipment Design Concerns

Overlap Regions

Overlap regions are a means of ensuring the integrity between two adjoining steam sterilized systems.

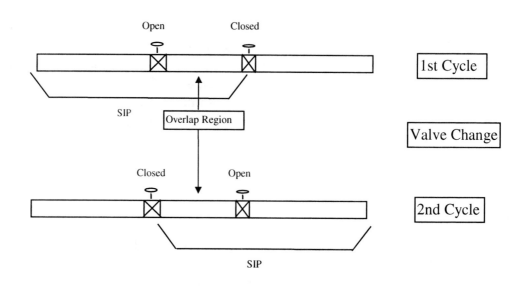

Steam Traps

Steam traps are check valves installed at low points on the SIP circuit that connect to the condensate drain. During start-up of a steam cycle, the steam trap element is fully open to discharge all air, non-condensable gases, and condensate. The heat of the entering steam causes the element to expand, closing the valve. Condensate then accumulates in the body cooling the element, causing the element to retract. The line pressure will then compress the element to open the valve and discharge condensate. The element self-adjusts to load conditions from a minimum opening on light loads to full opening at maximum load. The trap ensures that drain contents will not enter the SIP'd system and compromise sterility. If a steam trap is installed in an inverted orientation, it will prevent condensate from escaping and potentially expose the interior of the system to the drain. If condensate is not allowed to drain, it will form a cold spot that will not reach temperature. If the condensate is allowed to remain in the system, it may serve as a growth medium for microorganisms that may have survived in the cold spot during the SIP process.

Continued on next page

15.6

Equipment Design Concerns

High Points High points on a system, such as top mounted air filters, must be relieved of entrapped air to ensure steam penetration. This is accomplished by opening the top-most valve and allowing steam to escape. This action, often called a "bleed," removes the air and allows the steam to efficiently penetrate points higher than the steam inlet. If the air is not removed, it will take much longer for steam to adequately penetrate the high points. This may result in shorter exposure time at temperature for those points and potentially reduced kill rates.

Steam In Place

Sequence When performing SIP on a system, it is important to follow a sequence of actions that will accomplish the task in a safe, yet efficient manner.

Filters If there are hydrophilic filters within the steam circuit, they must be thoroughly wetted prior to the SIP process. This usually involves breaking the integrity of the system, and so should be completed prior to the pressure test.

Circuit Configuration Circuit configuration involves making the appropriate jumper, filter, valve, and hose connections to complete the SIP cycle. Again, this usually involves breaking the integrity of the system and should be completed prior to the pressure test.

Why Pressure Test? The pressure test is performed for two key reasons:
- Safety during SIP. Hot steam could escape through a system leak potentially burning the operator.
- System integrity post SIP.

Continued on next page

Steam In Place

Perform Pressure Test

The pressure test is performed to ensure the integrity of the system. Some systems have a PLC that will control the following actions, other systems must be manually tested.

- Ensure all fittings and valves are appropriately attached.
- Place appropriate high pressure warning signs.
- Slowly begin filling the system with air.
- Continue allowing air to enter the system until the appropriate pressure is reached.
- Close the air inlet valve, allow the system to "settle" for a few seconds.
- Begin timing the system.
- Integrity is determined by the pressure drop over time being less than the specified maximum.
- Release all pressure from the system in a safe manner.

SIP

Follow the appropriate area Standard Operating Procedure (SOP) to perform SIP. Ensure that the system that is being steamed is labeled accordingly, so as to prevent injury from someone unknowingly touching a hot surface.

1. Open steam trap valves.
2. Open steam inlet valve.
3. Monitor temperature and pressure.
4. When temperature is achieved:
   - Bleed high points
   - Begin timing
   - Confirm temperature with a Tempilstik melt
5. At exposure end time:
   - Close bleed valves
   - End timing
6. Close steam inlet valve.
7. Begin cooling (reconfigure).
8. Open air inlet valve to maintain appropriate air overpressure.
9. Complete appropriate documentation.

Continued on next page

Steam In Place

Air Overpressure

Air overpressure is used to maintain system integrity and/or sterility after SIP. This technique keeps a predefined pressure in the system following SIP and prior to use. If the system is compromised in some way, for instance a fitting loosens and begins to leak slowly, air would move from the sterile environment of the system out. If air overpressure is not maintained, that leak may draw nonsterile air into the system, thus compromising sterility.

Air overpressure is also used to ensure that the vessel is not damaged. Each vessel has a vacuum rating given by the manufacturer. If this vacuum rating is exceeded, the tank could implode on itself, there by destroying the tank.

Documentation

At the completion of the SIP cycle, the following appropriate documentation must be completed:
- Equipment Use Record (EUR)
- Equipment Status Card

Common Problems

Consequences of Ineffective SIP

If an SIP cycle is not effective, it may result in the following:
- The cycle may not kill all of the contaminants.
- If condensate remains, it may serve as a growth medium for those contaminants.
- Contamination of the system may lead to product loss.

Continued on next page

Common Problems

Possible Causes of an Ineffective SIP

The following table presents some possible causes and outcomes of ineffective SIP.

If	Then
The cooling system is left on	The system will not reach the required temperature set-point
A steam trap valve is closed	A dead leg is created and it will not reach the appropriate temperature set-point
A filter bleed valve is closed	Insufficient air removal could cause inadequate steam penetration
There is a high pressure differential across a filter	Damage to the integrity of the filter may result
Temperature set-point is held for less than the validated cycle time	There is potential for insufficient accumulation of F_0

Glossary

Condensate

Water that has condensed from the steam when it transfers its heat to the equipment.

High Points

Points in the system being SIP'd that are higher than the steam inlet.

Low Points

Areas where condensate tends to pool unless fitted with a steam trap to drain.

Steam Cycle

The entire process of SIP from prepping filters and pressure testing to applying air overpressure.

References

Arreola, Karen   SIP Concept Training. 1998.

Clean-Out-of-Place

Overview

Introduction   Clean-Out-of-Place (COP) is an automated method of cleaning used for small equipment or labware such as elbows, jumpers, valves, hoses, and gaskets. The parts are placed into the COP bath containing the cleaning solutions and are cleaned by utilizing mechanical force caused by the flow rate, chemical interaction of the cleaning agents with the soil being removed, and heat $\geq 70°C$.

Table of Contents   This document contains the following topics:

Clean-Out-of-Place

Objectives

1. Explain the concept COP.
2. Explain the types of things that require COP.
3. Explain the importance of effective cleaning in a biopharmaceutical facility.
4. Describe the equipment used for COP.
5. Describe the basic steps of a COP cycle.
6. Identify the safety hazards associated with COP.
7. Identify the critical parameters of a COP cycle.
8. Explain the problems generally encountered with COP.
9. Describe how equipment and labware are dried and wrapped following COP.

Background

Why Clean?   Cleaning is used to remove in-process residues, control bioburden, and reduce endotoxin levels within processing equipment and systems. Residue removal is accomplished during COP with a combination of heat, chemical action, and turbulent flow. The Code of Federal Regulations (CFR) 211.67(a) states, "Equipment and utensils shall be cleaned, maintained, and sanitized at appropriate intervals to prevent malfunctions or contamination that would alter the safety, identity, strength, quality, or purity of the drug product beyond the official or other established requirements."

Repeatability   Repeatable, reliable, and effective cleaning is of the utmost importance in a biopharmaceutical manufacturing facility. Adequate cleaning of all process equipment must be demonstrated and validated. COP cycles are validated to demonstrate that cleaning procedures are effective, reproducible, and under control. Procedures must be followed to ensure the validated cycles are used at all times.

Cleaning Agents   Appropriate cleaning agents must be selected that will ensure proper interaction with the residue to be removed. It is also important to recognize the interactions between the residues and the surfaces to which they may be adhered. Processing equipment made of different types of material may require different types of cleaning to remove the same residue.

Clean-Out-of-Place

COP Equipment

The required items for performing COP are:

- **COP Bath.** A COP bath is an automated method of cleaning small parts such as elbows, jumpers, gaskets, valves, and hoses. This system is used to clean equipment in a consistent and reliable manner. The components of a COP bath are a solution-holding tub, a pump, automatic valves, a heat exchanger, and a Programmable Logic Controller (PLC) to control the temperature of cleaning solutions.
- **Cleaning Agents.** CIP 100 (potassium hydroxide) is used as the caustic (alkaline) cleaning agent. CIP 200 (phosphoric acid) is used as the acidic cleaning agent.
- **Plant Steam Hose.** Plant steam is used to heat the solutions via a heat exchanger on the COP bath. Plant steam is hot and will produce serious burns if used improperly.
- **Hose and Valve Cleaning Manifold.** The COP bath pumps cleaning solution through the manifold, cleaning the hoses, and valves connected to it.

Preparation

When processing equipment has become soiled and is ready to be cleaned, the following steps will take place:

- Place all disassembled parts into the COP bath ensuring that all of the parts are completely submerged in the cleaning solution. Overloading the COP bath may result in inappropriate cleaning.
- Connect hoses and/or valves to the COP manifold to allow solution to flow through them. Note that the ends of the hoses and valves will need to be manually cleaned prior to connecting them to the COP manifold.
- Valves may also be completely disassembled and the valve bottom and diaphragm can be placed into the COP bath for cleaning. The valve top must be manually cleaned.
- Note that tri-clamps and valve tops should not be cleaned using the COP bath. The COP is extremely efficient at cleaning parts. It will remove all lubrication from the tri-clamp and valve threads and cause potential seizing of the threads. These parts are best cleaned manually. If they are cleaned in the COP, lubricate them after cleaning to ensure long life.
- Begin COP cycle per appropriate area SOP.

Continued on next page

Clean-Out-of-Place

COP Safety   There are several potential safety hazards associated with operating a COP bath because the COP bath is not fully enclosed.
- Hazardous chemicals (acid, base) can splash due to the turbulent flow in the bath. Ensure that the COP bath covers are in place prior to beginning a COP cycle.
- If hoses are being cleaned, attach several clamps to the ends of the hose to ensure they remain submerged. This will prevent the hose from splashing chemicals out of the bath due to the high flow rate.
- High temperatures. Ensure that the applicable "Caution Hot" signs are placed on the COP bath while running a COP cycle.
- High voltage. To avoid the risk of electric shock, ensure that the electrical components of the COP bath are protected from water.

COP Cycle   COP baths have different cycles, but generally they are as follows:
- Prerinse with PUR/WFI. This is performed to remove residue.
- Caustic wash. The caustic wash removes bacterial cell debris and is performed at $\geq 70°C$.
- PUR/WFI rinse. Rinses caustic detergent.
- Acid wash. The acid wash is used to remove mineral precipitates and proteinaceous residues and is performed at $\geq 70°C$.
- Rinse. Rinses residues from the acid wash.
- Hot PUR/WFI rinse performed at $\geq 70°C$. The purpose of this rinse is to flush out residual cleaning agents.
- Final rinse with PUR/WFI.

Critical Parameters   The following critical parameters must be met and remain within the specification for the duration of the COP cycle. If the specification is not reached or maintained, cleaning will not be ensured and will have to be repeated. The critical parameters of a COP cycle include:
- Temperature
- Chemical concentration
- Chemical contact time

If any of the above parameters are not reached or maintained for the duration of the COP cycle, the load must be rejected and will have to be recleaned.

Continued on next page

Clean Out of Place

Trouble-shooting

Since the COP is mostly a manual operation (parts, water, detergents added manually), the majority of the problems will occur with the temperature control system. If the cleaning solutions do not reach or maintain the proper temperature for the duration of the COP cycle, the operator must discern if the COP was set up incorrectly or if it needs to be repaired. First, ensure that the temperature control system was activated. If it was, then a work order must be initiated to correct the problem.

COP Completion

Perform the following at the completion of the COP cycle:
- Inspect the parts as they are taken out to ensure they have been cleaned and are not damaged.
- Complete the COP Equipment Use Record (EUR).
- The equipment status is considered "CLEAN" when the equipment has been cleaned per the appropriate SOP. If the SOP was not properly followed during cleaning, the equipment may not have been cleaned effectively and the use of it may compromise product. This would require that the equipment be recleaned.

Storage

Drying

Prior to storage, equipment and labware must be dry. Equipment may be air dried, or it may be dried as a step within an automated cycle. Residual moisture may support microbial growth and is not acceptable.

Packaging

When equipment and labware have been cleaned and dried, they must be wrapped prior to storage. Wrapping is necessary to prevent labware from becoming soiled while stored or during transport from storage to the processing area for use. Acceptable wrapping methods are:
- Inside a sealed pouch
- Inside a container in a parts drawer
- All open ports covered with a single layer of Biowrap that is secured with a rubber band or tape

Equipment and labware must also be identified as clean with the appropriate "Clean" sticker or status card per area SOP.

Sterility and Contamination Control

Overview

Introduction   Sterility and contamination control go hand-in-hand in the cell culture business. Contamination by microorganisms is a major problem in cell culture. Bacteria, mycoplasma, yeast, fungi, and viruses may be introduced via the operator, atmosphere, work surfaces, solutions, and many other sources.

The presence of contaminants in cell cultures is incompatible with the concept of standardized, defined systems. Presence of contaminants may produce both gross turbidity and rapid destruction of the culture, or no turbidity and moderate cytopathic effects in the culture. The latter type can remain undetected for prolonged periods and can have profound effects on the cell culture, the products produced, and/or the experimental results.

Catastrophes can be minimized if:

- Cultures are checked
- Cultures are kept antibiotic free for at least part of the time to reveal cryptic contaminants
- Reagents are checked for sterility prior to use
- Media is not shared with other groups
- The standard of sterile technique is kept high at all times

Table of Contents   This document contains the following topics:

Sterility and Contamination Control

Objectives

1. Describe the major types of contaminants in cell culture.
2. Explain why mycoplasma is so difficult to detect.
3. Describe the major sources of contamination.
4. Discuss the actions to be taken that will minimize contamination.
5. Describe the visual features of contaminated cultures that make them readily identifiable.
6. Discuss how a false positive may occur and how a culture is misjudged to be contaminated.
7. Describe the action to be taken should a culture become contaminated.
8. Explain why other cultures should be examined following a contamination.
9. Describe how you would attempt to identify the source of a contamination.
10. Explain possible consequences for repeated contaminations in a GMP facility.

Sterilization: What It Can and Can't Do

Introduction   Sterilization kills all the microbes in a solution or on a device, provided there weren't too many to begin with. The level of microbial contamination before sterilization is called the "Bioburden Load". It is the load of microbes that sterilization strives to kill. During sterilization the microbes die at a constant rate,; but they do not die all at once. The "kill rate" depends on several variable factors discussed below.

Key Features   This section discusses the following topics:

- Factors affecting kill rate
- Kill rate
- Sterilization of equipment
- Sterilization of liquids

Factors Affecting Kill Rate   Using standard sterilization practices, several factors should be given consideration regarding kill rates:

- Chemical concentration.
  In general, for chemical sterilization and also sanitization, the higher the concentration of the chemical, the faster the microbes die. Additionally, chemicals are more effective at higher temperatures.
- Temperature.
  In steam sterilization, the hotter the steam, the faster the microbes die. Steam is even more effective under acidic conditions.
- Humidity.
  A certain level of moisture speeds up the sterilization process in Ethylene Oxide (ETO) gas sterilizers.
- Resistance of the microbes.
  Some microbes are much more resistant than others. The sterilization formulas are carefully worked out for the microbes that are the most difficult to kill. In theory, if you can kill the most resistant microbes, then all the others should be killed as well.
- Presence of biofilms.
  Microbes often grow in association with other microbes on surfaces forming biofilms. The microbes at the deepest part of the biofilm are the most protected from the sterilizing agent and will require longer kill times than those microbes at the surface of the biofilm.

Continued on next page

Sterilization: What It Can and Can't Do

Factors Affecting Kill Rate

- Growth phase of microbes
  Microbes actively growing and metabolizing are more susceptible to killing agents than microbes in metabolically quiescent states.
- Presence of organic macromolecules
  The chemical environment of the microbes influences killing efficiency. Generally, an environment higher in organic macromolecules offers some protection for the microbes against killing agents, expecially chemical agents.

Kill Rate

If all the variables are kept constant, the microbes will die at about the same rate. Thus a certain percentage of all living microbes will die each minute. For example, let's assume there is a population of one million microbes in the steam sterilizer. Now, assume also that for each minute of moist heat at 121.1°C, 90% of all microbes will die. After one minute 900,000 microbes will be dead. 100,000 microbes are still alive. The next minute will kill another 90,000 and 10,000 are left. The next minute kills another 9,000 and only 1000 are left. After another minute only 100 microbes will be left. After six minutes there would be only one microbe left. And with that many minutes in the sterilizer itself (6 minutes in our example) the chances that any one microbe is still alive after 12 minutes are about one in one hundred billion. The process described would be 99.99999999% effective!

On the other hand, intense heat, extreme concentration of some bases, or extended time periods, can degrade, weaken, or otherwise damage the products or packaging. If such damage would happen, the product could be sterile, but unsafe. Therefore, it is important to select a sterilization method that will not interfere with the stability of the product that requires the sterilization. Not every technique can be used for every product.

Continued on next page

Sterilization: What It Can and Can't Do

Sterilization of Equipment

Sterilization procedures are designed not just to kill all of the microbial cells, but also to eliminate particularly resistant spores. Moist heat is more effective than dry heat but does carry the risk of leaving a residue. Dry heat is preferable but for a minimum of 160°C for 1 hour. Moist heat need only be maintained at 121°C for 15 to 20 minutes. For moist heat to be effective, steam penetration must be assured, and for this the sterilization chamber must be evacuated prior to steam injection. The type of sterilization used will depend on the material. Metallic items are best sterilized by dry heat. Silicone rubber, Teflon, polycarbonate, and some other plastics should be autoclaved for 20 minutes at 121°C, 100kPA with preevacuation and post-evacuation steps. Many plastics cannot be exposed to the temperature required for autoclaving or dry heat sterilization. To sterilize such items, immerse in 70% alcohol for 30 minutes and dry off under UV light in a laminar flow cabinet. Ethylene oxide gas may be used to sterilize plastics, but 2 to 3 weeks are required for the ETO to clear from the plastic surface. Gamma irradiation is the best method for plastics. Items should be packaged and sealed.

Sterilization of Liquids

The ultimate objective in preparing reagents and media is to produce them in a pure form. This includes avoiding the accidental inclusion of inhibitors and substances toxic to cell survival, growth, and expression of specialized functions. It is important the reagent is well defined and the functions of its constituents understood. Reagents or media can be sterilized by autoclaving, if they are heat stable. These would include reagents such as water, salt solutions, or amino acid hydrolysates. Filter sterilization is suitable for heat-labile solutions. Filters are prepared and may be sterilized by autoclaving or may be Steamed-In-Place by high-pressure steam. In addition, presterilized disposable filters may be purchased.

Contamination Control

Introduction

Bacteria, yeast, fungi, molds, and mycoplasma all appear as contaminants in cell culture. In general, it is necessary to note the type of contaminant, (bacterial rods or cocci, yeast, etc.), how the organism was detected, the location of the culture, how the culture was handled, and by whom.

Key Features

Some of the considerations for contamination control that are discussed in the document are:

- Characteristics of microbial contamination
- Potential sources of contamination
- Methods of prevention

Characteristics of Microbial Contamination

There are several key indicators of contamination in a cell culture:

- **pH**. Sudden change in pH is often a strong indicator of contamination. A decrease is often seen with most bacterial contamination. Very little change may occur with yeast until the contamination is heavy, and sometimes an increase in pH is seen with fungal contamination.

- **Turbidity**. Cloudiness in the medium may be visible sometimes with a light film or scum on the surface. Spots on the growth surface may be seen which also move when the medium is agitated.

- **Microscopic Evaluation**. During an examination with a low-power microscope spaces may appear granular and may shimmer. With heavy contamination the bacteria, yeast, or fungi are visible due to either motion or size.

- **Morphology**. Under the microscope, yeast may appear as round or oval particles. Fungi may appear as long thin strands.

- **Mycoplasma**. Mycoplasma contamination cannot be detected under the microscope. The culture must be tested using PCR, fluorescent staining, autoradiography, microbiological assay, orcein or Giemsa staining. It is important to note that the Mycoplasma contamination does not always show macroscopic alterations in the culture.

Contamination Control

Potential Sources of Contamination

Several significant sources of contamination are listed below:

- Equipment (such as the glassware, tools, instrument, culture flasks, incubators, etc.)
- Solutions (media or reagents)
- Room air
- Work surfaces
- Operators (hair, hands, breath, clothing)
- Hoods
- Incoming cell lines

Methods of Prevention

Incidences of contamination can be minimized by setting up effective methods of prevention. These would include:

- Proper training
- Gowning
- Using aseptic technique
- Sterilization of equipment
- Filtration of solutions
- Using disinfectants such as 70% alcohol

Mammalian Cell Culture

Overview

Introduction

Genetic engineering has made it possible to transfer a gene from one species to cells of another species. This process has led to the creation of the biotechnology industry. Many medically necessary bioproducts have been introduced in the past twenty years for the treatment of a wide range of diseases. Mammalian cell technology has flourished because many products require complex cellular processing steps in order for the protein to be biologically active. Prokaryotic host cells, such as *E.coli*, are incapable of performing these post-translational modifications. This document contains information about the cultivation and large-scale production of mammalian cells.

Breakthroughs

Breakthroughs with recombinant DNA technology and hybridoma technology in the 1970s and early 1980s have paved the way for mammalian cell production in the biotechnology industry.

Mammalian Cell Technology Applications

There are several important applications of mammalian cell technology:
- Production of vaccines
- Production of enzymes and protein hormones
- Production of monoclonal antibodies
- Production of native or modified proteins

Table of Contents

This document contains the following sections:

Mammalian Fermentation

Objectives

1. Explain how mixing is accomplished in a bioreactor.
2. Explain how pH can be controlled in a bioreactor
3. Define the term baffle and describe its function.
4. Explain how mixing would be different in a bioreactor with and without baffles.
5. Explain how temperature is controlled in a bioreactor.
6. Distinguish between a jacket, coil jacket, immersion coil, and heat exchanger.
7. Describe the function of a sparger.
8. Identify the following items on a bioreactor: stirrer, foam breaker, baffles, rupture disk, flat-bed turbine, sparger, jacket, valves, and sample port.
9. Identify three different types of processes that can be used to make product.
10. Explain what is done during a batch process.
11. Explain how batch feed differs from a batch process.
12. Explain what is done during a continuous feed process.
13. Describe the different parameters which need to be controlled during a process.
14. Explain why temperature control is important.
15. Explain why/where oxygen is required during cell metabolism.
16. Explain the basic steps of protein synthesis.
17. Discuss the reasons why glucose and lactate are monitored during mammalian cell culture.
18. State several reasons which may account for high lactate levels.
19. Explain the consequences of high lactate levels for extended periods.
20. Explain the course of action taken to remedy high lactate levels.
21. Explain what happens to the pH of a culture in a reactor as the cells grow and increase in number/density.
22. Explain how pH is controlled during mammalian fermentation.
23. Explain why bioreactors are on load cells.
24. Explain why there are redundant systems on the bioreactors.
25. Explain why there are acceptable volumes set for the contents of a bioreactor (high and low values).
26. Identify four different methods for separating product from cells.

Cell Enumeration and Viability Determination

Objectives

1. Explain the safety concerns when handling a trypan blue solution.
2. Explain the reason for using trypan blue to perform cell counts.
3. Demonstrate/explain the proper use of the inverted microscope.
4. Identify/set-up materials necessary for cell counts.
5. Demonstrate proper organization of workspace for cell counts.
6. Demonstrate aseptic removal of an aliquot from a culture requiring counting.
7. Perform appropriate dilutions of a cell aliquot to reach desired cell density for cell counts.
8. Demonstrate use of vortex mixer for cell dispersion.
9. Demonstrate set-up of hemocytometer.
10. Demonstrate proper loading of hemocytometer.
11. Demonstrate proper use of micropipettors.
12. Explain the use of the grids on the hemocytometer for performing cell counts.
13. State the desired cell numbers on the hemocytometer grids for obtaining accurate cell counts.
14. Perform cell counts using the hemocytometer.
15. Demonstrate proper use of a counter for cell enumeration.
16. Demonstrate the recording of viable cell number, nonviable cell number, and number of grids counted.
17. Explain how to distinguish viable from nonviable cells.
18. Explain how to count cells in an aggregate.
19. Perform calculations of viable cell density in cells/milliliter.
20. Explain how the volume of a hemocytometer chamber is determined.
21. Perform calculations of percent viability.

Cryopreservation

Objectives

1. Explain the purpose for cryopreservation of a cell culture.
2. Discuss the special role of cryopreservation in biomanufacturing.
3. Identify the necessary labware/materials for cryopreservation of a cell culture.
4. Identify the types of cryovials used for cryopreservation.
5. Describe the desired characteristics and conditions of a cell culture to be frozen.
6. Perform cell counts to determine cell density of culture to be frozen.
7. Determine the quantity of cell culture required to prepare a given number of vials at a specified density.
8. Identify the common cryoprotectants used for cell freezing and explain the theory behind their use.
9. Utilize an MFR to prepare freezing media.
10. Describe the steps in the procedure of cryopreservation.
11. Demonstrate preparation of cell culture for freezing and resuspension into freezing media.
12. Perform aseptic loading of cryovials with appropriate volume of cell suspension.
13. Identify the main factors that influence cell viability during cryopreservation/thawing.
14. Discuss the desired conditions for the freezing process.
15. Describe the proper storage conditions/temperatures for frozen cells.
16. Demonstrate thawing of a vial of cells and initiation of the culture.

Harvesting

Objectives

1. State two methods for separating cells from media.
2. Discuss the limitations of filtration.
3. Discuss the limitations of centrifugation.
4. Explain the role of a prefilter and a postfilter during a process.
5. Describe the function/appearance of a filter housing.
6. Identify the equipment needed to harvest.
7. Explain the function/contents of a harvest cart.
8. Describe the steps of a harvest.
9. Give a list of the types of samples that would be removed from a culture at the time of harvest.
10. Explain the purpose of testing a sample for bioburden.
11. Explain the purpose of testing glucose/lactate levels.
12. Explain why samples are taken for cryopreservation.
13. Explain the purpose of backup samples.
14. Explain how filter housings work.
15. Explain the purpose of a bleed valve on a filter housing.
16. Describe the role of ultrafiltration in harvesting.
17. State the equation for calculating generation number.
18. Demonstrate calculation of generations using initial and final cell densities.
19. Demonstrate the calculation to determine doubling time for a culture.
20. Explain why accurate cell counts are important for harvest.
21. Explain how previous inaccurate cell counts can be a problem at time of harvest.
22. Explain why generation number/time are important.

Section 1
Features of Mammalian Cell Culture

Overview

Introduction

This section describes distinct features of mammalian cells and how they are cultivated in the laboratory. This section includes information about:

- How mammalian cells produce proteins and how these proteins are processed
- Growth conditions and types of cells
- What is "sub-cloning"
- Long term storage of cells

Table of Contents

This section contains the following topics:

Features of Mammalian Cell Culture

Glycosylation

A distinctive feature of mammalian cells is their protein processing abilities. Processing includes complex folding, disulfide bond formation, and glycosylation (carbohydrate structures attached to the protein's amino acid backbone). The degree of glycosylation can affect *in vivo* clearance of protein, and therefore, the efficacy of dosage. The importance of glycosylation to a protein's activity can determine whether an animal cell is the host of choice. Proteins derived from other host classes, such as bacteria, insect cells, or yeast, have no or different patterns of glycosylation and protein folding.

Protein Secretion Machinery

Mammalian cell size ranges from five to hundred microns in diameter: about 10 times bigger than a bacterium and 1000 times bigger than a cold virus. An animal cell typically has a density of 1.7 g/ml, enabling it to be separated from most liquid water-based media (density ~ 1 g/ml) by centrifugation. The cell nucleus contains genes for the cell's own survival and can contain genes for producing a recombinant protein product.

The cell also contains the machinery for producing and secreting proteins. Before the protein can be secreted from the cell, a series of steps occurs to produce a protein product. These steps include transcription of the gene encoding the peptide sequence of the protein, clipping of the resulting heterogenous nuclear RNA (hnRNA) to make messenger RNA (mRNA), translation of the mRNA on the outside of the endoplasmic reticulum (ER) to make the peptide strand(s), post-translational modification of the peptide strand(s) within both the ER and the Golgi apparatus, and finally secretion of the correctly folded protein into the cell culture medium. The ER is the starting point of the secretory pathways, and the post-translational steps that occur in the ER and Golgi involve protein glycosylation and folding. These steps are thought to dominate the overall time needed to produce a protein from the gene. The half-time of exit from the ER can vary from fifeeen minutes to two hours compared to transcription or translation times of one to four minutes. The glycosylation that occurs during this processing time is determined by the glycoenzymes that are available in and particular to each cell type.

Continued on next page

Features of Mammalian Cell Culture

Growth
Cell culture describes a method by which cells must be treated in order to continue their growth and/or production ability. Animal cells grow with doubling times greater than 12 hours (12-36 hours typical for cell lines). A growth curve of a batch culture consists of three phases:

- **Lag phase.** After the culture is initiated and before cell growth begins, this indicates how well the cells are adapting to environmental conditions. The cells are synthesizing enzymes necessary for metabolism

- **Log phase.** The doubling time in the middle of this phase indicates the growth-promoting capacity of the culturing conditions.

- **Stationary phase.** Typically indicates the maximum cell number that can be supported by the culture conditions.

Cell growth during the growth phase can be modeled with an exponential equation:

$$X = X_0\, e^{\mu t}$$

X = cell density at time t
μ = cell growth rate in units of inverse time
X_0 = cell density at time 0

It is easier to put the growth rate into perspective by expressing it as a doubling time, t_d.

$$t_d = \frac{\ln 2}{\mu}$$

For example, a growth rate of 0.029/hr can be expressed as a doubling time of 24 hours, which means the cell density will double in one day during the exponential growth phase.

Continued on next page

Features of Mammalian Cell Culture

Medium
Cell culture medium usually consists of both essential and nonessential amino acids, glucose, vitamins, salts, minerals, organic supplements, and buffer components. The major carbon sources are glucose and glutamine, usually provided at 25 and 4mM, respectively, in a synthetic medium base [e.g., Dulbecco's Modified Eagle's Medium (DMEM)]. In cell culture, the concentration of amino acids usually limits the maximum cell density possible. The balance of amino acids can affect the cell growth rate or production ability. Animal serum (usually bovine) can be added to medium to provide even more nutrients (e.g., amino acids, ketoacids, and intermediary metabolites). However, the use of serum is not desirable due to the lot-to-lot variability, high cost, regulatory concerns regarding the use of bovine-derived components, and problematic downstream purification. The pH of the medium also affects the growth ability of the cells, and is usually controlled using a buffer. Bicarbonate in the medium, at equilibrium with carbon dioxide in the gas phase can be used to buffer the pH.

$$H_2O + CO_2 \rightarrow H_2CO_3 \rightarrow H^+ + HCO_3^-$$

Equilibrium is reached at pH 7.4. If bicarbonate is added to the medium by the addition of sodium bicarbonate which readily dissociates, $NaHCO_3 \rightarrow Na^+ + HCO_3^-$, then the equilibrium is shifted to the left and the medium becomes more basic (pH increases). Conversely, if carbon dioxide in the medium increases (from cell respiration, gas bubbling, or from an increase in atmospheric carbon dioxide concentration), the equilibrium is then shifted to the right and the medium becomes more acidic (pH decreases, i.e., the H^+ concentration increases). Animal cells are cultured at a pH range of 6.5 – 7.5. The pH can be controlled at an intermediate value using carbon dioxide gas and carbonate additions, as described above.

Medium should be stored in the cold (at 4°C) either in the dark or in incandescent lighting. Some forms of room fluorescent lighting will cause deterioration of riboflavin (a vitamin) and tryptophan (an essential amino acid) into toxic by-products. The shelf life of media can be determined based on the glutamine content. Glutamine has a half-life of approximately 1 month at 4°C, compared to a half-life of approximately one week at 37°C. Medium containing glutamine should not be used after 2-3 weeks of storage at 4°C.

Continued on next page

Features of Mammalian Cell Culture

Chinese Hamster Ovary Cells

Chinese Hamster Ovary (CHO) cells are widely used in the biotechnology industry. Cell lines of nonhuman origin are favored hosts for recombinant genes so that potentially serious human viruses cannot be associated with recombinant product. CHO cells are immortalized cells which are flexible enough to grow in various configurations, i.e., both attached and in suspension.

The host cells, into which the recombinant DNA containing the sequence for the protein product is transfected, are cells with no functional dihydrofolate reductase (DHFR) enzyme, and are known as "CHO DHFR minus" cells. The DHFR enzyme is essential for the synthesis of amino acids, purines and thymidine, and is required by all proliferating cells. CHO DHFR minus cells can be kept alive by supplementing the cell culture media with glycine, hypoxanthine and thymidine. These host cells are transfected with the DNA sequence of the protein product coupled to the sequence for DHFR. Glycine, hypoxanthine and thymidine are then removed from the media. Only those cells with successful transfection of the DHFR recombinant DNA for the protein product should survive. This process is known as "selection."

In addition, DHFR is useful in another way. DHFR activity can be inhibited by the drug methotrexate. Methotrexate binds to and disables the DHFR protein. In response to this, the number of DHFR genes increases as the cell tries to overcome the inhibition. This is known as gene amplification. In transfected cells, the DNA for the protein product is linked to the DHFR gene, so gene amplification of DHFR leads to similar gene amplification of product DNA, resulting in increased protein expression of product.

Continued on next page

Features of Mammalian Cell Culture

Generation of a Production Cell Line

A cell line suitable for use in a production process should ideally have a high specific productivity and be clonal. These requirements entail several steps in the derivation of a production cell line. As described above, CHO cells are transfected and selected. The cells may then be subcloned. This is a process by which cells are diluted, such that individual cells can be grown independently. The populations of cells which grow from a single cell can be considered "clonal," i.e., all identical to a single parent. Prior to, or after subcloning, the cells may be amplified.

A cell line which is suitable for production normally goes through two rounds of subcloning, and then a stock of the cell line is stored frozen. This is known as the Master Cell Bank (MCB). The MCB is tested to ensure the cells are free from any infectious agent, such as virus or mycoplasma. A vial from the MCB is then expanded to form another larger bank, from which each production run is derived. This bank is known as the Working Cell Bank (WCB).

Section 2
Large-Scale Production

Overview

Introduction   Many proteins of therapeutic use are produced in minute quantities in nature (e.g., insulin). Recombinant DNA technology has allowed for the large-scale production of clinically useful products for the treatment of disease in humans and animals.

Table of Contents   This section contains the following topics.

Large-Scale Production

Large-Scale Suspension Culture

Suspension cultures are often system of the choice for large-scale production of recombinant proteins. The reasons for this include the ease of operation, reliability, and flexibility. Critical to the success of this method of production is a cell line with high specific productivity and optimization of culture conditions.

Process Steps Involved in the Large-Scale Production Of Therapeutic Proteins

Steps involved in the production of a protein at large-scale include:
- Thawing a vial of frozen cells from the WCB.
- Scale-up to generate enough cells to inoculate the production vessel (bioreactor).
- Aseptic addition of cells to the production vessel (inoculation)
- Growth of cells to maximum densities in the production vessel. The goal of the production culture is to provide optimal conditions for cell growth such that the maximum cell density can be attained quickly and maintained in a viable condition for as long as possible.
- Culture termination. This is usually based on cell viability or product quality.
- Purification of the recombinant protein from the culture fluid. This step may or may not involve the removal of cells from the culture fluid.

Continued on next page

Large Scale Production

Scale-Up

Conditioned media (CM) is cell culture medium that cells have grown in and "conditioned" for a period of time. CM may contain growth factors, hormones, proteins, and other known and undefined components that support cell growth. In a serum-free process, the inoculum density is critical to ensure that sufficient cells and CM are added to the new vessel to guarantee cell proliferation. If the inoculum density is not adequate, the cells may enter a lag/stationary phase of nongrowth for an extended period of time or they may not survive.

In a typical scale-up, a vial of cells from the cryopreserved cell bank is thawed and expanded in T-flasks, spinner flasks, bioreactors, or a combination of the three. Increased volumes of cells and CM must be generated in order to inoculate larger and larger vessels. Scale-up can take from a few weeks up to a few months, depending on the cell growth rate and size of the final production vessel.

Bioreactor

A bioreactor is a controlled vessel in which cells grow and secrete recombinant protein into the culture media. The type of bioreactor used depends on the inherent nature of the cell line. Some cell lines, like CHO, are flexible enough to grow both attached and in suspension.

Cell Line	Bioreactor Options
Anchorage dependent: •Cells must be attached to a substrate to proliferate •Fibroblastic in appearance •Require serum for attachment	•Rollerbottles •Hollow fiber •Stirred tank (microcarriers)
Anchorage independent: •Cells grow freely in suspension cultures •Spherical in appearance •Serum-free	•Stirred tank •Airlift •Hollow fiber

Continued on next page

Large-Scale Production

Stirred Tank

Stirred tank bioreactors are the most widely used vessels for the production of recombinant proteins because they are versatile. With minor changes a stirred tank bioreactor can be adapted to grow both eukaryotic (e.g., mammalian, yeast) and prokaryotic (e.g., *E. coli*) cell lines.

Modes of Bioreactor Operation

Bioreactors are typically operated in one of three modes: batch, fed-batch, or perfusion. The mode of operation will depend on the cell line, nutrient requirements, and amount of recombinant protein needed at the end of culture.

Mode	Description
Batch	This is the simplest mode of reactor operation. Media and cells are added to the bioreactor and the culture grows without additions until harvest. Batch cultures usually operate between 5-8 days.
Fed-batch	This usually begins in batch mode, however, depleted and/or limited nutrients are added back to the reactor in the form of a liquid feed. Fedbatch runs frequently operate between 10 and 20 days.
Perfusion	This is a continuous culture in which equal volumes of fresh media are added and culture fluid is removed from the bioreactor. This maintains a steady culture volume. Perfusion cultures can typically last for periods of months.

Continued on next page

Large-Scale Production

Controlled Parameters

Mammalian cells are extremely sensitive to their immediate environment. A bioreactor must maintain adequate control of multiple parameters to preserve the health of the cells. *In situ* (pH and dissolved oxygen) and online (temperature) probes are used for real time measurement of critical parameters. Examples of parameters controlled by a bioreactor are:

Parameter	Bioreactor Options
Temperature	Mammalian cell cultures require an environment equivalent to normal body temperature. Cells are normally grown at 36 ±1°C with minimal fluctuation in temperature.
pH	pH (dissolved hydrogen ions) is a measurement of the acidity of the culture media. An optimum pH range for mammalian cells is usually between 6.8 and 7.2. Since most cell culture media are bicarbonate buffered, a liquid solution of sodium bicarbonate is used to increase the pH, while a carbon dioxide gas overlay is used to decrease pH.
Dissolved Oxygen	Cell cultures require oxygen for respiration and conversion of nutrients to energy. Dissolved oxygen (DO) content in media is usually expressed as the percentage of oxygen dissolved in the media or percent saturation. A DO setpoint of 50% saturation is usually a safe starting point for most cell lines. The DO level is maintained by overlaying air to the reactor headspace for diffusion of oxygen into the media at the gas/liquid interface. If oxygen demand is high, oxygen is bubbled directly into the media through a sparger located at the bottom of the vessel below the impeller. If the dissolved oxygen level is too high, nitrogen is added to the headspace to displace the oxygen in the media until the setpoint is achieved.
Mixing	Mixing in a bioreactor is important to preserve homogeneity and maintain cells in suspension. Mammalian cells can be shear sensitive and may not survive at high agitation rates for extended periods of time. Specialized low shear impellers, such as marine blade or pitched blade, can minimize shear damage.

Continued on next page

Large-Scale Production

Cell Stress   Eukaryotic cells lack a rigid cell wall, which is protective in prokaryotic cells. Therefore, mammalian cells are much more sensitive to stressful culture conditions than is *E.coli*. Even a relatively well-controlled bioreactor can exert stress on mammalian cells. For example, oxygen bubbles bursting at the air/liquid interface, foaming, mixing rates, and accumulation of waste products can all be detrimental to culture performance.

Cell Death   There are two modes of death in mammalian cell culture, necrosis and apoptosis. Necrosis is passive cell death and apoptosis is programmed cell death. The majority of cell death in a bioreactor is via apoptosis. Apoptosis is a process requiring metabolic activity by the dying cell. Classic characteristics of apoptosis include shrinkage of cells, DNA fragmentation, and condensation and margination of chromatin. Once a cell is committed to the apoptotic pathway, it is irreversible. Slowing down or inhibiting apoptosis can lead to increased product titers through extension of viable cell culture time.

Harvest   The timing of completion for a production culture varies from process to process, but is typically determined by viability or product integrity. Viability is important because as cells die, they eventually lyse and release their contents into the culture fluid. Cells contain proteases which can degrade the recombinant proteins. Also, excess cellular proteins may make it more difficult to purify out the product of interest.

Continued on next page

Large-Scale Production

Purification

Recombinant proteins are secreted into culture medium in the bioreactor. There are a number of approaches available to purify the product out of the culture fluid. The separation methods used in a particular purification scheme depend on the nature of the protein to be purified and the material from which it has to be separated (proteins, DNA, cell debris, etc.). The first decision is whether to purify the product with cells present or removed from the culture fluid. Removal of cells may include centrifugation or filtration through filtration membranes or hollow fiber units. Clarified culture fluid is then run over a series of chromatographic columns, each comprised of a different resin which separates out product depending on the characteristics of the protein. For example, the protein may be purified depending on its size, charge, or hydrophobicity. The protein may also be linked to another molecule (Fc, Peg, etc.) and that linker molecule may have characteristics which make it easier or more difficult to separate. Another option is to run the cell-containing fluid through a fluidized bed column (loosely packed column) and capture the product directly. The product binds to the resin while the cells and fluid pass through the column to a collection tank or drain. This captured product may then be eluted (removed) from the resin and run over a number of packed bed columns to complete the purification process.

Cell Enumeration and Viability Determinations

Laboratory

Laboratory Activity	Proficiency in cell viability determinations will be acquired by each student. Using their own cell cultures, students will learn use of hemocytometer, perform dilutions, learn appropriate calculations and acquire the ability to distinguish viable from nonviable cells.
Equipment	Microscopes Vortex Hemocytometers Calculators Micropipettors
Materials and Supplies	Cell culture Trypan blue solution Micropipettor tips Microfuge tubes Hemocytometers/cover slips 70% Ethanol
Activities at a Glance	1. Students will receive instruction on the use and care of the inverted microscope. 2. Students will remove samples from cell cultures for determination of cell number and viability. 3. Following instruction on the use of the hemocytometer, students will perform cell counts using trypan blue. 4. Students will perform calculations to determine total cell number, percent viability and precision of their counting procedure.

Cryopreservation

Laboratory

Introduction

Each student is required to establish their own "working cell bank" for use during the semester, if the need for backup cultures arises. During this exercise the students will learn the process of cryopreservation using their own existing cultures.

Equipment

Low temperature freezer
Centrifuge
Hemocytometer
Micropipettors
Automatic pipettors

Materials and Supplies

Viable cell culture
Trypsin (if attached cells are used)
Pipettes
Sterile centrifuge tubes
Cryovials
DMSO
Media
Fetal Calf Serum

Activities at a Glance

1. Prior to this laboratory, students should be instructed to set up a flask of cells for freezing.

2. Students will follow SOP for cryopreservation and create a working cell bank for themselves.

3. Following freezing of their cells, all students will thaw one vial in a subsequent laboratory, to determine if the cryopreservation was successful.

Bioreactor Operation

Laboratory

Introduction   A batch run will be set up in the bioreactor using CHO cultures prepared by the students. Students will learn bioreactor set-up, inoculation, and monitoring.

Equipment   Bioreactor
CO_2 cylinder
Compressed air cylinder
Vacuum pump

Materials and Supplies   Viable cell culture
Pipettes
Media
Sampling tubes
Syringes

Activities at a Glance

1. Prior to the inoculation of the bioreactor, students will set up cultures in spinner flasks so there is a sufficient number of cells for the inoculation. Cell counts will be performed and students will determine the amount of media and cell culture needed to inoculate the bioreactor.

2. Students will prepare the media and inoculate the bioreactor.

3. Students will pull samples each day of the run to monitor cell growth.

4. Students will monitor pH, DO, and temperature throughout the run.

Molecular Overview

Overview

Introduction   The manipulation of DNA is one of the most important tools in biotechnology. The ability to manipulate DNA is essential to the drug discovery process. In the area of protein expression, some of the most important techniques employed are:

- The initial cloning of a potential product
- Control of the protein expression
- Choice of the host

Table of Contents   This document contains the following topics:

Molecular Overview

Objectives

---

1. Explain the role of molecular biology in the biotechnology industry.
2. Define an expression system, include its function and significance.
3. Describe the different components of an expression vector.
4. State two examples of expression vectors.
5. Describe two main types of promoters.
6. Explain the difference between positive and negative control and give an example of each.
7. Explain the function of a polylinker or multiple cloning site.
8. Explain the role/function of selectable markers.
9. Define secretion sequence and explain its use in cloning.
10. Explain the use of protein tags and give an example.
11. Explain the use of protein fusions and give examples.
12. Describe the commonly used prokaryote/eukaryote hosts for expression of recombinant proteins.
13. Describe the advantages and disadvantages of using *E.coli* as a host.
14. Explain what is meant by refolding a protein expressed in *E.coli*.
15. Define inclusion bodies.
16. Explain the role of IPTG in induction.
17. Discuss the advantages and disadvantages of inclusion bodies.
18. Discuss the advantages and disadvantages of eukaryote hosts.
19. Discuss the advantages of yeast systems.
20. Describe the insect/baculovirus system of expression.
21. Discuss the advantages and disadvantages of a mammalian expression system.
22. Identify examples of recombinant products produced in mammalian cells.

Background

Techniques   The central dogma of biology is the concept that DNA is transcribed into RNA, which in turn is translated into protein. By manipulating the DNA sequence of a gene, the output protein may also be altered. Through the use of a variety of molecular techniques just about any known protein can be produced in a biological system.

Additionally, the initiation of product expression in a biological system is directly controlled at the molecular level. By taking advantage of different control systems inherent in the host organism, a different control system can be chosen which will drive production of a biological product at a time that is optimal for the host. Furthermore, control systems can be manipulated to provide other factors that are beneficial to expression. An example that is commonly exploited for recombinant protein expression is the use of metabolic promoter systems for control of the protein production.

The genetic makeup of the host organism can also be manipulated. These manipulations often involve the addition or removal of genes that affect either expression level or the final product quality. The removal of a wild-type protease that degrades the product, for example, may increase product yields or purity.

The Expression Vector

Introduction   An expression system incorporates the necessary factors for efficient control and production of the desired product. Most of these factors can be included on a single vector.

Key Features   The key elements of an expression vector are:
- Promoter
- Cloning site
- Selectable marker
- Other miscellaneous elements

Continued on next page

The Expression Vector

Promoter   Initiation of transcription occurs at the promoter site. The promoter is a DNA sequence that serves as a recognition site for RNA polymerase. Control of transcription is affected by the interaction of the promoter site with RNA polymerase and in some cases regulatory proteins.

There are three types of promoters, each defined by how it is controlled:

- **Constitutive Promoters**. Promoters that are not regulated; initiation of transcription is always occurring.

- **Negative Control**. Regulatory proteins (repressors) shut off transcription by binding to the DNA near or on the promoter site and interfering with the binding of RNA polymerase to the promoter, or by blocking the movement of the RNA polymerase toward the gene. The removal of the repressor protein activates transcription. An example of this type of promoter is the *E. coli lac* promoter that regulates the metabolism of lactose. A repressor protein blocks the RNA polymerase. The addition of lactose changes the ability of the repressor to bind to the DNA, thus allowing the initiation of transcription.

- **Positive Control**. Regulatory sites are used to turn on transcription. Activation of the promoter via regulatory proteins works by a variety of mechanisms, such as unwinding the DNA duplex or assisting with the binding and release of the polymerase to the promoter site. The *lac* promoter also provides an example of positive control (in the presence of cAMP). A regulatory protein called CAP will recruit RNA polymerase to a weak promoter allowing for initiation of transcription. When glucose levels are high and thus the cell does not need to metabolize lactose, cAMP levels are low. When glucose levels are low and the cell needs to metabolize another energy source, cAMP levels rise and then activate CAP, by binding to its regulatory site, which in turn activates the *lac* promoter.

Continued on next page

The Expression Vector

Cloning Site

The cloning site for an expression system is downstream from the promoter. The cloning site is a region of DNA that contains numerous unique restriction sites. Restriction enzymes cleave the DNA at specific sequences. The unique site allows for a single cleavage point on the plasmid. By placing that same unique sequence at the beginning of a gene via PCR or other molecular technique the two pieces of DNA can be joined together via complementary DNA binding. By placing numerous restriction sites in this region, any gene of interest can be cloned downstream from the promoter sequence.

Selectable Marker

Once a gene is cloned into an expression vector, it needs to be put into its host organism. The vector is introduced into a cell by various methods; however, the entire population of cells used will not contain the vector of interest. By using a selectable marker, those cells containing the vector can be isolated and selected. A common selectable marker used is an antibiotic resistance gene. A population of cells can be grown in the presence of an antibiotic after the introduction of the vector. Only those cells containing the antibiotic resistance gene found on the vector will survive.

Other Miscellaneous Elements

Other elements can be incorporated onto an expression vector. Examples of such elements are protein secretion signals, protein tags, and protein fusions.

- A secretion signal is a sequence of amino acids fused to the beginning of a protein that indicate to the host that the protein should be exported out of the cell.
- Protein tags are used for easy detection and/or purification of the protein of interest. These tags are usually short amino acid sequences that can be placed at either end of the protein. One example of this is the His tag. This tag is a series of six or more histidine residues. This tag binds well to nickel. By taking advantage of this, the protein can be detected using nickel conjugated to a detection reagent (such as horseradish peroxidase) or purified by passing a cell lysate through a purification column that contains bound nickel.
- Protein fusions can be useful in many ways. Some fusions are used to make a protein more soluble for purification, while others have clinical applications, for example extending the protein's half-life.

Microbiology/Host Selection

Overview

The selection of the appropriate organism for the production of a product is an important decision. The nature of the protein often determines the host type. The different hosts can be divided into two types: eukaryotic and prokaryotic. Commonly used hosts of each type will be discussed in this section.

Prokaryotic Hosts

Prokaryotes are single-celled organisms defined as lacking a membrane-bound nucleus and lacking membrane-bound organelles. These types of organisms are used extensively throughout the biotechnology industry. They are used in a variety of applications ranging from expression of proteins for therapeutic uses to bioconversion of waste products. Examples of commonly used expression hosts are *Escherichia coli* and *Bacillus subtilus*.

Advantages of *E. coli*

E. coli is the most commonly used host in the biotechnology industry. It is the most extensively studied organism with its entire genome completely sequenced. Advantages of *E. coli* include:

- It is easy to grow. *E. coli* can be grown very rapidly and also grown to very high cell densities without compromising the health of the culture or affecting final product.
- Most proteins can be inexpensively produced in large quantities.
- There are a large number of expression systems commercially available.

Continued on next page

Microbiology/Host Selection

Disadvantages of *E. coli*

The disadvantages of *E. coli* include:

- Prokaryotes do not have the same internal machinery as eukaryotes. Prokaryotes do not have the capability to add sugar moieties to the protein (a process called glycosylation) which can affect the activity of the therapeutic molecule. Additionally, *E. coli* has inferior secretion and processing capabilities in comparison to eukaryotes.
- Proteins expressed in *E. coli* are often incorrectly folded and inactive. Each protein has a specific structure that it must form for it to be active. Disulfide bonds between cysteines are major contributors to the structure of a molecule. Unfortunately, the internal environment of *E. coli* is not conducive to the formation of these bonds. Thus, proteins must be refolded into their proper configuration during purification before they can be useful as a product.
- Large amounts of protein can aggregate into insoluble inclusion bodies. These bodies are both a disadvantage and an advantage in the purification of product. Prior to purification the protein must be solublized and refolded. These steps can be cost prohibitive in a process. The advantage of inclusion bodies again involves purification. Most of the host proteins are soluble. By breaking open the cells, the inclusion bodies can be separated from a majority of the host proteins by simply centrifuging out the heavier inclusion bodies.

Eukaryotic Hosts

Eukaryotes are more complex cell systems characterized by membrane-bound organelles, most notably the nucleus. Because most therapeutic proteins are of human origin, it is logical to use eukaryotic hosts for the production of these products. The general disadvantages of prokaryotic hosts are the advantages of using eukaryotes, including N-glycosylation and proper processing and folding of proteins. The general disadvantages of eukaryotic systems in comparison to prokaryotic hosts are the time it takes to establish a cell line that is expressing product and the low expression levels of the product. Specific eukaryotic systems have their own advantages and disadvantages that will be discussed below.

Continued on next page

Microbiology/Host Selection

Yeast Expression Systems

Yeast has been used for centuries in the food industry in a variety of ways (fermentation of alcohol, bread product, etc.). Yeasts are the simplest of the eukaryotes, living as single-celled organisms in the wild. Because of this they can be manipulated similarly to bacteria.

Advantages:

- Yeast can be grown to high densities similar to bacteria.
- A production strain can be established in a fraction of the time it takes for other eukaryotic systems.
- Extensively studied genome (especially in the case of *Saccharomyces cerevisiae*)
- A large number of commercially available expression vectors are available.

(Examples of yeast systems include *Saccharomyces cerevisiae*, *Kluvermyceslactis*, *Pichia pastoris*, and *Schizosaccharomyces pombe*.

Disadvantages:

- Glycosylation of proteins is not the same as in mammalian cells.

Continued on next page

Microbiology/Host Selection

Insect/ Baculovirus Expression Systems

One of the more recent expression systems developed is the use of insects and insect specific viral systems. In this system the gene of interest is cloned into a virus (called a baculovirus) that only infects specific types of insects. The product is only produced once the host cells are exposed to the virus. Once exposed, the cells survive only a short period of time. The product of the gene-of-interest replaces a highly expressed viral protein called the polyhedrin protein. In nature this protein coats the virus to protect it in the environment and represents approximately 25% of the dry weight of the carcass at the end of infection. However, in cell culture this protein is not needed, and thus can be replaced by the product.

Advantages:
- Cloning and virus production are faster than the establishment of a stable mammalian cell line.
- Because of the transient nature of this viral system, toxic proteins can be expressed easily.

Disadvantages:
- Cells are not mammalian, and thus do not yield proteins with native glycosylation.

Mammalian Expression Systems

Mammalian cells have been used for the production of proteins for the past two decades. Host cell lines vary from Chinese Hamster Ovary cells to human fibroblasts. These cells are typically the ideal environments to produce a product, because the final product will more likely resemble the natural protein. However, there are distinct problems with using these cells. The time and effort it takes to produce a stable production line is considerable. Furthermore, these cells grow extremely slow in comparison to bacteria. Therefore extra precautions must be taken while handling. The biggest disadvantage to the use of mammalian cell lines in comparison to all the others is the amount of protein that is typically produced. The small amounts can be economically challenging to the marketing of a product. However, there are many examples of proteins being produced with mammalian systems, for example, Enbril produced by Immunex.

Protein Expression

Laboratory

Introduction

The induction of protein expression is a key molecular event in producing recombinant proteins. *E.coli* containing an IPTG inducible protein will be utilized for this laboratory exercise. This laboratory enables students to induce protein expression under a variety of conditions and monitor the production of the protein through the appearance of inclusion bodies.

Equipment

Incubator shakers, $30^{\circ}C$, $34^{\circ}C$ and $38^{\circ}C$
Spectrophotometers
YSI glucose analyzer
Microscope, Oil Immersion

Materials and Supplies

LB
Glucose, 400g/l
IPTG
Overnight culture of *E.coli*
Sterile shake flasks (6 per group)
Disposable tubes for 4 ml samples.

Laboratory

Activities at a Glance

Students will induce expression of a recombinant protein under various conditions. Inoculum level, temperature, and glucose levels will be varied as shown below.

<u>LB</u>	<u>LB + glucose</u>
1 X inoculum not induced	1 X inoculum not induced
1 X inoculum + IPTG	1 X inoculum + IPTG
3X inoculum + IPTG	3 X inoculum + IPTG

1. Students will be divided into 3 groups. Each will set up 6 flasks as above (50 mls) and incubate at either 30°C, 34°C, or 38° C. 1X inoculum is 2 mls of overnight culture and 3X is 6 mls. Glucose is added to 0.5 g/l.

2. Students will measure initial O.D. and pH in one 1X flask and one 3X flask.

3. O.D. and pH will be measured at zero, one hour, and 2 1/2 hours.

4. At 2 1/2 hours students will also prepare an aliquot of cell paste to be used
   for SDS-PAGE. One mg of cell paste is needed.
   Each group should determine how much volume is needed for the gel run.

5. Cultures will be examined with the light microscope to monitor the appearance of inclusion bodies.

Microbial Media Design and Preparation

Overview

Introduction

The design and preparation of media for growth of *E.coli* has several purposes and goals. Effective media design ensures that all nutrients required are present in sufficient amounts for the amount of growth required and for the amount of product to be synthesized. The amounts should be controlled so that the accumulation of toxic or wasteful metabolites is kept to a minimum. Only those materials that are safe for human consumption (even if they are not very palatable!) should be used. Finally, cost of the raw materials must be weighed against the value of the product which results from the use of these materials.

Table of Contents

This document contains the following topics:

Microbial Media Design and Preparation

Objectives

1. Give the basic nutrients required for *E.coli* growth.
2. Define the term auxotroph.
3. Explain the chemical function of H, C, N, O, and P in biological systems
4. State six considerations in the choice of media ingredients.
5. State the primary concern in media choices for pharmaceuticals.
6. State the primary concern of TSE in media choices.
7. Discuss the difference between defined media and complex media and the advantages/disadvantages of each.
8. Explain why misincorporation can be a problem with defined media.
9. Identify the available sources and types of glucose used for production.
10. Identify the various sources of complex nitrogen used in media.
11. Explain the AN/TN ratio.
12. Explain how O_2 is delivered to media and the limiting factors in its delivery.
13. Explain why cells need the following: phosphorous, sulfur, trace metals, and vitamins, and explain how each is delivered to the media.
14. Discuss the considerations given to water quality in media preparation.
15. Distinguish between RO, DI, and WFI water.
16. Explain why highly purified water can be a disadvantage for media preparation.
17. Explain how the proper proportions of media components are chosen for a process.
18. Discuss the use of factorial design.
19. Discuss how batching is used in media preparation.
20. Distinguish among the various options for sterilization of media.
21. State the fundamental equation used in sterilization theory.
22. Define F and discuss its significance in sterilization.
23. Explain the role of *Bacillus stearothermophilus* in sterilization procedures.
24. Discuss several factors affecting steam sterilization.
25. Define HTST.
26. Distinguish between depth filtration and absolute filtration and their use in filtering media.
27. Demonstrate ability to perform media preparation with a given recipe.
28. Demonstrate media sterilization using an autoclave.
29. Perform media sterilization using filtration devices and proper aseptic technique.
30. Demonstrate proper washing, wrapping, and sterilization of shake flasks.
31. Demonstrate aseptic dispensing of media to shake flasks.
32. Demonstrate ability to perform calculations for required amount of glucose stock into prepared media.
33. Demonstrate ability to aseptically dispense stock glucose into LB or TB.
34. Demonstrate inoculation of shake flasks with bacterial overnight culture.
35. Demonstrate operation of spectrophotometer to determine optical density of bacterial cultures.

Media Design

Introduction   A suitable starting point for the design of media for growth of *E.coli* would be to consult a table showing the elemental composition of *E. coli*, particularly the strain being studied. As *E. coli* actually has very simple nutritional requirements (glucose, ammonium, phosphorus, sulfur, magnesium, vitamins, and trace minerals), a very simple medium can be prepared, provided that all of the above materials are present in the proper proportions. A more complex medium can be used to ensure faster or denser growth than the simple medium described above. Of course, cost must be factored into the decision. For low-volume, high value products, relatively expensive media can be used without a large impact on process economics. However, for a high-volume, low value product, cost can be an important factor. Media containing materials derived from bovine or other animal sources are now considered suspect, due to the current concerns with Transmissible Spongiform Encephalopathies (TSE's), such as "Mad Cow Disease," and should be avoided, if possible.

Key Features   This section discusses the following considerations for media design:
- Compatibility of ingredients
- Oxygen requirements
- Heat
- Supply and availability
- Amounts of components

Each is described below.

Compatibility of Ingredients   Special care should be taken to ensure that the media ingredients are compatible with each other in the proportions that they are mixed. A frequent problem is precipitation of media components (e.g. ammonium phosphate) which can remove needed nutrients from solution, thereby making them unavailable to the organisms being cultured.

Continued on next page

Media Design

Oxygen Requirements

An easily overlooked media component is oxygen. For efficient growth, organisms such as *E.coli* require a constant supply of oxygen, which must be effectively dissolved in the fermentor broth. A very rich medium, supporting rapid growth to high density, will necessitate a correspondingly high oxygen demand, which must be met by the fermentor. Modifications to the agitation rate, airflow rate, fermentor backpressure, and possibly oxygen supplementation may be used to meet this demand. If these factors are not effective, the media may need to be "scaled-down" or made more dilute so as to lower the amount of oxygen required by the culture.

Heat

Although not strictly a nutrient, removal of excess heat produced by the metabolic activity of the organisms is essential. Again, as in the case of oxygen, if existing equipment is not able to remove heat as fast as the organisms generate it, the media may need to be adjusted or diluted in order to limit the amount of metabolic heat produced.

Supply and Availability

An important consideration in the choice of media is that of supply. Is the material available in sufficiently large amounts to support product synthesis over the expected lifetime of the product and anticipated scale of production? Can alternative sources of the media components be identified and guaranteed?

Quantities of Components

The amounts of different components of the media must be adjusted in order to produce efficient growth of the organism. A general approach is to have all nutrients present in excess (for the desired amount of cell growth) with the exception of one single nutrient (the limiting nutrient). Therefore, the growth rate of the culture can be regulated by the addition rate of the limiting nutrient. If all nutrients are present in excess, the culture may begin to produce wasteful by-products or metabolites (such as acetate). If these accumulate to any great extent, they may begin to become inhibitory to the growth of the culture.

Media Preparation

Key features

This section discusses the following considerations for media preparation:
- Equipment
- Solubility
- Water
- Component shelf life
- Considerations for sterilization
- Weight per weight

Each is described below.

Equipment and Supplies

For the preparation of media, the following equipment is useful or needed:
- **Scales or balances**. These range from analytical balances for the measurement of small amounts of vitamins or trace minerals up to floor scales which can weight 10's or 100's of kilogram for large amounts of media. It is important the scales and balances are functional in the range of weights needed.
- **Buckets**. For making up laboratory scale batches, a collection of stainless steel or plastic buckets is needed. These should accommodate all batch sizes.
- **Mixers and stir plates**. A variety of mixers and stir plates (heated, if possible) will speed up the process of making lab batches of media.
- **Filters and vacuum source**. For sterilization of heat sensitive materials, a range of sizes of disposable filters and a vacuum source should be available.
- **Water**. To dissolve very concentrated feed solutions, a source of heated water (80°C) is necessary.
- **Labels**. Autoclavable labels are used to label feed bottles which are placed in the autoclave.

Solubility

Often feed media is made as a very concentrated solution, to minimize dilution of the culture and product in the batch. These are often very difficult to dissolve, so the use of heated water can prove useful in accelerating this process. In many cases nutrients (glucose, yeast extract) are present in the media at the limit of their solubility. This poses a danger of precipitation as the media cools after autoclaving. Often this precipitation can occur several days after the sterilization is completed.

Continued on next page

Media Preparation

Water
The researcher must decide what type of water to use. Purified waters, such as deionized (DI) or reverse osmosis (RO), provide a highly consistent source of makeup water, but are expensive, require frequent testing and do not supply any nutrients. Tap or industrial water is inexpensive and can supply trace metals, often in amounts sufficient for growth of the culture. However, it can introduce inconsistency to the process, as the exact chemical composition can vary from day to day, and particularly, from season to season. Most very large-scale fermentations (tens of thousands of liters) use tap water as a matter of cost control.

Component Shelf Life
Information concerning the expected shelf life of prepared media is useful. Is there any breakdown of nutritional content after extended storage? For very concentrated feed solutions, how long may they be held before precipitation begins? This information can be very useful when processes are scaled-up, and feeds must be prepared several days to a week before it is actually used.

Considerations for Sterilization
During sterilization, two processes are taking place. Contaminating organisms are being killed and heat sensitive components of the media are being altered and/or destroyed. Some of these heat sensitive components may be valuable or necessary nutrients. The amount of heat sterilization used to achieve a sufficient kill of contaminating organisms must be balanced against the loss of nutritional quality of the media. This is more of a problem for complex feeds, which contain nitrogen sources or vitamins, than for sugar solutions. In some cases, this may necessitate the use of high-temperature short time (HTST) sterilization techniques to minimize loss of nutritional quality. These not only provide the same "kill" of contaminating organisms with minimal degradation of heat sensitive components, but may also be more economical for very large-scale processes.

Testing
For processes used to produce human therapeutics, which will be manufactured under GMP conditions, methods for testing media and feeds are desirable. These might include density, percent total soluble solids, conductivity, color, and pH, before and after sterilization. In addition, the actual concentration of a nutrient could be tested, if a suitable analytical method is available. This is fairly straightforward for a nutrient like glucose. However, no methods are available for complex nutrients such as yeast extract.

Continued on next page

Media Preparation

Weight per Weight

One point that can aid the researcher when it is time to scale-up the media, and can also help the person who prepares the media, is to write media recipes in terms of weight per weight. Very often, laboratory media is made up on a weight per volume (i.e., grams per liter). This does not pose any great problem for small volumes of dilute solutions. However, for very concentrated media prepared in very large volumes (hundreds of liters) this can be difficult to achieve. Concentrated solutions have densities, which can be very different from water or dilute solutions. (700 g of glucose dissolves in only 400 ml of water to produce one liter of a 70% glucose solution, with a density of approximately 1.25 kg/l). Also, measurement of large volumes gets increasingly difficult and less accurate as the volume increases. In addition, it is very useful to be able to measure the amount of a feed solution actually used during a process after it is completed. It is a fairly simple matter to weigh a large tank at the beginning and the end, and calculate the amount used. For example, 235 kg of feed were used out of the original 350 kg. It is not so easy to measure out 115 liters of remaining feed. Who wants to fill a one-liter cylinder 115 times, counting each one?

Microbial Media Preparation

Laboratory

Introduction The media used for supporting the growth of *E.coli* will be prepared for use in subsequent fermentation laboratory exercises. Several different types of media will be made by students and sterilized using the autoclave.

Equipment Stir plates
pH meters
Balances
Vacuum pump

Materials and Supplies Tryptone
Yeast extract
NaCl
NaOH
KH_2PO_4
K_2HPO_4
Glucose
IPTG
Stir bars
Storage bottles
Glycerol
0.2 micron filter unit

Laboratory

1. Students will prepare the media needed for the three microbial labs. Students will be divided into small groups and each group will prepare the following:

   500 mls of LB

   300 mls of glucose

   500 mls of saline

   500 mls of TB

2. RECIPES

   LB: (per liter)

         10 g tryptone

         5 g yeast extract

         6 g NaCl

         pH to 7.0 with NaOH

   TB: Part A   (per liter)

         12 g tryptone

         24 g yeast extract

         4 ml glycerol

         Add water to 90% of final volume

         Add 4 mls phosphate (Part B) to Part A and bring to volume.

         Part B   (per 100 ml)

         2.3 g KH_2PO_4

         12.5g K_2HPO_4

   Glucose: 400g/liter

   Saline: 9 g/liter

   IPTG: 0.238 g/l   Filter sterilize.

Fermentation of Recombinant *Escherichia coli*

Overview

Introduction

Fermentation technically refers to cell metabolism in the absence of oxygen, such as the conversion of glucose to ethanol by yeast cells. Industrial microbiologists use this term to refer to the production of product by the mass culture of a microorganism. This document contains information about the various stages of the fermentation process for Recombinant *E. coli*.

Table of Contents

This document contains the following sections:

Fermentation of *Escherichia coli*

Objectives

1. Outline a basic strategy for the production of therapeutic recombinant proteins.
2. Explain why *E.coli* is the organism of choice in the biotechnology industry.
3. State the major limitations in the use of *E.coli*.
4. Give examples of the various promoters used for expression in *E.coli* and the advantages/disadvantages of each.
5. Discuss the methods of induction for the above promoters.
6. Distinguish between a master cell bank and a working cell bank.
7. Discuss the role of an inoculum train in a fermentation process.
8. Describe the considerations during the growth phase of a culture.
9. Explain the considerations during the growth phase of a production campaign and with induction.
10. Distinguish between batch, fed-batch, and continuous processes.
11. Identify the various components of a fermentor and explain their functions.
12. Explain the function of a load cell on a fermentor.
13. Demonstrate/discuss three ways to estimate the cell number of a culture.
14. Explain why DO, pH, temperature, and CO_2 evolution are monitored during cell growth.
15. Describe the conditions under which *E.coli* will produce acetate.
16. Explain why acetate formation is a problem during a fed-batch process.
17. Discuss various general solutions to limit glucose uptake and acetate production.
18. Describe the events in *E.coli* which lead to heterogeneity in the recombinant proteins produced.
19. Discuss how such events can be prevented or circumvented.
20. Discuss the following operational considerations: production of metabolic byproducts, heat transfer, mixing, foaming, O_2 uptake, and pH.
21. Discuss the buffer of choice for fermentation.
22. Discuss the choice/use of acid/base additions.
23. Discuss control strategies.
24. Demonstrate the replica plating technique and explain its use in determining plasmid retention.
25. Descibe OUR and OTR.
26. Demonstrate the determination of O.D. measurements with a spectrophotometer and explain how it can be used to infer cell number.

Continued on next page

Objectives

27. Describe how glucose concentrations change during a fed-batch process.
28. Define inclusion bodies.
29. Identify inclusion bodies within induced cells.
30. Discuss the advantages/disadvantages of inclusion bodies.
31. Describe the effect of inclusion bodies on optical density.
32. Explain why the calculation of generation time is important during a campaign.
33. Discuss the problem and implications of plasmid loss.
34. Identify a baffled shake flask and explain the functions of the baffles.
35. Perform inoculation of a culture.
36. Describe the relationship of shaker speed to OAR of a culture.

Section 1
About the Fermentation Process

Overview

Introduction

This section describes how the fermentation process is used to bring a biopharmaceutical product to market. This section includes information about:

- The steps used to develop a product and bring it to market
- How the fermentation process works
- A high-level description of the batch, fed-batch and continuous processes

Table of Contents

This section contains the following topics:

Background

Introduction   Starting in the late 1970's, the techniques for the production of "foreign proteins" in microbial cells were developed and molecular biotechnology was born. Called genetic engineering, these techniques form the basis for the production of human therapeutics in many biotechnology companies.

Fermentation Technology Applications   There are four important applications of fermentation technology in commercial fermentation:

- Production of biomass, such as yeast for the baking industry
- Production of enzymes, such as proteases for the improvement of dough texture
- Production of microbial metabolites, such as vitamins and antibiotics
- Modification of a compound which is added to the fermentor such as conversion of ethanol to vinegar.

Developing a Product

Background   Many activities need to be carried out in order to move a product to commercial manufacturing. The fermentation process involves the efforts of several different departments, each contributing their specialized technologies to develop the product. This topic describes the activities used to bring a product to market.

Bringing a Product to Market   The table below provides a brief description of the stages involved in bringing a product to market.

Stage	Description
Discovery of a product of interest	Identify a protein as a candidate to control or reverse the course of some disease
Cloning	Clone the protein into a micro-organism
Cell fermentation	Culture the host cells of interest
Purification and formulation	Purify and formulate the product
Clinical trials	Demonstrate safety and efficacy of the product
Regulatory process	Gain approval for testing and sales

Continued on next page

Developing a Product

How the Fermentation Process Works

The table below describes the stages of the fermentation development process.

Stage	Who Does It	Description
1	*Cloning*: Research	Provides a cell containing a cloned protein that has been shown at bench-scale to produce the product of interest
2	*Strain Assessment*: Process Development	Assesses the storage conditions of a pure culture in order to • Maintain cells for subsequent experiments, and • Use as an inoculum for the production fermentors
3	*Product Expression Assessment*: Analytical Group	Assesses a project by assaying the product for quantity and quality
4	*Media Development*: Process Development	Evaluates the media to be used for the growth of the microorganism and the needs for production of product
5	*Equipment Design*: Process Development	Chooses or designs the fermentor and ancillary equipment. This is important for scaling-up the process to commercial production
6	*Process Optimization*: Process Development	Determines the optimum conditions for producing the product in the fermentor *Note*: This stage is an ongoing project. While never really completed, conditions are chosen based on product yield, quality, stability, and projected market demand.

Continued on next page

Developing a Product

Recovering Product

Once cells have produced product, the product must be recovered. The harvesting of the product involves either
- Insoluble inclusion bodies(IB) contained in the cells
- The soluble fraction of the cells
- Product secreted to the media

Conditions are selected for optimum product recovery, based on the nature of the product and issues such as stability of the protein and the equipment necessary for product recovery.

Fermentation typically stops at the IB capture step or the concentration of whole cells. In order to bring any potential products to market quickly, stages 2, 3, 4, 5, and 6 of the fermentation process are carried on concurrently.

Batch, Fed-Batch and Continuous Processes

Introduction

Fermentations are typically carried out in batch, fed-batch, or continuous processes. This topic describes the general fermentation strategy and the three processes.

General Fermentation Strategy

The manufacture of therapeutic proteins using recombinant *E. coli* generally uses a fermentation process that is divided into two phases:

- A growth phase to increase cell density
- A production phase to produce the recombinant protein

The separation of the growth phase from the production phase is necessary because:
- First, *E. coli* that are making recombinant proteins generally grow poorly, which makes it difficult to achieve high cell densities
- Second, the metabolic burden of making recombinant protein causes selective pressure which favors the growth of cells that have lost the ability to produce product

Continued on next page

Batch, Fed-Batch and Continuous Processes

Advantages/ Disadvantages of Batch Fermentation

In a batch process, all ingredients used during the fermentation are added prior to the introduction of the cells. Further additions are not made, except possibly an inducer, such as lactose. The advantages and disadvantages of batch fermentation are described below.

Advantages of Batch Fermentation:
- Ease of operation, resulting from less operator interaction. This saves labor and equipment costs and reduces risk of lot failure due to errors.
- Lower production costs due to the
  - lack of feeds
  - reduction of labor involved in preparing and adding the ingredients to the fermentor

Disadvantages of Batch Fermentation:
- Limits to the concentrations of nutrients that can be added to the fermentor
- Limited ways to control cell growth rate and production of undesirable metabolic by-products
- Limits to the cell density and productivity

Batch, Fed-Batch and Continuous Processes

Fed-Batch Process

Fed-batch processes involve adding nutrients to the fermentor after the inoculation of the culture into the production fermentor. Several factors are involved in the fed-batch process which influence the feeding strategy, as described in the table below.

Factor	Description	Result
Nutrient limitation	The addition of limited nutrients is controlled by the feeding strategy	By controlling the addition rate of the feeds: • Cell growth rate can be controlled • High cell densities can be achieved • Toxic by-products produced by the cells can be minimized

Mixing capacity	Mixing capacity of a fermentor is determined by physical characteristics, including:
	• Vessel geometry
	• Baffle configuration
	• Impeller
	  – size
	  – type
	  – RPM
		Adequate mixing capacity ensures
		• Even distribution of feed media throughout culture
		• Increased availability of oxygen to cells

Oxygen transfer rate	The rate at which oxygen is available to the cells depends on the: • Fermentation media • Gas dispersal • Fermentor design *Note*: Oxygen transfer rate can be evaluated by measuring the volumetric transfer rate, K_La, of the system.	Sufficient oxygen is necessary for aerobic growth. High cell density can: • Increase volumetric productivity • Reduce operating costs

See next page for rest of table

Continued on next page

Batch, Fed-Batch and Continuous Processes

Fed-Batch Process

Factor	Description	Result
Oxygen uptake rate	A measure of the rate at which cells are able to remove the dissolved oxygen from the liquid in the fermentor. This oxygen is used for metabolic needs.	Provides an indicator of the level of metabolic activity of the cells and the efficiency of utilization of added nutrients.
Heat transfer capacity	Heat transfer capacity of a fermentor is determined by: • Vessel jacket type and surface area • Coolant type and temperature • Mixing rate.	Adequate heat transfer capacity ensures removal of excessive heat generated by increased: • Nutrient metabolism (metabolic heat) • Agitation rate (mechanical heat).

Addressing Precipitate Formation

The possibility of precipitate formation has to be addressed when developing feeds. It is possible by using fed-batch to have the proper amount of nutrients available for the cells at all times. These ingredients may, if added as a bolus precipitate, cause operational problems and render the nutrients unavailable in a form useful to the cells.

Continuous Process

In continuous processing the product is removed at a predetermined rate. However, some or all of the cells are maintained in the fermentor and production continues. This technique is more commonly used in yeast fermentation and cell culture.

Section 2
Fermentation Parameters

Overview

Introduction   This section describes the parameters used during the fermentation process. It includes information about:
- Design of media
- Optical density
- pH
- Temperature and heat removal
- Dissolved oxygen
- Control of foaming
- Harvesting product
- Scale-up

Table of Contents   This section contains the following topics:

Media Design

Background

Even though *E. coli* can grow using only glucose, ammonia, and salts, these are not the nutrients for optimal growth. More optimal nutrients would include a carbon source, usually glucose or glycerol, a nitrogen source, usually a digest of animal or plant protein, along with minerals, trace metals, and vitamins. Some of these minerals, trace metals and vitamins are provided by the yeast extract and peptones. *E.coli can* synthesize all vitamins required for its growth.

Importance of Media Design

For fed-batch fermentations, a media is designed for optional cell growth and a different media is designed for optimal product synthesis. The same concentrations of nutrient media used in developing lab-scale fermentation processes are generally used in the scaled-up version of the process.

To achieve high cell densities, it is necessary to concentrate nutrients as much as possible. However, this can lead to media precipitation. Because of reduced mixing rates at large-scale, the formation of media precipitates can cause operational problems and lead to nonhomogeneous environmental conditions for cells, which causes less reproducible fermentations.

Cost of Media

At large-scale, it is important to take media cost into account. For example, ammonium nitrogen is one-tenth the cost of yeast extract nitrogen.

Media Sterilization

The mode of sterilizing the media at large-scale may also be significantly different than at the small-scale. For example, an autoclave may be suitable for small-scale experiments, but a continuous-flow, short-contact/high temperature mode of sterilization may be necessary for generating large quantities of sterile media in a reasonable length of time. These different modes of sterilization may lead to the formation of different media breakdown products.

The breakdown products can be toxic to the cells. Media prepared at production-scale needs to be evaluated for its effect on cell growth and product synthesis.

Continued on next page

Media Design

Purpose of Yeast Extract

Yeast extract is especially rich in trace elements and factors beneficial for the growth of microorganisms. It is a good basic media and usually only magnesium, iron, and phosphate need to be supplemented. The choice of feed ingredients is based on:

- Nutritional needs
- Effect on productivity
- Solubility
- Cost
- The absence of any compounds that would interfere with down-stream processing, including purification

Optical Density

Description

Absorbance or optical density (OD) is a measure of how much the intensity of a beam of light is reduced by passing through a suspension.

Turbidity measures cell mass, which is determined by using a spectrophotometer that passes a fixed wavelength (600 nm) of light through a fixed distance (path length) and then onto a detector.

Absorbance is the amount of light removed by the solution and the turbidity is determined by the amount of light which passes through the solution without deviation to reach the photocell.

Purpose

Using the absorbance is an easy way to determine the cell mass of a culture, which is a function of both cell number and size. The concentration of the solution must be within the linear range of the instrument and can be adjusted by dilution of the sample. Careful operation and calibration of the instrument is critical.

Optical Density Formula

The following formula is used to measure absorbance:

$$\textbf{Optical Density} = \textbf{Absorbance} = \textbf{log} \, (I_0/I)$$

Where:
- I_0 = intensity of incident light
- I = intensity of unscattered light

Importance of Optical Density Measurement

The OD measurement must accurately determine the cell related density. The nutrient and inducer concentrations, feed additions, and dissolved oxygen levels are all designed to provide the cells with the optimum environment, and are based upon cell concentration.

Importance of pH

Introduction   This topic describes how a proper pH balance is maintained during the fermentation process.

Description of pH   pH is a measure of the hydrogen ion concentration in a solution. It is desirable to maintain constant pH by adding acid or base. The media may also be buffered to be stable at a desired pH. Common buffers are citrate, borate, and phosphate. All organisms have a pH growth range and a pH optimum at which they grow best. As the media diverges from this optimal pH, the cell growth will be affected and eventually cease.

pH Levels   The table below describes the three types of pH levels.

pH Level	Description
Neutral solution	pH of 7, which has equal numbers of hydrogen ions and hydroxide ions Pure water has a pH of 7.
Acidic solution	pH lower than 7, which has more hydrogen ions than hydroxide ions
Alkaline solution	pH greater than 7, which has fewer hydrogen ions than hydroxide ions

Continued on next page

Importance of pH

pH Control

The change in pH can tell a lot about the state of the fermentation. In manufacturing, the process should be reproducible and acid/base usage is one of the best ways to monitor the status of the fermentation.

When *E. coli* grows on glucose as its carbon source, it produces organic acids as by-products. In addition to becoming toxic at high levels, these acids decrease the pH of the broth, which can halt growth if the pH is not neutralized. The production of large amounts of acid requires base for neutralization with the formation of salts as a by-product. These salts can also be toxic.

It is common practice to use ammonium hydroxide to control pH in cultures growing on glucose. The ammonia, in addition to maintaining the proper pH, provides a form of nitrogen favored by the cells.

The pH can increase when the cells use complex nitrogen, such as peptones, as a nutrient, because ammonia is released in this reaction. In this case, acid must be added to reduce the pH.

Temperature and Heat Removal

Introduction

This topic describes the importance of:
- The proper temperature to grow *E. coli*
- Removing the heat generated by *E. coli*

Maintaining an Optimal Temperature

The optimum temperature for growth of wild type *E. coli* is 37°C, however strains using the p_L promoter system are often grown at lower temperatures. The p_L promoter system is temperature-sensitive and the cells must be kept below 39°C for proper control. In other control systems promoters are not affected by the temperature, but the plasmid replication may be. The cells can grow faster at higher temperatures, which can reduce fermentation time.

However, the ability to maintain a high growth rate can be problematic. Rapid growth rates require increased supplies of oxygen, nutrients, mixing, and the ability to remove the heat generated by both the equipment (agitator, sparging) and the metabolism of the cells. Processes have to be designed with a particular temperature integrated with the other fermentation parameters.

Purpose of Heat Removal

In large-scale processing, it is important to consider removing the heat generated by *E. coli*. Metabolic processes in the cells primarily combust the carbon source to carbon dioxide. Some of the combustion energy is converted to chemical energy within the cells and the remainder is dissipated as heat. The rate of this heat generation can be regulated in fed-batch fermentation processes by adjusting the rate of carbon addition.

Continued on next page

Temperature and Heat Removal

Heat Generation Equation

It has been shown that heat generated by *E. coli* is proportional to substrate consumption. Additionally, the rate of heat generation (Q) is related to the oxygen uptake rate (OUR) by the following equation:

$$Q = (0.124) \cdot (OUR)$$

Where:
- Q is in units of kcal/L·hr
- OUR is in mmol/L·hr

(Should the constant in the above equation contain the units needed to convert OUR to units of energy, maybe kcal/mmol O_2 consumed?)

In batch fermentations, the choice of substrate determines the amount of heat generated. For example, glycerol is metabolized more slowly than glucose, and its consumption generates heat at a lower rate than glucose consumption. *E. coli* typically grows in the range of 20°C to 45°C.

Maintaining Adequate Cooling

For cells with temperature-sensitive promoter/induction systems such as p_L and p_R, induction could occur due to the heat generated by the culture, if temperature control is inadequate. Consequently, it is important to design the fermentation vessel to provide adequate cooling to maintain optimal growth and protein production temperatures.

Typical laboratory fermentors use either a single cooling loop of tubing directly submerged in the fermentation broth, or the vessel is jacketed. At scales larger than 5000 L, it is generally necessary to provide both a cooling jacket and cooling coils submerged in the fermentor to maintain adequate temperature control. The addition of internal coils complicates production, because vessel cleaning becomes more difficult, and the potential for leaks in cooling coils increases the risk of contamination.

Oxygen

Introduction

Oxygen can be considered a nutrient that is necessary for the growth of *E. coli*. Oxygen has to be provided constantly due to its low solubility. Air contains 21% oxygen and can usually provide the needed oxygen until it becomes the limiting parameter in scale-up.

This topic describes the effects of oxygen on the fermentation of *E. coli*.

Factors Affecting Oxygen Supply

The amount of air or oxygen demanded by the cells indicates their metabolic state. If the feed rates are higher or lower than normal, or some other environmental parameter is out of specification, the oxygen demand will be different. The table below describes the factors that can affect the supply of oxygen.

Factor	Description
Agitation rate	The agitation rate has the greatest influence. Agitation decreases the size of the gas bubbles and therefore increases the surface area available for oxygen transfer.
Temperature, back pressure, and the media	Determines the amount of oxygen that can dissolve in the liquid phase of the broth.
Foam level	Foam level may be controlled with small additions of antifoam. Because antifoam can reduce the oxygen transfer rate, it is a good practice to closely monitor the fermentor's dissolved oxygen level after adding antifoam.

Effects of Oxygen Starvation

When the *E. coli* are starved for oxygen, they change to a different metabolism (anaerobic respiration) which is not as efficient. Under these conditions the growth rate will decrease and too much glucose may be added, compounding the problem.

Increasing the amount of glucose also increases the amount of oxygen required to metabolize the glucose aerobically.

Continued on next page

Oxygen

Use of Dissolved Oxygen

There is a wide range of Dissolved Oxygen (DO) that can support cell growth. When the DO drops too low for aerobic growth (called the critical DO level), the changes in the cellular metabolism are rapid and dramatic. The fermentation processes are designed to operate at a sufficient dissolved oxygen level to avoid this critical level.

Control of Foaming

Cause of Foaming

E. coli fermentations generally foam. Foam forms when proteins in the fermentation solution stabilize air bubbles that were sparged through the fermentor broth to maintain the concentration of dissolved oxygen. The air sparged through the fermentor can carry foam out the top of the fermentor and significantly reduce the volume of the culture.

Control of Foaming

High agitation, aeration, and cell density can lead to foam formation. This foam can overflow the condenser and foul the exit filter, making pressure control impossible. To control foaming, a number of different surfactants can be added to the broth, including silicon and polypropylene glycol. However, these antifoaming agents reduce the value of K_La* and therefore reduce the rate of oxygen transfer from the sparged gas to the fermentor broth. Also, silicon has been shown to foul filter membranes that are used in downstream processing.

Consequently, the best strategy is to add a minimal amount of antifoaming agent to the fermentor broth to ensure that the foam does not exit the fermentor.

Note: K_La is the volumetric mass transfer coefficient.

Growth Rate of Cells

Introduction

All the conditions described in this section interact to determine the growth rate of the cells. The type of cell, genotype, nutrients, environmental parameters, and control strategies each play a part in cell growth. Cell growth which is different from past experience with a known process implicates a deviation in some of the fermentation parameters. This topic describes the cell growth process.

How Cell Growth Works

Bacteria divide by binary fission where one cell becomes two daughter cells, two become four, and so on. This continues at a constant rate in a steady state condition. The rate will be the maximum growth rate for that particular organism, unless something exists at a less than optimal level. This is called mu(μ) max. In a batch or fed-batch fermentor, this steady state is not achievable, because some nutrients are depleted and by-products accumulate as cell concentration increases. The growth rates will differ in the batch and fed-batch phases.

Effect of OD on Growth Rate

The correlation between cell mass and OD prior to induction is linear for cells before they are producing IBs. After induction, the refractile IBs contribute to the scattering of light, and the absorbance is not an accurate measure of cell mass. The increase in OD can be used as an indication of the accumulation of IBs, since the more IBs form, the more light is scattered.

Measuring Cell Growth

In order to measure cell growth, one can use a spectrophotometer absorbance reading as an indication of cell mass. The optical density can be used to calculate the specific growth (μ). Using the following formula, you can calculate when a target OD will be reached or determine if the growth rate of the culture is changing. The formula is:

$$X = X_0 \ e^{\mu t}$$

Where:
- X = OD
- X_0 = OD at time zero
- μ = specific growth rate in reciprocal hours (1/hr)
- t = time in hours

Harvesting Product

Purpose

The goal of harvesting is to reduce the processing volume, increase the percentage of solids, remove contaminating materials and unused media, inactivate the cells, and provide a stable product to be stored while recovering an acceptable amount of product. In most cases this stored product will be washed inclusion body paste. Harvesting conditions can have a large effect on the ease of purification and the final product purity and yield.

Typical Harvesting Process

The figure below illustrates the typical harvesting process.

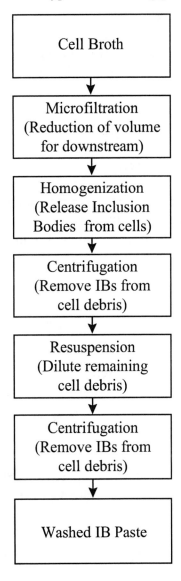

Continued on next page

Harvesting Product

How Harvesting Works

Harvesting includes the steps from the fermentation broth to the starting material for purification. This material can be in the form of:

- Cell broth
- Washed broth
- Cell paste
- Inclusion bodies
- Washed inclusion bodies

In some cases it will be the cell lysate that is recovered if the product is a soluble protein. This intermediate stage must be proven stable if storage is necessary. There may be some products that require immediate processing due to stability issues or the desire for continuous processing with no holding of intermediate steps.

Description of Centrifugal Harvesting

Centrifugal harvesting uses the differences in density between the cells or inclusion body (IB) and their medium to achieve a separation. Stokes' law defines the important parameters involved in using gravitational force for separation. Centrifugation just increases the gravitational force. The velocity of a particle in a gravitational field can be characterized as shown below:

$$\text{Velocity} = \frac{D^2 (r_p\text{-}r_m)}{8\,h}\ \omega^2 r$$

where:

- D = particle diameter
- $r_p\text{-}r_m$ = density difference of the particle and medium
- h = viscosity
- $\omega^2 r$ = centrifugal acceleration

It can be seen that increasing the density difference by having larger inclusion bodies or reducing the density or viscosity of the medium will improve the recovery. This holds true for cells, IBs, and any material denser than the process fluid.

Scale-Up Challenges

Introduction

Scale-up presents many challenges. Large-scale fermentors require an increased amount of necessary ancillary equipment, which in turn increases the chance of mechanical failure. Retaining a constant fermentor geometry eliminates many sources of inconsistency. This includes maintaining the same tank height/diameter ratio, impeller diameter to tank diameter ratio, and impeller number and design.

Maintaining Sterility

One of the first scale-up concerns is sterility. The piping of the fermentor becomes more complicated. The amount of necessary ancillary equipment and the number of possible contamination sites increases.

Since sterilization consists of killing any unwanted organism in the fermentor or feed tank, the risk increases that an organism will survive this treatment with larger scale since there are more organisms present at time zero.

Providing Nutrients

Providing nutrients to the cells can be complicated by the volumes involved and the route the feed has to travel to reach each cell. The homogeneity of the broth can vary depending on the scale. Due to variations in characteristics such as mixing and heat transfer, it is sometimes not feasible to operate a large-scale fermentor under the same conditions as in a pilot plant.

Oxygen Levels and Temperature Controls

Before a process is transferred to manufacturing, the issues of sufficient oxygen and temperature control should be addressed.

One of the biggest challenges for scale-up is to provide sufficient oxygen and mixing to obtain a homogenous mixture. There is no consensus about the best way to scale mixing. Most often, a constant power-to-volume ratio or agitator tip speed is used to maintain the same shear rates and/or dissolved oxygen levels.

Temperature control can put demands on the system. The metabolic heat generated by the cells and the heat from the equipment and sparged gases may be more than the cooling system can remove. As the volume of a tank increases by the cube, the surface area available for cooling increases only by the square. Therefore, the effective area for removing heat does not scale linearly with volume, making it harder to remove heat from the fermentor.

Continued on next page

Scale-Up Challenges

Scale-Up Options

Harvesting at large scales is very different than working with volumes under ten liters. Microfuges and bottle centrifuges can easily handle pilot plant volumes. Beyond the ten to fifteen liters scale, bowl and continuous disc stack centrifuges or filtration are used.

Continuous centrifugation is the most scalable option because the small-scale unit operations are not preferred for large-scale harvesting.

Section 3
Stages of Fermentation

Overview

Introduction

This section describes the stages used in the fermentation process, including:
- The Seed Train
- Batching and sterilization
- Induction

Table of Contents

This section contains the following topics.

The Seed Train

Introduction

The fermentation process starts with a Seed Train that provides cells for the production fermentor, which involves growing the inoculum from a frozen seed vial. Frozen cells can be used because they are viable and the cloned genes are stable at -120°C for over ten years.

Choose media components, incubation conditions and target cell density for the inoculum to minimize the lag phase in the production fermentor.

The Seed Train Process

The table below describes the stages in the Seed Train process.

Stage	Description
1	Thaw the cells and aseptically add them to the media in a shake flask.
2	Place the shake flask in the incubator shaker. *Result*: The cells will start to divide after a lag phase in which there is no measurable growth, but the cells are making enzymes necessary to start growing.
3	Transfer the cells when a sufficient cell mass is obtained, but before the cells become limited for some nutrient or oxygen is depleted. *Result*: The cells are transferred to the seed fermentor.
4	Depending on the scale inoculate one or more intermediate seed fermentors to increase the size of the inoculum. This is done when the process cannot go from the shake flask to the final production-scale fermentor because the volume increase is too great. *IMPORTANT*: This stage can also be used to reduce the time in the production fermentor. Fermentation processes for manufacturing therapeutic recombinant proteins have been reported at scales ranging from 45 L to 1500 L. Inoculum for such large-scale fermentations must be of sufficient size to ensure successful growth in the production fermentor.

Media Components in Inoculum Culture vs. Production Culture

Media components in the inoculum culture are generally similar to those in the production culture. For example, if the production fermentor uses a minimal, defined media, the inoculum media should also be minimal. Otherwise, growth in the production fermentor may not occur for at least 24 hours. An inoculation volume that is approximately 1% of the production fermentor volume is typical.

Batching and Sterilization

Introduction   Batching and sterilizing the production fermentor is carried out prior to inoculation.

Sterilization Considerations   Steam heat is the most common method used for sterilizing fermentors. This eliminates any viable organisms from the components added in the batch or remaining in the fermentor after cleaning. Clean is not good enough. There must be *no* living organism present other than the recombinant host cell. Sterilization parameters are chosen to inacativate highly resistant spores of *Bacillus* species. Yeast extract and peptones are rich in these spores.

The batch should include ingredients that can safely be steam sterilized together. Any heat sensitive ingredients are filter sterilized and added as a poststerile addition (PSA). Ingredients incompatible with the batch ingredients, due to undesired chemical reactions at high temperature, are autoclaved separately and then aseptically added to the fermentor.

Equation Used to Describe Steam Sterilization   The following first order chemical equation is used to describe the destruction of microorganisms by heat:

$$\ln N_t / N_o = k\,t$$

where:
- N_o = number of viable organisms present at the start
- N_t = number of viable organisms present after treatment
- t = time of sterilization
- k = reaction rate constant or the specific death rate

k will differ among types of organisms and also differ depending on whether the cells are spores or in their vegetative growth phase. The important controllable parameters are the number of contaminants present and time. *Note*: Nutrients also have a rate (k) at which heat will destroy them. Times must be chosen to ensure sterility without destroying needed nutrients.

Continued on next page

Batching and Sterilization

Environmental Changes

If the inoculum was grown in a shake flask, there is no method to control pH, and the media has to be designed to remain close to pH 7. When going into the fermentor, the conditions and media are different because:

- The dissolved oxygen level is higher
- The temperature is different
- There is a higher concentration of nutrients in the fermentor media
- There is a lower concentration of cells following inoculation

Any time the cells are inoculated into different nutritional or environmental conditions, they can go into a lag phase or period with little or no cell growth.

Description of Lag Phase

The inoculum enters a lag phase when introduced into the fermentor. This is due to a change in nutrients from Luria broth to the batch media. Luria broth contains a carbohydrate source that results in the production of organic acids by the cells. Shake flasks do not have a way of controlling pH and the acid would create an inhospitable environment.

Cells adapt to the batch media and start to grow. This growth can be monitored by the change in:

- Dissolved oxygen
- Consumption of some nutrient such as glucose
- An increase in turbidity.

Purpose of the Fed-batch Phase

The purpose of the fed-batch phase is to increase the cell density without the added burden for the cell to produce recombinant product. When the cells are induced, there are limited intracellular resources, and cell division slows down or stops.

Continued on next page

Batching and Sterilization

How the Fed-Batch Phase Works

The table below describes the fed-batch process.

Stage	Description
1	Once the cells are in the fermentor, their environment is constantly changing. The cells start to use the available nutrients and produce by-products. The consumption of these nutrients, along with the production of these by-products, can limit growth or become toxic. *Example*: Acetate is a common by-product that becomes toxic at higher concentrations.
2	When the cells have metabolized most of the glucose, the glucose becomes limiting and cell growth starts to slow down. The media in the batch is not able to obtain a large increase of cell mass and a feed is initiated.
3	Feed is pumped into the fermentor from the external reservoirs.
4	Cell growth is controlled at some predetermined rate by the addition of feed. *Note*: The feed rate schedule is determined during the process development stage.

Importance of Feed Rate

The feed rate not only controls the growth rate, but concomitantly controls:
- Acid/base usage
- Oxygen requirements
- Heat evolution
- Byproduct formation
- Elapsed fermentation time

Deviations in any of these parameters indicates improperly controlled feed rates may be implicated. Growth rates that are too high will cause the cells to overproduce by-products. Growth rates other than those specified in the manufacturing procedure can affect productivity and product quality.

Induction

Background

When the cell density reaches a predetermined level, fermentor conditions are adjusted to *induce* the cells to begin the protein production phase. The requirements for the production phase may be quite different than for that of the growth phase. The growth phase requires more carbon source. The production phase requires more nitrogen source.

Promoter System

The promoter system used also determines the conditions for the production phase. The inducer is determined at the time of cloning by the choice of promoter system. The most frequently used promoters are based on changes in temperature or the addition of a chemical "inducer." If the promoter is constitutive, then the cells are producing the foreign protein usually as long as they are growing.

Note: Promoter systems are determined mostly by the idiosyncrasies of the product protein.

Induction Times

Induction times are based on experiments that assess the level of production and quality of product at a number of elapsed times post-induction. When the cells are induced normally, cell division slows down or stops completely and recombinant protein production begins. The time necessary to produce protein depends upon the:
- Promoter
- Fermentation conditions
- Protein being expressed

Depending on the system used, induction continues from 5 to 20 hours. The length of induction depends on many things, including yield, ease of recovery, and product quality. The goal is to achieve the highest titer with the highest product quality.

Quality is determined by the final purified product and is an interaction of fermentation and purification conditions; both processes have to be developed together.

Bacterial Growth Lab

Laboratory

Introduction This laboratory provides an opportunity for students to study the growth of bacterial cultures under different nutritional and environmental conditions. Students will assess growth by monitoring several parameters including optical density, wet weight, pH, and glucose concentrations.

Equipment Micropipettors
Analytical balances
3 Incubator shakers
Microcentrifuge
Spectrophotometers
YSI glucose analyzer

Materials and Supplies Sterile shake flasks, 250 ml
Luria broth
Terrific broth
Glucose, 400 g/l
Overnight culture of *E. coli*.
Sterile pipettes
Saline for dilutions
Microcentrifuge tubes
Tubes for serial dilutions
Pipette tips

Laboratory

Activities at a Glance

Students will monitor the growth of bacterial cultures under several different conditions. Students will be divided into three groups, and each group will incubate their cultures at a different temperature ($24°C$, $30°C$, and $37°C$).

1. Each group will aseptically set up shake flasks containing the following:
   40 mls of Luria broth
   40 mls of Luria broth + 0.5g/l glucose
          (50 microliters of 400 g/l stock)
   40 mls of Terrific broth
   40 mls of Terrific broth + 0.5g/l glucose
          (50 microliters of 400 g/l stock)

2. Each flask will be inoculated with the overnight culture at 10% final volume.

3. Students will make the following measurements at time 0 and at 30 minute intervals over a three-hour period.
   a. Optical density: A_{600} using the spectrophotometer
      Dilutions in saline must be performed to stay within the linear range of the instrument.
   b. Glucose concentration: YSI Glucose analyzer
      1.0 ml samples will be taken for glucose determinations.
   c. Wet weight
      1.0 ml samples will be placed in microcentrifuge tubes and centrifuged.
      Obtain weights of tubes with/without cells to make wet weight determination.

4. Initial and final samples will be diluted to 10^{-5} and 10^{-6}, and 0.1 ml plated on LB and LB/Ampicillin plates for colony counts and replica plated to determine plasmid retention.

Integrity Testing

Overview

Introduction   Filter integrity testing is a nondestructive procedure to evaluate whether a filter unit is integral or contains a flaw. A filter that is nonintegral or flawed will not perform as designed in production.

To assure that a critical filter remains integral during use, integrity testing is typically performed before use (after steaming, if possible) as well as after use of the filter. The most common cause of damage to a filter, causing a failure of integrity, is applying too high of a pressure differential to a hot filter. (filter cartridge at steaming temperature can be damaged by a differential pressure > 5 psid.)

Filter integrity testing can only be used on membrane filters. Depth filters such as "pad filters" or "spun wound" filters are not integrity testable.

Table of Contents   This document contains the following topics:

Integrity Testing

Objectives

1. Explain why integrity testing is performed.
2. Describe when/where integrity testing is performed.
3. Distinguish between destructive and nondestructive integrity testing.
4. Define bubble point.
5. Describe the bubble point test.
6. Describe bubble point dependencies.
7. Explain when bubble point is applicable.
8. Describe the factors which affect bubble point.
9. Define diffusion testing.
10. State a reason why bubble point is preferred to diffusion testing.
11. State a reason for performing diffusion testing.
12. Explain when diffusion testing is applicable.
13. Describe the factors which affect diffusion tests.
14. Set up/prepare equipment for a bubble point and diffusion test.
15. Perform a manual test of bubble point.
16. Perform a manual diffusion test.
17. Demonstrate assembly of 10" filter housing with hydrophilic cartridge.
18. Demonstrate proper use of pressure vessel and connections.
19. Perform interpretation of diffusion results and make determination of filter integrity.
20. Perform interpretation of bubble point test results and make determination of filter integrity.
21. Describe the effects of temperature on manual bubble point and diffusion tests.
22. Identify an automatic integrity tester.
23. Describe the function/use of an automatic integrity tester.
24. Explain the purpose of a filter autopsy.

Background

Validation
The most important function of filter integrity testing is to verify in a nondestructive manner that an individual filter being used in a critical process application meets the manufacturer's integrity test criteria so that it can be correlated to data for bacterial retention. Once a particular filter has been validated for a sterilizing application, continued integrity testing is required to assure that each individual filter is equivalent in performance.

Integrity Tester
Automated integrity testers use calibrated pressure transducers and/or flow meters to accurately and reproducibly determine if a filter meets its manufacturer's specifications. Automated testers also have the capability of printing out a hard copy of the test results. With an automated tester, integrity tests can be performed with the filter in-place or at an integrity test station. In-place testing can often be done without compromising the sterility of the system.

General Considerations
Integrity tests should be performed in a controlled environment. Drafts and changes in temperature can alter the results of an integrity test.

An integrity test failure can often be due to environmental effects or insufficient stabilization time during the test. If the first test on a filter fails, rewet the filter (hydrophilic) or refill the housing (hydrophobic), check all seals and connections (including the filter mounting) and run the test a second time. If the test fails a second time, it is possible that the filter is defective or is the incorrect type. Consult a supervisor.

Integrity test parameters are specific to the filter being used, the wetting liquid, and the gas used for pressurization. Be sure that you are using the right filter, liquid, and gas for the test program you are running.

Filter Wetting Methods

Hydrophobic Filters

Hydrophobic filters are filters that repel liquid. They are used in applications such as gas filtration and tank vent filters.

Hydrophobic filters are wetted using a 60% Isopropyl alcohol (IPA), 40% PUR/WFI solution pumped through the filter. This allows the membranes to become thoroughly wetted. Hydrophobic filters should be blown down using clean air after testing to ensure their hydrophobic qualities are not affected by the wetting agent.

When performing a water intrusion test, it is not required to wet the filter with the 60% IPA, 40% PUR/WFI solution prior to integrity testing.

Hydrophilic Filters

Hydrophilic filters are filters that allow solutions to flow through them. They are used to filter solutions such as vitamins, trace metals, and miscellaneous buffers, as well as final product.

Hydrophilic filters are wetted by flushing the filter with PUR/WFI. Hydrophilic filters should be blown down using clean air after testing as well.

Water Intrusion Testing

Water Intrusion

Water intrusion testing is used to measure the largest pores of a hydrophobic filter by measuring the volume of water that is able to enter these pores at a given pressure. This measurement may be made by pressure drop on the upstream side of the filter, or by the flow of gas (typically air) that displaces the water entering the filters pores.

Type of Filters

Water intrusion testing is used to test hydrophobic filters such as air, gas, and tank vent filters. These filters typically contain membrane manufactured with PTFE or polyvinylidene fluoride (PVDF).

Continued on next page

Water Intrusion Testing

Principles of Water Intrusion Testing	Water intrusion testing requires a very sensitive integrity test instrument and can easily be influenced by environmental effects. When performing water intrusion testing, care should be taken to avoid changes in temperature or drafts in the area where the test is being performed. It is also a good practice to allow the water used for the test a chance to equilibrate to ambient conditions before performing testing.
Performance	To perform the water intrusion test, all ports on the upstream side of the housing must be capped off except for the top (instrument) port. The housing must be completely filled with water. (*It is very critical that the filter is completely submerged and has several centimeters of water above it as well. If any part of the filter membrane becomes exposed to air during the testing, the test will fail.*) The integrity tester is then connected to the housing, and the proper program is selected. During the integrity test, the filter housing must remain upright and should not be handled. After a successful test, water must be drained from the housing before use in production. (Water remaining in the housing will blind the filter to the flow of gas and decrease its performance.)

Bubble Point

Bubble Point	Bubble point refers to the pressure required to displace the liquid from the largest pore in a wetted filter. Since a tighter rated filter typically has smaller pores, bubble point increases as the retention rating of the filter decreases.
Types of Filters	Bubble point testing can be used on hydrophilic or hydrophobic membrane filters.

Continued on next page

Bubble Point

Principles of Bubble Point

In bubble point testing, gas pressure is gradually raised on the upstream side of a wetted filter until the gas is able to pass through the filter. At the "bubble point" of a filter membrane, the gas has reached sufficient pressure to overcome the surface tension of the liquid in the largest filter pore and displaces it from the pore. At this point, gas is able to freely flow through the pore and a noticeable decrease in pressure drop or gas flow on the upstream side of the filter can be measured. In a manual bubble point test, tubing from the outlet of the filter is held under water and the pressure is increased until a steady stream of bubbles emerges from the tubing. The pressure when this occurs is the bubble point.

Performance

To perform bubble point testing, the filter must first be flushed with the solution to be used for wetting. All ports on the upstream side of the housing must be capped off except for the top (instrument) port. The integrity tester is then connected, and the appropriate program is selected. During the test, the filter housing should remain upright and should not be handled.

Pressure Hold

Pressure Hold

Pressure hold testing entails pressurizing the upstream side of a wetted filter at a pressure below the bubble point and measuring the drop in pressure over time.

Types of Filters

Pressure hold testing is not a sensitive test of a filter's integrity, but is often used to test the overall integrity of a "system" including piping, seals, and connections. Pressure hold testing is also sometimes used with ultrafiltration systems as a test for a gross failure of the filter's or system's integrity.

Continued on next page

Pressure Hold

Principles of Pressure Hold

The primary use of the pressure hold test is to test the integrity of a system rather than a filter. A wetted filter is expected to allow some diffusion of air over time. So a pressure hold test on a filter is actually measuring the same thing as a diffusion test, only the acceptance criteria are different. To reduce the pressure drop that occurs over time with a pressure test, a low test pressure is often chosen. Pressure tests are often a simple way to determine if the cause of a failing filter integrity test is due to the filter or the system (i.e. housing). A common cause for failure in integrity testing is incorrect sealing of the filter or of the housing. With the downstream side of the filter housing capped off, a failed pressure hold or diffusion test is most likely due to a misaligned seal.

Diffusion

Diffusion (Forward Flow)

Diffusion (or forward flow) testing is a measure of the diffusion rate of a gas through a wetted filter membrane. The rate of diffusion can be calculated by a pressure drop on the upstream side of the filter or by direct measurement of the flow of gas into the filter housing during a diffusion test. In diffusion testing the pressure on the upstream side of the filter is maintained throughout the test at a constant value (unlike the pressure hold test).

Types of Filters

Diffusion testing can be performed on hydrophilic or hydrophobic membrane filters.

Continued on next page

Diffusion

Principles of Diffusion

Diffusion testing is the most common method of testing hydrophilic filters. The rate of diffusion of a gas (typically air) into the liquid (typically water) entrained in a filter's pores and out the downstream side is the diffusion rate of a membrane. As the retention rating of a filter becomes tighter, the rate of diffusion will decrease. Diffusion testing must take place at a pressure less than the bubble point of the membrane so that diffusion is being measured, not bulk flow of the gas through the filter pore. If a filter is not fully wetted, or is damaged, the flow of gas will increase such as to resemble the bubble point bulk flow of gas. For large filter areas, diffusion is preferred to bubble point due to the potential of detecting a "false" bubble point based on the large amount of diffusion that may be seen through a large membrane surface area.

Performance

To perform diffusion (forward flow) testing, the filter must be thoroughly flushed with the solution to be used for wetting. All ports on the upstream side of the housing must be capped off except for the top (instrument) port. The integrity tester is then connected to the housing, and the proper program is selected on the integrity tester. During the test, the filter housing should remain upright and should not be handled.

Manual Integrity Test

Manual Integrity Test

Integrity testing can also be done manually. A manual integrity test is typically performed by wetting a filter and applying pressure to the upstream side of the membrane. The rate of gas diffusion/time is measured by capturing the gas on the downstream side of the membrane into a graduated container that has been flooded and inverted in a tank or bucket of water and timing the rate of displacement of the liquid by the gas with a calibrated stopwatch.

Manual testing is susceptible to operator error and is difficult to reproduce. It cannot be performed in-place on a sterile system. Manual testing is typically not sensitive enough to test very small filters or perform certain procedures such as water intrusion testing.

Glossary

Downstream	The side of the filter where the process stream has already passed through the filter membrane. The downstream side of a filter is also referred to as the outlet or clean side of the filter, and the process stream here is called the filtrate.
Filter Integrity Test	A nondestructive test that shows a filter meets the specifications required by the manufacturer to perform as designed or to correlate to the manufacturer's bacterial challenge.
Upstream	The side of the filter that is facing the direction of flow. The upstream side of a filter is also referred to as the inlet or "dirty" side of the filter.

References

Books	*Filtration in the Pharmaceutical Industry,* Meltzer, T. H. and Jornitz, Maik W.

Filter Integrity Testing

Laboratory

Introduction   Filter integrity testing will be performed by students using both diffusion testing and bubble point. In addition, students will gain experience in the assembly of filter housings and the use of pressure vessels and gauges.

Equipment   10" Stainless steel housings
Stainless steel pressure vessels
Compressed gas source (air or nitrogen)
Pressure regulator
Pressure gauges

Materials and Supplies   10" filter cartridge to be tested: Durapore, Catalog # CVGL71TP3
                    0.22μm hydrophilic cartridge
Purified water
6' tubing section with quick disconnect inlet and outlet connections
6' tubing section with quick disconnect inlet/sanitary flange outlet
3' (¼ " I.D.) tubing section with sanitary flange fitting
Graduated cylinder
4 liter beaker
Stopwatch

Activities at a Glance   Students will conduct tests to determine the diffusional flow rate and bubble point of a Millipore hydrophilic cartridge.

Protocol for these tests are outlined on a handout from Millipore.

Tangential Flow Filtration

Overview

Introduction	Membrane-based Tangential Flow Filtration (TFF) unit operations are used for clarifying, concentrating, and purifying proteins and molecules.

Examples	A typical use for TFF is to take a large, dilute volume of liquid and concentrate it to a small, concentrated volume. A good example is orange juice. When made, orange juice contains a lot of water. TFF can be used to concentrate the orange pulp and flavor molecules and pass all the water. This is how we get concentrate from orange juice. The benefits of this include helping to lower shipping costs and reducing space required for storage of the product.

Table of Contents

This document contains the following topics:

Tangential Flow Filtration

Objectives

1. Describe the basic concepts of TFF.
2. Describe the basic concepts of NFF.
3. State the three different streams in TFF.
4. Explain how TFF differs from dead-end filtration.
5. Discuss the limitations of normal flow filtration.
6. Identify the four types of TFF.
7. Describe the separation of solutes and particles in microporous filtration.
8. Describe the separation of solutes and particles in ultrafiltration.
9. Describe the separation of solutes and particles in RO.
10. Discuss which industries utilize TFF and the type of TFF applicable.
11. Identify what products are made using TFF.
12. Describe the uses of TFF in the biopharmaceutical industry.
13. Outline a potential production process and give examples of where TFF could be utilized.
13. Describe the appropriate use of Pellicon, Prostak, and Helicon filters.
14. Give the components of a TFF system.
15. Demonstrate assembly of Pellicon-2 mini-filters and cassettes.
16. Perform integrity testing on such filters.
17. Describe the concept of a TMP and explain its significance to TFF.
18. Define crossflow rate.
19. Define NMWL and its significance to TFF.

What Is TFF?

What Is Tangential Flow Filtration?

Filtration is a pressure driven separation process that uses membranes to separate components in a liquid solution or suspension based on their size and charge differences. Filtration can be broken down into two different operational modes: Normal Flow Filtration and Tangential Flow Filtration. The difference in fluid flow between these two modes is illustrated in Figures 23.1and 23.2 on the next page.

Normal Flow Filtration

In Normal Flow Filtration (NFF), fluid is convected directly toward the membrane under an applied pressure. Particulates that are too large to pass through the pores of the membrane accumulate at the membrane surface or in the depth of the filtration media, while smaller molecules pass through to the downstream side. This type of process is often called dead-end filtration. However, the term "normal" indicates that the fluid flow occurs in the direction normal to the membrane surface, so NFF is a more descriptive and preferred name. NFF can be used for sterile filtration of clean streams, clarifying prefiltration, and viruses.

Tangential Flow Filtration

In Tangential Flow Filtration (TFF), the fluid is pumped tangentially along the surface of the membrane. An applied pressure serves to force a portion of the fluid through the membrane to the filtrate side. As in NFF, particulates and macromolecules that are too large to pass through the membrane pores are retained on the upstream side. However, in this case the retained components do not build up at the surface of the membrane. Instead, they are swept along by the tangential flow. This feature of TFF makes it an ideal process for finer sized-based separations. TFF is also commonly called cross-flow filtration. However, the term "tangential" is descriptive of the direction of fluid flow relative to the membrane, so it is the preferred name.

What is TFF?

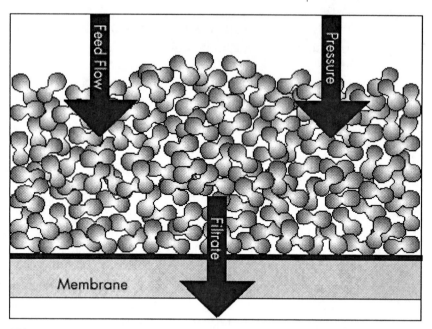

Figure 23.1: Normal Flow Filtration

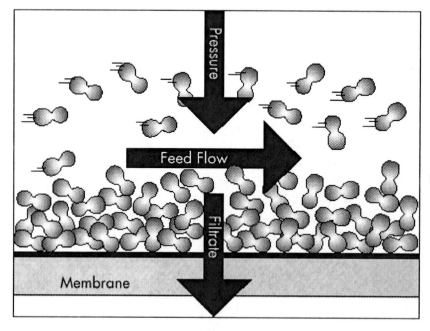

Figure 23.2: Tangential Flow Filtration

TFF Basics

Tangential Flow Filtration Basics

In a TFF unit operation, a pump is used to generate flow of the feed stream through the channel between two membrane surfaces. A schematic of a simple TFF system is shown in Figure 23.3 below.

During each pass of fluid over the surface of the membrane, the applied pressure forces a portion of the fluid through the membrane and into the filtrate stream. The result is a gradient in the feedstock concentration from the bulk conditions at the center of the channel to the more concentrated wall conditions at the membrane surface. There is also a concentration gradient along the length of the feed channel from the inlet to the outlet (retentate) as progressively more fluid passes to the filtrate side.

Figure 23.3: Schematic of a Simple TFF System

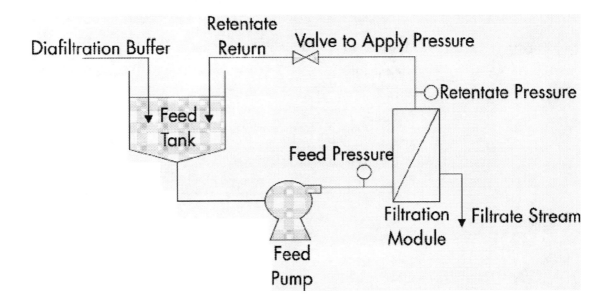

Types of TFF

Application Modes

Several different modes of application exist for TFF including:

- Microfiltration (MF)
- Ultrafiltration (UF)
- Virusfiltration (VF)
- Nanofiltration (NF)
- Reverse Osmosis (RO)

Membranes Types

The types of membranes used in TFF include:

- Polyethersulfone (PES)
- Regenerated Cellulose
- Polyvinylidene fluoride (PVDF)
- Polyamides

Devices

The devices employed for TFF include:

- Hollow Fibers
- Prostaks
- Cassettes
- Spiral Wound

How TFF is used in Protein Processing

How is TFF Used in Protein Processing?

TFF can be further subdivided into categories based on the size of components being separated. For protein processing, these can range from the size of intact cells to buffer salts. In addition, it shows the range of membrane pore size ratings or nominal molecular weight limits (NMWL) that generally fall into each category.

A membrane pore size rating, typically given as a micron value, indicates that particles larger than the rating will be retained by the membrane. A NMWL, on the other hand, is an indication that most dissolved macromolecules with molecular weights higher than the NMWL and some with molecular weights lower than the NMWL will be retained by the membrane. A component's shape, its ability to deform, and its interaction with other components in the solution all affect its retention. Different membrane manufacturers use different criteria to assign the NMWL ratings to a family of membranes. The technical references at the end of this document provide more detail on membrane retention determination, as well as additional information on other related topics.

Microfiltration (MF) is usually used upstream in a recovery process to separate intact cells and some cell debris/lysates from the rest of the components in the feed stream. Either the retained cells or the clarified filtrate can be the product stream. Membrane pore size cutoffs used for this type of separation are typically in the range of 0.05 µm to 1.0 µm. Ultrafiltration (UF) is one of the most widely used forms of TFF, and pH is used to separate proteins from buffer components for buffer exchange, desalting, or concentration. Depending on the protein to be retained, membrane NMWLs in the range of 1 kD to 1000 kD are used.

Integrity and Permeability Testing

Introduction
- Integrity testing ensures the TFF membrane is void of major defects.
- Permeability testing is an indication of membrane cleaning.

Integrity Explanation

In order to ensure that the installed membranes have not sustained any damage during storage and handling, Millipore recommends integrity testing all TFF assemblies prior to startup and after each post-use cleaning. An air diffusion test identifies problems such as macroscopic holes in the membrane, cracks in the seals, or improperly seated modules. When air is applied to the retentate side of the membranes at a controlled pressure, it diffuses through the water in the pores at a predictable rate. If there are defects, the air will be able to flow through them at a much higher rate than the background diffusion, giving a failing test value. To obtain accurate test results, fully wet the membranes with water and then completely drain the modules. In the "Maintenance Procedures" manuals, Millipore provides instructions on performing integrity tests and lists test pressures and diffusion specifications for all of its membranes.

Permeability Explanation

Prior to the first use on protein and after each post-use cleaning, measure the clean membrane permeability to establish a baseline for flows and pressures. This value, also called the normalized flux, is determined by recording crossflow and filtrate flow rates, feed, retentate, and filtrate pressures, and temperature during recirculation of a solution. Then, calculate:

Normalized flux = (Flux x Temperature correction factor) / TMP

For a given TFF setup, always take the measurement at similar operating conditions, preferably at a low transmembrane pressure (TMP), using the same solution. Refer to the "Millipore Maintenance Procedures" for specific instructions and temperature correction factors.

Millipore Literature References

Literature Number	Title
VG059	Validation Guide: Pellicon-2 Cassette Filters
AB002	Selecting a Membrane for Concentration, Desalting, and Buffer Exchange of Macromolecules (Ultrafiltration)
SD011	Pellicon Laboratory Unit Operations, Holders, and Assemblies
DEF056/U	Pellicon-2 Filters and Holders
SD206	Helicon-UF Modules
P34000	Helicon-UF Spiral Wound TFF Cartridge
P34552	Prep/Scale TFF Cartridges
P35696	Prep/Scale TFF Cartridges Flushing Procedure
P30164	Installation Instructions for Pellicon
P35430	Pellicon-2 Cassettes and Maxi Filters Installation Guide
P35471	Pellicon-2 Mini Filters Installation Guide
P35472	Pellcon-2 Filters Flushing Procedure
SD002	Maintenance Procedures for Tangential Flow Filters and Unit Operations
P17514	Maintenance Procedures for Helicon-UF Ultrafiltration Cartridges
P17512	Maintenance Procedures for Pellicon and Pellicon-2 Cassette Filters
SD227	Pellicon-2 Filters
99516	Pellicon-2 Instructions Manual
EB004/U	Understanding Solution Capabilities Brochure
TB0010000	A Guide to the Development of an Ultrafiltration/Diafiltration System for Protein Processing
PC099	Millipore Pharmaceutical Process Separations Catalogue
PB022	Pellicon Tangential Flow Filtration Cassettes Brochure

Technical References

Cheryan, M. 1986. *Ultrafiltration Handbook*. Technomic Publishing Co., Inc., Pennsylvania.

Koros, W.J., Ma, Y.H.; Shimidzu, T. 1996. "Terminology for Membranes and Membrane Processes (IUPACRecommendations 1996)." *Pure & Appl*. Chem. 68: 1479 – 1489.

Ng, P., Lundblad, J., Mitra, G. 1976. "Optimization of Solute Separation by Diafiltration." *Separation Science* 2: 499-502.

Tkacik, G., Michaels, S. 1991. "A Rejection Profile Test for Ultrafiltration Membranes and Devices." *Bio/Technol*. 9: 941-946.

van Reis, R., Gadam, S., Frautschy, L.N., Orlando, S., Goodrich, E.M., Saksena, S., Kuriyel, R., Simpson, C.M., Pearl,S., Zydney, A.L. 1997. "High Performance Tangential Flow Filtration." *Biotech. Bioeng*. 56: 71-82.

van Reis, R., Goodrich, E.M., Yson, C.L., Frautschy, L.N., Dzegeleski, S., Lutz, H. 1997. "Linear Scale Ultrafiltration." *Biotechnol. Bioeng*. 55: 737–746.

van Reis, R., Goodrich, E.M., Yson, C.L., Frautschy, L.N., Whiteley, R., Zydney, A.L. 1997. "Constant C-wall? Ultrafiltration Process Control." *J. Membrane Sci*. 130: 123-140.

van Reis, R., Zydney, A.L. 1999. Protein Ultrafiltration. In M.C. Flikinger, S.W. Drew (eds.) *Encyclopedia of Bioprocess Technology*. John Wiley and Sons, Inc. New York.

Zeman, L.J.; Zydney, A.L. 1996. *Microfiltration and Ultrafiltration: Principles and Applications*. Marcel Dekker, New York.

Trademarks

Millipore, Pellicon, Proflux, Labscale, Ultracel, Helicon, Prostak, and BioMax are all trademarks of Millipore Corporation or an affiliated company. Tri-Clamp is a trademark of Ladish Company.

Tangential Flow Filtration

Laboratory

Introduction

The purpose of this laboratory is to provide students the opportunity for hands-on experience with tangential flow filtration. The laboratory exercise will involve the use of Pelicon filters, housings, and equipment used in tangential flow filtration, in order that the student understand the concepts and applications of TFF within the biotechnology industry.

Equipment

Pellicon-minis
Cassettes
Stainless steel pressure vessel
Pressure regulator
Automated filter integrity tester

Materials and Supplies

Compressed gas source (air or nitrogen)
Purified water
1-6' tubing sections with quick disconnect inlet and outlet connections
1-6' tubing sections with quick disconnect inlet/sanitary flange outlet
1-3' ¼ "I.D. tubing sections with sanitary flange fitting
Pressure gauge
Graduated cylinder
4 liter beaker
Stopwatch
Pressure regulator

Activities at a Glance

1. Practice assembly of Pellicon-minis in cassettes.
2. Perform diffusional flow rate and bubble point determinations with Pellicon-minis.
3. Demonstration of automated filter integrity tester.

Protein Recovery

Overview

Introduction   This document is divided into the following three sections:
- Section 1: "Protein Recovery Concepts" contains information required for understanding the process
- Section 2: "Safety Concerns" contains information about related safety concerns
- Section 3: "The Protein Recovery Process" contains a description of the process

Table of Contents   This document contains the following sections:

Protein Recovery

Objectives

1. State the goals of protein recovery.
2. Describe the different classes of impurities that are a challenge in protein recovery.
3. Explain why the removal of host cell proteins is challenging.
4. Explain the considerations for removing both human and bacterial impurities.
5. Describe two immunoassays used to measure host cell impurities.
6. Explain the removal of host cell nucleic acids.
7. Explain how and when variants of the product arise.
8. Explain how the specifications for variants are determined.
9. Explain why removal of endotoxin is necessary.
10. Describe the LAL assay used to test for endotoxin.
11. Describe several process design considerations and how they reduce contaminants.
12. Describe prion diseases and their concern to the biotech industry.
13. Explain where potential introduction of prions may occur in the process.
14. Summarize the stages of the protein recovery process.
15. Explain methods for separating cells from liquids.
16. Give a brief description of inclusion bodies.
17. Describe the steps for inclusion body solubilization.

Section 1
Protein Recovery Concepts

Overview

Introduction   This section contains information about concepts related to protein recovery that are required background information for understanding the protein recovery process.

Table of Contents   This section contains the following topics:

Topic	See Page
Goals of Protein Recovery	24.4
Classes of Impurities	24.6
Removal of Host Cell Proteins	24.7
Removal of Nucleic Acids	24.10
Removal of Product Variants	24.11
Removal of Pryogenic Endotoxins	24.13
Removal of Contaminants	24.15

Goals of Protein Recovery

Primary Goal

The Hippocratic Oath begins by stating, "First, do no harm." Accordingly, the primary goal of the recovery process is to ensure a high level of safety of the drug produced.

Secondary Goals

Other goals of a good recovery process are that the process will
- Allow the manufacturer to produce ample supplies of the drug at reasonable cost to the patient
- Operate predictably and reproducibly
- Be implementable with minimum development time in order to help bring the new drug quickly to market
- Have minimal impact on the environment

Relationship of Purity to Safety

Setting criteria for purity and consistently meeting them in the recovery process strongly influence the safety of the drug. Taken together, the final product specifications and the nature and purity of the starting material define what the recovery must accomplish, and therefore directly affect the choice of specific recovery unit operations.

Continued on next page

Goals of Protein Recovery

Acceptable Amounts of Impurity and Establishment of Safety

One of the oldest axioms of protein chemistry is, "A protein may only be proven to be homogeneous as evidenced by the application of n+1 analytical assays, where n = the number of assays that exist."

Analytical assays get more informative, more sensitive, and more numerous as a new molecule moves through development toward approval (and even after approval). This information has the following implications:

- A drug does not suddenly become unsafe just because of a newly acquired ability to detect a previously hidden impurity.
- We should not ignore opportunities to improve product quality.
- We are not expected to continue to purify things away until we reach zero impurities. Such an attempt would make the process never-ending and too expensive.

In the final analysis, safety is established by the accumulated weight of *in vivo* data from animal toxicity studies and human clinical trials.

Since all drugs, even biotechnology proteins, have side effects, the safety is ultimately limited by effects arising from the drug's inherent activity (the therapeutic ratio). The chance of achieving zero impurities, like the chance of achieving a zero risk-to-benefit ratio, is zero. Neither goal is attainable, and neither goal is worthwhile.

Classes of Impurities

Introduction
One of the goals for achieving purity in the protein recovery process is the removal of impurities that may detract from the safety of the preparation.

Definition
Impurities are substances that are *expected* to be present either as a result of their production by the host organism or because of their use in the manufacturing process.

Classes of Impurities
The principle classes of impurities that arise from recombinant microorganisms and present a challenge to the recovery scientist are
- Host cell proteins
- Nucleic acids
- Lipids
- The cells themselves

Other impurities in certain processes include:
- Pyrogenic lipospolysaccharide (endotoxin), when the process uses a gram-negative bacterial host such as *E. coli*
- Impurities intentionally added in the manufacturing process, such as acetonitrile (a solvent often used in preparative reversed phase chromatography of proteins).

Each is described in the topics that follow.

Removal of Host Cell Proteins

Introduction

In removing impurities in the protein recovery process, host cell proteins are not the molecules of greatest concern. However, their removal poses one of the greatest challenges in developing the purification of recombinant proteins.

Challenges of Removing Host Cell Proteins

Removal of host cell proteins is challenging because the various proteins in a mixture are generally much more similar to each other than to other classes of molecules, such as polynucleotides or lipids.

Example:

In a unit operation such, as cation exchange chromatography at pH 5, there is likely to be a very high degree of separation of DNA (high net negative charge) from most proteins, which will be slightly to moderately positively charged, while individual protein species may be poorly resolved or even unresolved from each other during elution of the column.

Continued on next page

Removal of Host Cell Proteins

Influence of the Host: Human vs. Bacterial

Whether the host is human or bacterial is an important factor in host protein impurities. Because bacterial hosts bear lower homology than those of the human recipient, they pose a risk of provoking an immune response in the patient.

Human host considerations:
Prior to the advent of biotechnology drugs, most protein biologics were derived from human sources. Because the host protein impurities in products derived from human sources are homologous with those of the recipient (such as in a preparation of human immunoglobulin, Factor VIII or growth hormone, there is no concern about potential immunogenicity of the impurities. Therefore, it is acceptable that the drug contain levels of host cell protein impurities that can be expressed in *percentage* terms.

Bacterial host considerations:
The suite of protein impurities produced by a bacterial host bears much lower homology with those of the human recipient and may provoke an immune response that can affect the patient's well-being or reduce the efficacy of the drug.

In addition, bacteria are noted for producing a variety of proteolytic enzymes which, if present in the purified drug, might adversely affect its potency and stability.

For these reasons, regulatory agencies expect that recombinant protein drugs be purified to unprecedented low levels of residual host proteins, often in the range of a few *parts per million*.

Influence of the Starting Material

Fortunately for the recovery scientist, the nature of the recombinant starting material makes it easier to achieve this high purity level.

Example:
Growth hormone is present in human serum at only a few nanograms per milliliter and is only a few parts per million of the mass of pituitary tissue. In contrast, it is the most abundant cytoplasmic protein when expressed in recombinant *E. coli*. Thus, when starting from the recombinant source material, a lower-fold *purification* is needed because the titer (and relative abundance) is higher.

Continued on next page

Removal of Host Cell Proteins

Host Cell Immunoassays

Host proteins need to be detected and quantified at a level of parts per million to:
- Prove that purity at the parts per million level has actually been achieved
- Assess the relative merits of two purification alternatives in removing trace levels of protein impurities

There are two host cell immunoassays used to measure impurities at this level are
- Blank run
- Direct measure of impurities

Each is described below.

Blank Run

In a blank run immunoassay, fermentation and recovery are performed using a host cell that has identical genetic composition to the production strain but lacks the product gene. Host cell impurities are prepared and quantified in the absence of the "noise" of the product.

Direct Measure of Impurities

The direct measure of impurities method employs a polyantigen immunoassay based on antibodies to host cell proteins. It is the most useful method and is often aided by the blank run. Although this type of assay is not trivial to develop, it provides an extremely sensitive way to directly quantitate the spectrum of host cell proteins in process fluid.

Developing Processes for Subsequent Products

Many different therapeutic proteins may be expressed using the same type of host and expression system. After one product is purified, it is known how the product behaved and how all the impurities behaved. This information can be used to develop a process for the next product by beginning to predict the partitioning of all the components but one.

In addition, the host cell immunoassay used can be applied with some validation and fine tuning to subsequent products that are produced in the same host.

Removal of Nucleic Acids

Nucleic Acids in Bacterially-Derived Products

The presence of residual nucleic acids in bacterially-derived recombinant products does not represent any special safety concern. The properties of DNA and RNA are so different from proteins that they can easily be purified away to virtually undetectable levels.

Nucleic acids (like endotoxin) bind with high affinity to anion exchange resins and positively charged filter media. Therefore, their removal during the recovery becomes almost incidental.

Bacterial-Origin DNA vs. Mammalian-Origin DNA

In the past, there has been some confusion among manufacturers about whether bacterial-origin DNA was equivalent to mammalian-origin DNA. In the case of products derived from mammalian cell lines (which are transformed and therefore tumorigenic), the potential for residual oncogenes posed a specific risk factor and it has long been required that residual DNA be reduced to less than about 100 picograms per dose. However, even that requirement has been eased recently to the level of approximately 10 nanograms per dose, in light of a decreased concern about the efficiency of transforming events.

However, such requirements have never applied to bacterially-produced products. It is generally necessary only to:
- Characterize the extent of DNA removal that is obtained
- Show that the recovery process reproducibly achieves that level from batch to batch.

Removal of Product Variants

Introduction Variants of the product itself are another aspect of product purity. Because these variants are, by definition, so structurally similar to the product, they are almost always the hardest impurities to remove.

Sources of Variants Variants arise from a number of sources and occur in the stages listed in the table below.

Stage	Variants
Fermentation	Several types of variants may be produced including: • Amino acid misincorporation • Misprocessing at N-terminus • Modification of N-terminus • Proteolysis at C-terminus • Endoproteolysis
Downstream Processing	The protein may undergo proteolysis; deamidation of asparagine may lead to internally clipped or modified forms containing the cyclic imide, isopeptide bond, or aspartic acid residue.
Recovery	The thioether sulfur of methionine is frequently oxidized to the sulfoxide form.

Continued on next page

Removal of Product Variants

Specifications for the Permissible Level of Variant

Specifications for the level of a variant to be permitted in the final formulation must be set on a case-by-case basis. Sometimes it is possible to isolate small quantities of a variant using analytical procedures, or to at least obtain a fraction in which it is highly enriched. Then, properties such as receptor binding, activity, or serum half-life can be tested in the available model systems and compared with those of the native sequence. Such tests often show that the variant behaves almost identically to the native sequence. However, if the properties of the variant are substantially different, it may need to be purified away or, at the least, its abundance will need to be carefully controlled from batch to batch.

Examples in which production-scale HPLC (high pressure liquid chromatography) has been used to substantially remove all variants, creating virtually "monocomponent" preparations, include:
- Recombinant human insulin
- Growth hormone
- Insulin-like growth factor-I

Removal of Pryogenic Endotoxins

Introduction   Because humans are exquisitely sensitive to *E. coli* lipopolysaccharide, the removal of pyrogenic endotoxin is an important part of any recovery process starting from a gram negative bacterium such as *E. coli*.

Guideline   As a general guideline, a single dose should contain less than about 100 endotoxin units (EU), equivalent to roughly 10 nanograms, of endotoxin. Amounts higher than 10 nanograms will elicit a febrile response.

Removing the Endotoxin from *E. coli*   The broth of an *E. coli* fermentation may contain as much as 10^8 EU/mL; therefore, the purification must provide for several logs of endotoxin removal. In some cases the initial mass of endotoxin may exceed the mass of the desired product.

The hydrophobicity and negative charge of lipopolysaccharide allow it to be removed with relative ease. Anion exchange chromatography resins and positively charged membrane filtration media (to which endotoxin binds with high affinity) are economical materials that give tremendous pyrogen removal capacity.

Continued on next page

Removal of Pryogenic Endotoxins

Endotoxin Removal from Other Organisms

The requirement for endotoxin reduction is not limited to products derived from gram negative organisms. Most protein recovery unit operations are carried out under the following conditions that permit the growth of organisms:
- Ambient temperatures
- Aqueous buffers
- Near-physiologic pH

Bacterial contamination is indicated if endotoxin is present in any of the following:
- Downstream buffers
- Column eluates
- Iin-process intermediates

Purpose

Characterization of a recovery process with respect to the absence of endotoxin is a useful complement to direct bioburden testing for demonstrating that the process is sanitary.

Assay Used to Monitor Endotoxin

The universally accepted monitoring test for endotoxin is the Limulus Amoebocyte Lysate (LAL) assay. This assay:
- is rapid
- is economical
- has a very high sample throughput
- is extremely sensitive, capable of detecting as little as 0.05 EU/ml

The LAL uses a solution of components isolated from blood cells of the limulus or horseshoe crab. Small quantities of endotoxin are added to this lysate to initiate a proteolytic cascade (somewhat analogous to blood clotting in humans), which in turn causes gelation of the lysate in a test tube.

Removal of Contaminants

Contaminants from Live Organisms

Live organisms present during the purification may contaminate the product with proteases, glycosidases, or toxins.

These may in turn
- Lead to partial degradation of the product, affecting its activity or stability
- Pose a direct threat to the patient.

Minimizing Contaminants

Considerations to minimize adventitious bioburden pervade all aspects of process design. The table below lists process design considerations and their intended effect in reducing contaminants.

Design consideration	Effect
Proper design of air handling and filtration equipment	Reduces airborne organisms
Careful choice of: • Flooring materials • Floor sloping • Drain placement	Minimizes: • Puddling • Spread of organisms by foot traffic
Gowning requirements	Reduces contamination by operators
Specifications for equipment design to eliminate: • Dead legs • Rough or porous surfaces	Reduces growth environments
Control of access and directional flow of material and personnel	Reduces contamination from outside sources
Processing at cold temperatures	Reduces growth rates
Scheduling practices and coupled operations	Reduces processing time
Regular heat sterilization or chemical sanitization of process equipment	Reduces bioburden

Section 2
Safety Concerns

Overview

Introduction This section contains information about safety concerns related to the protein recovery process.

Table of Contents This section contains the following topics:

Risks from Recombinant Organisms

History

In the early days of the biotechnology industry little was known about the risks posed by recombinant organisms to the environment, workers, or patients. Special precautions were therefore taken to kill and contain recombinant bacteria in order to avoid release or exposure.

Current Thinking

It has become generally accepted that the recombinant bacteria typically used in biotechnology production pose no greater risk to operators and the environment than conventional microorganisms. Thus the steps that are taken to reduce initial process bioburden are prompted primarily by ordinary concern for hygiene.

Use of Sterilizing Membrane Filters

During processing, the presence of organisms *per se* is not regarded as problematic for the recovery scientist or for patients, since intact live organisms are reliably and completely removed by sterilizing membrane filters that have been used in the pharmaceutical industry for decades.

Risks from the Prion Gene

History

In the early 1970's (around the time that Boyer and Cohen first showed that genes could be cloned) Stanley Prusiner, investigating the disease known as scrapie in sheep, made the heretical proposal that the causative agent was not, as had been long supposed, a so-called "slow virus," but was instead a simple protein devoid of any nucleic acid.

Twenty years later Prusiner's discovery (for which he received both the Lasker Award and the Nobel Prize), represents a fascinating new mechanism for information exchange at the molecular level and, unfortunately, a potentially huge issue for the pharmaceutical industry. Prusiner named the infectious agent a 'prion.'

The Prion Gene's Effect

The prion gene, which is apparently present in the genome of all mammals, encodes a protein of unknown function that is normally expressed in the brain. Apparently, if this protein somehow becomes conformationally altered, it can, in turn, catalytically alter the conformation of other normal prion molecules, leading to accumulations of insoluble protein and subsequent death of the brain cell.

Prion Diseases

Several familial prion diseases of man are now recognized, and certain mutations in the gene sequence greatly increase the risk of developing the disease.

Creutzfeld-Jacob disease is one well known example. In the mid-1980's the occurrence of several cases of CJD was linked to administration of human growth hormone derived from human cadaver pituitaries. This caused the FDA to remove such preparations from the market, which led the way for approval of the bacterially-produced recombinant drugs Protropin (Genentech) and Humatrope (Lilly).

Risks from Bovine Spongiform Encephalopathy

History

In the early 1980's the practice of adding sheep offal (which contains brain tissue) to cattle feed became widespread in Great Britain. It is now widely accepted that this practice caused infectious scrapie to jump from sheep to cattle, giving rise to an epidemic of what is called bovine spongiform encephalopathy (BSE), or mad cow disease.

The BSE epidemic led to the slaughter of hundreds of thousands of cattle in Britain, as well as an embargo on British beef products. Evidence now strongly suggests that the disease has been transmitted from cows to people.

Repercussions for the Biotechnology Industry

Repercussions for the biotechnology industry have come in the form of insistence from regulatory authorities (primarily European) that raw materials from bovine sources *not* be used in the production of human drugs. A comprehensive ban on the use of bovine-source materials is being considered. Such a ban will have an enormous impact on the production of biotechnology drugs.

Purchasing agents and process development scientists are currently under considerable pressure to redesign processes and reformulate products.

Use of Beef By-products in Mammalian Cell Culture

The carcass-rendering industry processes about 40 billion pounds annually in the U.S. alone, and beef by-products are the starting point for a surprisingly wide variety of process raw materials.

Mammalian cell culture technologists began to confront this issue several years ago, because they were already motivated to reduce the use of components such as bovine serum, insulin, and transferrin because of cost issues and potential contamination by mycoplasma or viruses.

Continued on next page

Risks from Bovine Spongiform Encephalopathy

Use of Beef By-products in Downstream Processing

Beef by-products are also widely used in bacterial fermentation and downstream processing. Many compounds, including lipids, detergents, vitamins, and trace minerals, may have bovine origins.

Examples of beef by-products used in downstream processing include
- Beef hydrolysates used as nutrient sources for bacteria
- Glycerol
- Gelatin

Each is described below.

Beef Hydrolysates Used as Nutrient Sources for Bacteria

Beef hydrolysates are commonly used as complex nitrogen sources for bacteria. It is thought by some that because of the extreme destructive conditions under which they are produced, and the fact that they are additionally autoclaved prior to use, they could not possibly be a source of infectious prions.

Glycerol

Glycerol is frequently used in fermentation as a carbon source and in recovery as a solvent. It is also a common excipient component in oral medications. Much glycerol is produced as a by-product of the saponification of tallow in the soap industry. Following alkaline hydrolysis, it is further purified by distillation at a very high temperature (above 200°C). Even though these conditions should destroy any protein present, there is still a move toward glycerol derived from petroleum (propylene) for pharmaceutical applications.

Gelatin

Gelatin is used in a large number of capsule formulations. Even though its production involves high temperature hydrolysis, it is still being demonized as a potential source of infectivity.

Continued on next page

Section 3
The Protein Recovery Process

Overview

Introduction   This section describes the protein recovery process.

Table of Contents   This section contains the following topics:

Stages in the Protein Recovery Process

Stages of Downstream Processing

There are several options for initial downstream processing. Which option to use is dictated by the nature of the expression system.

Summary

The table below summarizes the stages in the protein recovery process. Each stage is described in detail later in this section.

Stage	Description
	Protein recovery
1	Cell-liquid separation. Whether or not the product is secreted determines the next stage. <table><tr><th>When the product is …</th><th>Then the next stage is …</th></tr><tr><td>secreted</td><td>"Stage 4: Concentration/ buffer exchange.""</td></tr><tr><td>not secreted</td><td>"Stage 2: Cells are broken."</td></tr></table>
2	Cells are broken. Whether the product is in inclusion bodies or soluble determines the next stage. <table><tr><th>When the product is …</th><th>Then the next stage is …</th></tr><tr><td>in inclusion bodies</td><td>"Stage 3: Inclusion body soublization."</td></tr><tr><td>soluble</td><td>"Stage 4: Concentration/ buffer exchange."</td></tr></table>
	Protein purification
3	Inclusion body soublization.
4	Concentration/buffer exchange.
5	Final purification.
6	Formulation.

Protein Recovery Process Diagram

Diagram   The diagram below represents the protein recovery process.

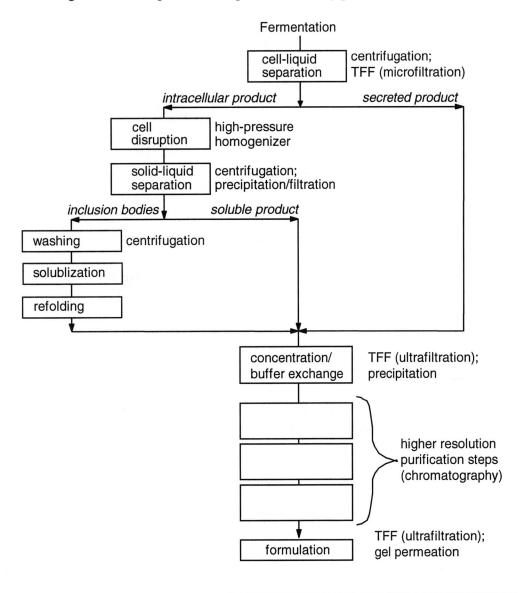

Stage 1: Cell-Liquid Separation

Description   The first stage in downstream processing is usually a solid-liquid separation. In this stage, the soluble components of the broth are separated from the cells.

Centrifugation is usually used for this stage; however, tangential flow microfiltration (TFF) is sometimes used.

Reference: Refer to the following documents for additional information about this stage:
- "Centrifugation"
- "TFF"

Next Stage   The next stage depends on whether product is secreted by the cells or not, as described in the table below.

If product is ...	Then the next stage is ...
not secreted	"Stage 2: Cells are broken."
secreted	"Stage 4: Concentration/buffer exchange."

Note: If the product titer is not high enough, a volume reduction step such as precipitation or ultrafiltration may be carried out prior to capture. However, with modern recombinant expression systems, the product titer is usually high enough that preconcentration is not necessary.

Stage 2: Cells are Broken

When This Stage Applies	This stage applies if product is not secreted by the cells.
	Reference: Refer to the document "Cell Disruption" for additional information about this stage.
Tasks in This Stage	This stage consists of the following two tasks: • Cells are broken • Solids-liquids are separated. Each is described below.
Breaking Cells	There are several ways to break microbial cells. High-pressure mechanical homogenization is the most widely used because it is: • Predictable • Economical • Scaleable.
Solid-Liquid Separation	After the cells are broken, they are again subjected to a solid-liquid separation, usually centrifugation. If the product is in the liquid phase, the centrifugation is usually done under conditions that give the greatest possible removal of solids.
Next Stage	After breaking and solid-liquid separation, the next stage depends on whether the product is in inclusion bodies or soluble as described in the table below.

If product is ...	Then the next stage is ...
in inclusion bodies	"Stage 3: Inclusion body solublization."
soluble	"Stage 4: Concentration/buffer exchange."

Stage 3: Inclusion Body Solublization

When This Stage Applies

This stage applies if product is in inclusion bodies at the completion of Stage 2.

Tasks in Stage 3

Stage 3 consists of the following three tasks:
- Washing
- Solublization
- Refolding.

Each is described below.

Washing

Which method to use for this task is dictated by the nature of the expression system and the best equipment to use for a given unit operation.

If the product is in the solid phase, such as an inclusion body, the centrifugation is carried out under conditions that are more selective, in an attempt to maximize the sedimentation of the product particles while allowing as much cell debris as possible to escape in the supernatant liquid.

Subsequent solublization of the inclusion body, followed by a controlled renaturation and oxidation to establish the correct disulfide pairings, is then almost always required.

Description of Inclusion Bodies

Cells may contain several inclusion bodies that may occupy as much as half of the cell volume. Inclusion bodies are often made up almost entirely of the heterologous protein, with little cross contamination by host cell proteins. The protein is in the reduced state (that is, the cysteine residues are in the free thiol form, not in disulfide bonds) and is not properly folded into its native conformation.

Continued on next page

Stage 3: Inclusion Body Solublization

Inclusion Bodies in _E. coli_	When a heterologous protein is expressed in _E. coli_ in very high yield, it is often sequestered in dense insoluble particles called inclusion bodies. In most cases they are found in the cytoplasm, although if a periplasmic secretion expression system was used they can be found in the periplasmic space as well. The larger particles, also called _refractile bodies_, are easily viewed under phase-contrast light microscopy.

Solublization

Before the product can be taken through final purification, it must be solublized and refolded into its native conformation with properly paired disulfides.

Inclusion bodies are easily solublized with high pH, detergents, or with solutions of chaotropic agents (such as 8 M urea or 7 M guanidinium chloride). The protein is then usually diluted or exchanged into a solution of lower chaotropic strength to facilitate correct refolding.

The yield of solublization is highly dependent on a number of factors, including:
- Concentration of the product
- Type and concentration of denaturant
- pH
- Temperature
- Ionic strength
- Solvent polarity

Refolding

Determining the optimal refolding conditions is a laborious empirical process requiring high throughput screening over a very large parameter space. The aim is to achieve high yield at high product concentration (thus minimum volume) with minimal reagent use. Success is highly variable and is dictated by the information contained in the primary sequence of the product itself.

Stages 4, 5 and 6

Introduction

The remainder of the process consists of the following three stages:
- Stage 4: Concentration
- Stage 5: Final purification
- Stage 6: Formulation

Each is described below.

Stage 4: Concentration/ Buffer Exchange

During this stage, TFF and precipitation take place.

Reference: Refer to the following documents for information about this stage:
- "TFF"
- "Centrifugation"

Stage 5: Final Purification

After a soluble, properly folded product (free from cells and other gross particulates) is obtained, one or more high resolution separations is carried out.

Column chromatography is usually used for this stage. Because column chromatography is a sequential orthogonal method (the steps it uses to fractionate are based on different molecular properties), it provides for a higher purity and greater process robustness.

Stage 6: Formulation

During this stage, TFF and gel permeation take place.

Reference: Refer to the document "Formulation" for additional information about this stage.

Cell Disruption

Overview

Introduction

This document contains information about the various classes of cell disruption methods and detailed description of how homogenization is used for cell disruption.

Table of Contents

This document contains the following topics:

Cell Disruption

Objectives

1. Describe where proteins over expressed in *E.coli* accumulate.
2. Describe the four different classes of cell disruption.
3. Describe the different types of nonmechanical approaches and discuss their effectiveness.
4. Describe the use of ultrasonic bombardment and discuss its effectiveness.
5. Describe how grinding is performed and discussed its effectiveness.
6. Describe high-pressure homogenization and discuss the advantage of using this method.
7. Describe the use application of high-pressure homogenization in microbial cell processing.
8. Give a description of high-pressure homogenization in microbial cell processing.
9. Discuss the application of high-pressure homogenization in microbial cell processing.
10. Explain why homogenization is a favored method for cell disruption.
11. Describe the multiple objectives of high-pressure homogenization in microbial cell processing.
12. Draw a flow diagram of a typical homogenization operation with a self-priming homogenizer.
13. Describe the parts and functions of the components in the above diagram.
14. Describe the steps in a process that follow high-pressure homogenization.

Background

Background   Most recombinant proteins overexpressed in *E. coli* fail to make it outside the cell. These proteins are:

- Secreted into the periplasmic space between the plasma membrane and cell wall
- Accumulated in dense insoluble inclusion bodies in the cytoplasm
- Found properly folded and soluble in the cytoplasm

In all these cases, the cells must be broken open or disrupted to release the product. This document contains information the methods used to achieve cell disruption, especially homogenization.

Cell Disruption Methods

Introduction   This section describes the following four classes of cell disruption methods:

- Nonmechanical approaches
- Ultrasonic bombardment
- Grinding
- High-pressure homogenization

Cell Disruption Methods

Four Classes of Cell Disruption Methods

The table below contains a description and an evaluation of the effectiveness of the four classes of cell disruption methods.

Class	Description	Effectiveness
Nonmechanical approaches	Performance by using chemicals, enzymes, or freezing/thawing.	• Chemical or enzyme disruption is readily scaled, but may degrade the desired protein, which can present a purification challenge for the recovery scientist. • Freezing/thawing is the least effective method for disrupting cells. However, it is also the least disruptive to soluble production. *Note*: There is at least one example of the large-scale use of urea and reductants to extract insulin-like growth factor I from *E. coli*.
Ultrasonic bombardment	Involves inserting a probe into a liquid suspension of cells which sends bursts of high frequency sound o ultrasonic waves into the liquid. The ultrasonic waves cause the fluid inside the cells to cavitate, causing the cell to break open.	Effective, but not easily scaleable.

Continued on next page

Cell Disruption Methods

Four Classes of Cell Disruption Methods

Class	Description	Effectiveness
Grinding	Performance: • A device called a bead mill • A grinding media of glass or ceramic beads that have diameters of about 100 to 500 microns	Can: • Generate the very high shear forces necessary to disrupt rigid organisms, such as yeast and • Achieve a capacity of up to approximately 40 liters per minute *Note:* The grinding media must be purchased, tested, removed, and disposed of.
High-pressure homogenization	Under very high-pressure, this forces cells though an outlet orifice to create very high shear forces.	Considered to be the simple and most readily scaled option.

Note: For more information on high-pressure homogenization, refer to the topic " High-Pressure Homogenization" on the next page.

High-Pressure Homogenization

Background   For decades, high-pressure homogenizers have been used in a variety of other industries. Some examples include the homogenization of:

- Milk, which is probably the most large-scale application of homogenization
- Household and automotive paints to achieve smoothness and uniform pigment dispersion
- Products such as cosmetics and detergents to produce a certain consistency and appearance though the creation of a stable emulsion of otherwise immiscible components

Description of a High-Pressure Homogenizer   A high-pressure homogenizer is essentially a piston pump capable of generating extremely high outlet pressure. Laboratory and pilot-scale devices that process up to a few liters per minute can generate pressure as high as 20,000 psi. The largest machines can process several hundred liters per minute at pressure up to about 10,000 psi.

The critical component of a homogenizer is the outlet orifice, which consists of a valve and a seat. At the process fluid passes though the orifice, the fluid components experience tremendous accelerative and shear forces, as well as simple physical impingement against the wall of the valve. Some investigators also feel that as the pressure drops from several thousand psi to zero in the orifice, cavitation develops which helps burst cells by internal gas bubble formation.

Continued on next page

High-Pressure Homogenization

Homogenization Process

High-pressure homogenization is a commonly employed unit operation in microbial cell processing. In this process, the homogenizer used is a high-pressure positive-displacement pump capable of attaining pressure several thousand times greater than atmospheric.

The table below describes the homogenization process.

Stage	Description
1	The material to be homogenized (i.e., the feed suspension) is: • Drawn into the homogenizer • Forced though a small orifice, called the disruption valve
2	A combination of forces act on the fluid as it passes over the disruption valve which leads to the: • Lysis or rupture of the cells • Micronization or break-up of the cellular debris
3	The exit steam or lysate leaves the homogenizer at a substantially higher temperature, because large amounts of mechanical energy are absorbed by the fluid.

Homogenization in Cell Disruption

Homogenization is a favored method for cell disruption because:

- It can be scaled to very high capacity in a relatively predictable manner
- *E. coli* can be broken with a high efficiency rate (i.e.>90%) with a single pass though the unit
- Performance is fairly independent of feed composition
- The only "reagent" that needs to be removed is the heat generated by the operation

High-Pressure Homogenization

Objectives of Homogenization

High-pressure homogenization may be used to simultaneously achieve multiple objectives. The table below describes these objectives.

Objective	Description
Cell kill	A reduction in the total number of living cells. Cell kill is particularly important when: • Downstream operations contain long hold times (which may allow the cells to grow) • The microbial consumption of oxygen may inhibit downstream biochemical manipulations *Note:* Cell kill may be quantified by viable counts.
Protein release	The release of the protein of interest from inside the cell
Reduction in viscosity	During homogenization, viscous species (e.g., carbohydrates, nucleic acids, and lipopolysacharides) are released into the lysate. *Notes:* • Additional homogenization can break up these components and improve the efficiency of downstream centrifugation operations. • Lysate viscosity is the primary measure of viscosity reduction.
Micronization of cell debris	Cell wall fragments may be broken into smaller fragments with multiple passes though the homogenizer. The size distribution of this can have an effect on the: • Debris sedimentation rate • Purity of downstream inclusion body harvest operations *Note:* The lysate particle size distribution is a measure of micronization efficiency.

Self-Priming Homogenization Operation

Introduction	This topic describes a typical homogenization operation using a self-priming pump.

Self-Priming Homogenizers	The following homogenizers are self-priming homogenizers and therefore do not require a feed pump: • APV-Gaulin® • Gaulin-Rannie® • Microfluidics®

Flow Diagram	The flow diagram below depicts a typical homogenization operation with a self-priming homogenizer.

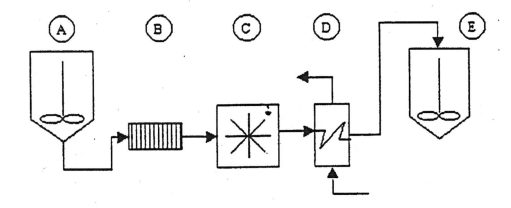

Note: For more information on the above diagram, refer to "Parts and Function" on the next page.

Continued on next page

Self-Priming Homogenization Operation

| Parts and Functions | The table below describes the parts and functions of the operation flow diagram for self-priming homogenizers. |

Part	Name	Function
A	Feed tank	• Provides temperature control • Prevent the suspensions from settling *Note*: The feed tank is typically jacketed and mixed.
B	Inline strainer	Prevents large particulates from damaging the homogenizer internal
C	Homogenizer	Disrupts cells using high pressure and shear forces
D	Heat exchanger	Used to remove the heat generated during homogenization
E	Lysate tank	• Provides temperatures controls • Prevents the suspensions from settling *Note:* The lysate tank is typically jacketed and mixed.

Nonself-Priming Homogenization Operation

Introduction

This topic describes a typical homogenization operation using a nonself-priming pump.

Nonself-Priming Homogenizers

Nonself-priming homogenizers require a feed pump to maintain flooded suction. This type includes the Nitro® homogenizer.

Continued on next page

Nonself-Priming Homogenization Operation

Flow diagram   This topic describes a typical homogenization operation using a nonself-priming pump.

Nonself Priming Homogenizer   Nonself-priming homogenizers require a feed pump to maintain flooded suction. This type includes the Nitro® homogenizer.

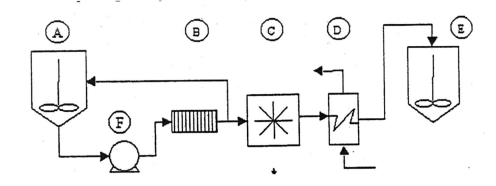

Note: For more information on the above diagram, refer to "Parts and Functions" on the next page.

Continued on next page

Nonself-Priming Homogenization Operation

Parts and Functions

The table below describes the parts and functions of the operation flow diagram for nonself-priming homogenizers shown above.

Part	Name	Function
A	Feed tank	• Provides temperature control • Prevents the suspensions from settling *Note*: The feed tank is typically jacketed and mixed.
B	Inline strainer	Prevents large particulates from damaging the homogenizer internals
C	Homogenizer	Draws a portion of the circulating fluid *Note:* The remainder of the fluid is returned to the tank.
D	Heat exchanger	Used to remove the heat generated during homogenization
E	Lysate tank	• Provides temperature control • Prevents the suspensions from settling *Note:* The lysate tank is typically jacketed and mixed.
F	Feed pump	Circulates the feed suspension though the strainer

Note: During the flooded suction operation, the flow rate from the feed pump must be greater than the draw rate from the homogenizer.

Total Recycle Mode Homogenization Operation

Introduction

Both self-priming and nonself-priming homogenizers can be operated in total recycle mode, in which the lysate existing in the heat exchanger is returned to the feed tank.

Flow diagrams for total recycle mode for self-priming homogenizers are depicted below.

Advantages of Recycle Homogenization

The advantages of recycle homogenization over stepwise homogenization operations include:
- Reduced tankage requirements
- The elimination of operator intensive turnarounds
- Constant volume operation

Note: Due to the long processing times required for large feed volumes, recycle homogenization is not typically practiced at pilot or manufacturing scales.

Flow Diagram for Self-Priming Homogenizers

The flow diagram below depicts a total recycle homogenization operation using a self-priming homogenizer.

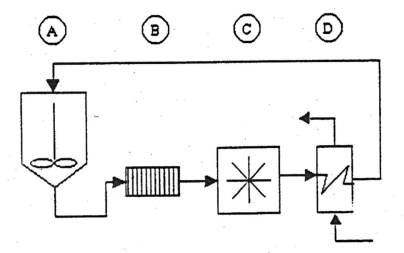

Note: For more information on the above diagram, refer to the topic "Self-Priming Homogenization Operation" on previous pages.

Continued on next page

Total Recycle Mode Homogenization Operation

Flow Diagram for Nonself-Priming Homogenizers

The flow diagram below depicts a total recycle homogenization operation using a nonself-priming homogenizer.

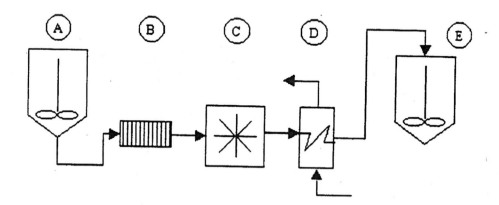

Note: For more information on the information on the above diagram, refer to the topic "Nonnself-Priming Homogenization Operation" on previous pages.

Centrifugation

Overview

Introduction   Centrifugation is a versatile and widely used unit operation in biotechnology processes. Most applications involve the separation of solids from liquid, although as discussed later, there are some applications in which two immiscible liquids are separated from each other. Centrifugation is the method of choice for removing:

- Cells from whole broth
- Cell debris after disruption
- Particulates that are formed during precipitation operations

Table of Contents   This document contains the following topics:

Centrifugation

Objectives

1. Explain the basic concepts of centrifugation.
2. Discuss the applications of centrifugation in biotechnology processes.
3. Describe the function/use of a sample centrifuge (ie. J6B) in harvesting.
4. Demonstrate/describe how to balance a centrifuge.
5. Explain the consequences of running an unbalanced centrifuge.
6. Identify the matched buckets in a J6B centrifuge and explain how to determine whether they are matched.
7. Demonstrate the use of the J6B centrifuge.
8. State the two types of centrifuges that are predominantly used in large-scale protein production.
9. Describe the function/use of a tubular bowl centrifuge.
10. Explain why this type of centrifuge is called a clarifier.
11. Describe the advantages/disadvantages of tubular centrifugation.
12. Describe the applications of a tubular bowl centrifuge in a process.
13. Diagram the basic components of a tubular bowl centrifuge, and explain the function of such components and the operations of the centrifuge.
14. Describe some of the problems encountered with using a tubular bowl centrifuge.
15. Explain how samples are removed from a tubular bowl centrifuge.
16. Describe the function of a liner in such centrifuges, and explain how cells are properly removed from the liner.
17. Distinguish between the use of a tubular bowl centrifuge for clarification or concentration.
18. Describe the use of a disk stack centrifuge.
19. Diagram the basic components of a disk stack centrifuge.
20. Discuss the basics of the centrifugation process in a disk stack centrifuge.
21. Explain the advantages/disadvantages of disk stack centrifugation.
22. Explain the process of dislodging.
23. Explain the drawbacks of the disk stack centrifuge.
24. Identify the parts of a disk stack centrifuge, and locate the feed inlet and supernatant outlet ports.
25. Diagram the flow of a process and indicate the appropriate use of centrifuges.
26. Describe how a process and the use of centrifugation will differ for soluble versus insoluble proteins.

Background

Types of Centrifuges

There are many different sizes and designs of centrifuges.

Most researchers are familiar with tabletop and laboratory centrifuges that accept test tubes and small bottles that spin at either a fixed angle or swing from a supporting hinge. These machines typically process up to a few liters per batch at forces up to about 20,000 x g.

For large-scale protein production a very different design is needed. The two machine types that predominate are:
- Discharging disk stack centrifuge
- Tubular bowl centrifuge

Disk Stack Centrifuge Design

Introduction

The disk stack centrifuge is the most widely used centrifuge in bioprocessing. The disk stack centrifuge consists of a bowl that contains a stack of closely spaced cones (disks) which rotate about their vertical axis.

The disk stack centrifuge, more commonly called a centrifugal *clarifier*, is by far the most versatile and sophisticated. Since it is capable of continuous solids discharge, it is essentially infinitely scaleable.

Key Features

The three key features of the disk stack centrifuge include the centrifuge's:
- Rotor disks
- Rotor disk construction
- Feed inlet and supernatant outlet ports

Each is described below.

Rotor Disks

The first key feature of this rotor are the disks themselves. They are a stack of stainless steel cones spaced 0.5 to 1.5 mm apart. The disk stack is analogous to a hugely distorted centrifuge bottle having an enormous width (cross-sectional area), but a depth of only about a millimeter. The short sedimenting distance is what allows this design to process fluids at very high feed rates.

Feedstock flow. The important point is that as the feedstock flows through the stack from the periphery toward the central core, solids sediment outward. And, they need only migrate a fraction of a millimeter in order to reach the "outer" disk and therefore, be removed from the flow path. Solids then continue to flow along the disk until they eventually spill against the wall of the rotor.

Processing capabilities. Even small pilot-scale machines have 50 to 100 disks with areas of several square meters and can clarify fluid at a few liters per minute. The largest machines, typically used in food and dairy processing, will process several hundred liters per minute.

Continued on next page

Disk Stack Centrifuge Design

Rotor Disk Construction

A second key feature of this design is that the rotor is actually constructed of two halves which can be momentarily separated from each other, while the whole assembly (the largest rotors weigh almost a ton) is spinning at 8,000 rpm. This feature enables continuous operation because as solids build up inside the rotor they can be periodically discharged through the narrow gap that forms when the rotor halves separate.

There are two modes of discharging:

Partial desludging mode. In a typical application of "partial desludging," the unit is programmed to open the gap (about five millimeters wide) for a duration of 0.1 to 0.5 seconds at intervals of 30 seconds up to a few minutes. By opening the gap for only a fraction of a second one can limit the volume that shoots out of the rotor during discharge. This is useful for:
- Obtaining solids that have minimal dilution by the feedstock
- Avoiding loss of the supernatant in the pellet fraction

Note: The higher the solids content of the feed, the more frequently the rotor will have to be opened.

Total desludging mode. In "total desludging" mode the gap is held open for a full second or more, causing the entire contents of the bowl to be shot out. This is useful when:
- Solids are especially viscous and do not flow well
- Machine must be cleaned in place

Feed Inlet and Supernatant Outlet Ports

The final feature of this design pertains to the feed inlet and supernatant outlet ports, which enable large feedstock volumes to be processed in a continuous mode.

Reference: For more information on processing, refer to the topic "Stages of Centrifugation" in this document.

Modifications for Protein Drug Isolation

When these clarifiers are used for protein drug isolation, the feed inlet, distributor plate, and paring disk assembly are specially modified to reduce shear and avoid foaming during acceleration and deceleration of the fluid in order to preserve the activity of the product.

Tubular Bowl Centrifuge Design

Description of a Tubular Bowl Centrifuge

The tubular bowl design is also used in biotechnology applications. This centrifuge consists of a hollow cylindrical element with a large length-to-diameter ratio that rotates at high speed in a stationary casing about the vertical axis.

Advantages and Disadvantages

Because the rotor is simpler in design, these centrifuges can often spin faster and thus achieve higher g forces than the disk stack centrifuge.

However, because there is no mechanism for solids discharge, the machine has to be shut down and disassembled when the bowl fills up.

Uses of the Tubular Bowl Centrifuge

The tubular bowl centrifuge is limited to:
- Smaller scale applications
- Feedstocks with very low solids content

Harvesting Product

Manton-Gaulin Homogenizers

Manton-Gaulin homogenizers are very efficient, providing over 99% cell breakage, depending on the operating pressure. Multiple passes through the homogenizer may be used to:
- Increase cell breakage efficiency
- Reduce the size of cell debris

Homogeniza-tion Process

If the product is in the form of an insoluble inclusion body (IB), the cells need to be ruptured (lysed) to release the IB. This can be done by freeze/thaw, osmotic stress, detergents, or high-pressure. The table below describes the homogenization process using the Manton-Gaulin homogenizer.

Stage	Description
1	Lyse the cells using high-pressure.
2	Draw the cells through a check valve into the pump cylinder.
3	Force the cells through the discharge valve assembly on the pressure stroke. *Result*: After cell lysis the IBs exist with a mixture of cell fragments, released proteins, and some remaining feed medium. *IMPORTANT*: The IBs are not affected by the pressure of the break, but the homogenizer generates a large amount of heat, which does affect the IB so the process stream must be cooled.
4	Wash the IBs in water or buffer to improve downstream processing, in a manner similar to cell capture. *Note*: Since the IBs are not as large as whole cells, the recovery is more sensitive to the parameters in Stokes' Law.
5	Reduce the feed into the centrifuge to allow for longer residence times in the centrifuge bowl. *Result*: There is a large loss of product relative to other processing steps.

Stages of Centrifugation

Introduction   This topic describes the centrifugation processes for:
- Disk stack centrifuge
- Tubular bowl centrifuge

Disk Stack Centrifugation Process   The table below describes the stages of the disk stack centrifuge process.

Stage	Description
1	Feed enters the centrifuge through essentially an open pipe at the bottom of the bowl on the axis of rotation.
2	Feed is radially accelerated by vanes on a distributor plate on the bottom half of the rotor.
3	Feed travels outward along the underside of the disks and the solids are deposited on the undersides of the disks.
4	Solids are collected in the solids space within the bowl. *Note*: The solids can be ejected continuously or intermittently from the bowl, depending on the type of machine. *See stages 5 + 6 on next page.*

Continued on next page

Stages of Centrifugation

Disk Stack Centrifugation Process

Stage	Description
5	As clarified supernatant exits the disk stack, it moves to the paring disk chamber, which is basically the inverse of a centrifugal pump. The table below describes the differences. <table><tr><td>When the clarified supernatant exits the disk stack via a ...</td><td>Then the ...</td></tr><tr><td>Centrifugal pump</td><td>Fluid • Enters a stationary housing • Is accelerated • Is flung outward by the pump's impeller</td></tr><tr><td>Centrifuge</td><td>• Spinning rotor is the housing and • Rapidly rotating fluid is flung inward by the vanes of the stationary "impeller" or paring disk</td></tr></table>
6	The clarified liquid flows out the top of the bowl.

Tubular Bowl Centrifugation Process

The table below describes the stages of the tubular bowl centrifugation process.

Stage	Description
1	Feed enters at the bottom of the bowl.
2	Solids sediment to the periphery within the tube.
3	Clarified liquid leaves through the top.

Operational Goals of Centrifugation

Introduction   Centrifugation is regularly used in cell processing and acid precipitate clarification. Centrifugation is an extension of gravity sedimentation and can be used to separate particles between 100 μm and 0.1 μm. Differences in the particle's size, as well as the densities of the solids and process liquid, facilitate the centrifugal separation. Centrifuges can be used for:

- Solids recovery
- Clarification
- Drying of solids
- Solids classification

Goals   The table below describes the operational goals of centrifugation.

Goal	Description
Solids Recovery	The operational goal is to maximize solids recovery. This is achieved by: • Lowering the flow rate (increases residence time) • Increasing the settling rate, such as by use of flocculants ***Examples***: Cell harvest and inclusion body recoveries
Clarification	The operational goal is to clarify a process stream, while minimizing the losses of the process stream. This is achieved by: • Lowering the flow rate (increases residence time) • Increasing the settling rate, such as by use of flocculants ***Examples***: Clarification of acid precipitation and lysate pools

See next page for rest of chart

Continued on next page

Operational Goals of Centrifufation

Goals

Goal	Description
Drying of Solids	The operational goal is to remove the process liquid from the collected solids. This is achieved by: • Lowering the flow rate (increases residence time) • Increasing the settling rate (increasing the centrifugal acceleration) *Example*: Removal of fermentation components during cell harvest
Solids Classification	The operational goal is the selective capture of a specific particle. This is achieved by: • Adjusting the flow rate until the desired separation between particles of different sizes has been achieved • Removing undesirable solids, which results in a lower step yield *Example*: Inclusion body recoveries

Advantages and Disadvantages of Tubular Centrifugation

Advantages

The tubular bowl centrifuge is the most efficient industrial centrifuge because of its:
• High speed
• Thin settling zone

Advantages and Disadvantages of Tubular Centrifugation

Disadvantges   The tubular bowl centrifuge has a limited capacity because the solids:
- Remain in the tube
- Must be manually removed from the centrifuge
- Collection within the bowl reduces the
  - effective bowl volume
  - residence time, which results in a reduction of the centrifuge's efficiency

Advantages and Disadvantages of Disk Stack Centrifugation

Introduction   The disk stack centrifuge is the most widely used centrifuge in bioprocessing. As previously explained, it is the most versatile and sophisticated, and allows for continuous processing. However, feed zone shear can be a problem.

Problems with Feed Zone Shear   Feed zone shear can have a dramatic effect on the ability of the centrifuge to recover the solids in the feed stream. The shear can reduce the size of the particles in the feed stream, thereby reducing the solids recovery. Acid precipitates can be disrupted to the point where the disk stack is not a viable option for the clarification of the feed stream.

Moving a Shear Sensitive Process   When moving a shear sensitive process from one centrifuge to another, the inlet shear must be taken into consideration. If the solid to be separated is shear sensitive, moving to a machine with equivalent or lower inlet shear can potentially improve the clarification. However, if a machine with equivalent or lower inlet shear is not available, investigation of a less shear sensitive solid could provide a reasonable solution.

Note: Processing the material to downstream end point can also yield valuable information.

Examples of Unit Operations in Action

Introduction   This topic provides examples of unit operations in action for soluble proteins and insoluble proteins.

Soluble Proteins   These are unit operations for soluble proteins.

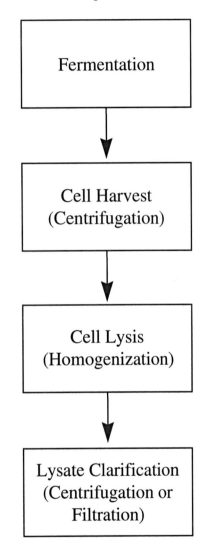

Continued on next page

Examples of Unit Operations in Action

Insoluble Proteins

These are unit operations for insoluble proteins.

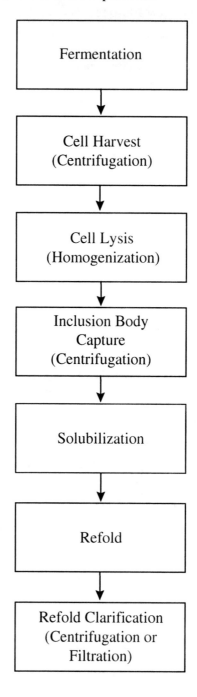

Centrifugation

Laboratory

Introduction   Centrifugation in this laboratory will be approached utilizing several different types of centrifuges. Students will dismantle the disk stack centrifuge to gain an understanding of its function and use. When available, students will receive a demonstration of the operation of this centrifuge by an industry instructor. Additional centrifuges in the lab will be used for harvest of cell culture or microbial fermentation.

Equipment   J6B centrifuge
Disk stack centrifuge
Tools for disk stack centrifuge
Microscopes

Materials and Supplies   Culture for harvesting from induction lab
Centrifuge tubes/bottles
Oil for immersion lens
Microscope slides

Laboratory

Activities at a Glance

1. Students will learn use of J6B centrifuge by processing cell culture from the induction lab. Each student will prepare and spin down cultures. Each student will learn proper balancing of tubes and the operation of the centrifuge.

2. Students will receive instruction on the components, operation, and application of the disk stack centrifuge. Under the supervision of the industry instructor, students will disassemble and then reassemble the disk stack centrifuge. Students will gain knowledge in the use of the tools for this centrifuge as well.

3. Using culture from the induction lab, students will view the cells with the light microscope to identify inclusion bodies.

4. Students will view cells following disruption to identify free inclusion bodies.

Chromatography

Overview

Introduction   This document describes the chromatography process and the methods used in purification procedures for protein recovery.

Table of Contents   This document contains the following topics:

Ion-Exchange Chromatography

Objectives

1. Describe the different types of ion-exchangers.
2. Explain why a protein is suitable for purification with ion-exchange chromatography.
3. Explain the basic theory of ion-exchange chromatography.
4. Describe the six basic steps of ion-exchange chromatography.
5. Explain what a resin slurry is and describe how to create one.
6. Make determinations of amount of resin for a given column volume.
7. Describe the different types of packing.
8. Demonstrate/describe the steps for packing small columns.
9. Explain why a column is packed at a different flow rate than that used for a run.
10. Explain HETP, why it is determined and the significance of the values obtained.
11. Given output from a column run, determine the HETP value.
12. Explain why HETP is determined for each column before it is used for a production run.
13. Define resolution.
14. Describe zone broadening and channeling.
15. Explain the theory of the equilibration step in ion-exchange chromatography.
16. Describe the events following application of the sample, during absorption.
17. Explain why a wash step is performed before the column is run.
18. Describe desorption or elution of sample.
19. Describe the steps of regeneration and sanitization.
20. Identify/describe the equipment needed for ion-exchange chromatography.
21. Distinguish between resolution, retention factor, efficiency, selectivity, and resin capacity.
22. Distinguish between column volume and bed height.
23. Perform calculations for determining column volume.
24. Perform calculations for determining linear flow rate.
25. Perform determinations of protein concentrations based on absorbance.
26. Explain why columns are not run at capacity.
27. Distinguish between flow velocity and flow rate and perform calculations to determine each.
28. Describe preventive maintenance of chromatography columns.
29. Describe the benefits of column maintenance.

Continued on next page

Objectives

30. Describe preventive maintenance of chromatography columns.
31. Demonstrate assembly, set-up, and use of an XK-50 column.
32. Perform packing of ion-exchange column.
33. Demonstrate column equilibration, washing, loading, and elution.
34. Interpret output of chart recorder and evaluate success of column run.
35. Explain how protein peaks could be identified in the absence of the chart recorder data.
36. Demonstrate/describe resin washing and regeneration.
37. Demonstrate disassembly and washing of column and disassembly of remaining equipment.

Affinity Chromatography

Objectives

1. Explain the basic concepts of affinity chromatography.
2. Explain why affinity chromatography is such a useful technique in the biotechnology industry.
3. Explain the role of Protein G/Protein A in affinity chromatography.
4. Describe the natural role of these molecules.
5. Describe the structure of the agarose beads used in affinity chromatography.
6. Explain how Protein G has been genetically engineered for use in affinity chromatography.
7. Describe the basic structure of an antibody molecule and identify which portion is bound by Protein G.
8. Describe the types of interactions which lead to the Ab/Protein G complex.
9. Identify what other molecules that may be bound to the Protein G column.
10. Explain the process of elution at the molecular level.
11. Demonstrate assembly of the column.
12. Demonstrate ability to adjust the column for a specified column bed height.
13. Perform calculations for column height for a given volume of resin slurry.
14. Perform calculations for determining flow rate.
15. Demonstrate calibration/use of the peristaltic pump.
16. Demonstrate use/knowledge of the UV monitor.
17. Perform test to determine reasonable settings for the UV monitor.
18. Demonstrate use of the chart recorder.
19. Demonstrate knowledge of chart recorder settings and ability to make needed adjustments.
20. Describe information required on chart recorder output.
21. Perform proper recordings of information on chart recorder output.
22. Perform packing of affinity column.
23. Demonstrate ability to troubleshoot during packing procedure to obtain a well-packed column.
24. Identify significant changes in chart recorder output during column run.
25. Demonstrate ability to prepare buffers for use in affinity chromatography.
26. Explain the reasons for changing buffers during the chromatography run and explain specifically what each buffer accomplishes.
27. Explain why a column should not be allowed to run dry.
28. Explain the consequences of incorrect determinations of flow rate.
29. Describe channeling and its consequences.
30. Determine protein concentrations in load, flow through, and eluate.

Continued on next page

Objectives

31.   Explain measurements for determining concentration of antibody in the above.
32.   Explain the use of an extinction coefficient.
33.   Perform data analysis for the affinity purification step.
34.   Calculate/explain percent purity and purification factor.
35.   Diagram the set-up for the affinity chromatography laboratory.
36.   Explain the role of producer and verifier.
37.   Explain the concept of mass balance and why it is significant.
38.   Explain what regeneration of a resin accomplishes and why it is done.
39.   Write a batch record for the affinity chromatography purification.

Chromatography Scale-Up

Objectives

1. Explain what is meant by a chromatography scale-up.
2. Describe the stages in a typical chromatography run.
3. Explain the differences between analytical and production purposes.
4. Explain the concept of "theoretical plates."
5. Explain how the number of theoretical plates is determined.
6. Describe what influences HETP.
7. Demonstrate ability to perform HETP calculations.
8. Explain the screening or mapping approach to scale-up.
9. State the advantages/disadvantages of this approach.
10. Explain the experimental design approach to scale-up.
11. State the advantages/disadvantages of this approach.
12. Explain the mechanistic approach to scale-up.
13. State the advantages of this approach over others.
14. Explain the role of mass balance in the use of mechanistic models.
15. Describe the use of the Yamamoto Simplified Model.
16. Describe some of the assumptions of the Yamamoto model.
17. Given a set of chromatograms run under different conditions, select the conditions desired for a given process and provide specific reasoning.
18. Explain IR and how to determine the value.
19. Perform measurements of retention time and peak width.
20. Explain GH and how to calculate.
21. Explain the difference between an isocratic elution and gradient elution.
22. Describe the use of a GH-IR curve.
23. Explain what a GH-IR curve is dependent on.
24. Define the coefficient K and explain its significance.
25. Describe the types of molecular interactions between a protein and a resin.
26. Explain the factors that influence these molecular interactions.
27. Explain the relationship between coefficient K and the GH-IR curves.
28. Explain what a KR value of 9 means.
29. Describe the information that can be obtained from a K-IR plot.
30. Explain purity, productivity, and recovery and how they are used in selecting conditions for scale-up.
31. Given a chromatogram with two prepeaks eluting too close to the main peak, describe how the conditions could be altered to better separate these prepeaks.
32. Describe how a very sharp gradient will affect elution.

Large-Scale Column Packing

Objective

1. Explain why it is important to have good column packing.
2. Define resolution and explain the factors which affect it.
3. Describe the parameters which affect peak width.
4. Describe a homogenous versus a heterogeneous bed density.
5. Explain which bed density is desirable and the reasons for the choice.
6. Demonstrate removal of 20% ethanol from resin and exchange buffer.
7. Explain the desired slurry resin and explain the purpose of this step.
8. Make determinations of the settled volume of the slurry media.
9. Calculate the packed column volume for a desired bed height.
10. Calculate the resin slurry volume required.
11. Calculate the maximum packing flow rate.
12. Calculate the integrity test flow rate.
13. List all of the column parts required for assembly.
14. Identify each of the components of a large chromatography column.
15. Demonstrate the ability to inspect and clean all of the column parts.
16. Demonstrate assembly of 35 cm column.
17. Demonstrate set-up/connections of pumps, valves, flow meter, pressure gauges, and UV monitor.
18. Explain the function of each of the above.
19. Explain the function of the frits, flow adapters, gaskets, o-rings, and paddles.
20. Demonstrate ability to level column.
21. Demonstrate removal of air bubbles/pockets from frits and flow adapters.
22. Discuss four different methods for bed consolidation.
23. Explain the challenges of packing large-scale columns.
24. Demonstrate operation of peristaltic pumps.
25. Describe the steps performed for equilibrating in packing buffer.
26. Demonstrate the ability to reslurry the resin.
27. Determine the quality of the column packing.
28. Explain the use of integrity tests with chromatography columns.
29. Define HETP and describe its use in testing columns.
30. Explain the types of molecules used for HETP.
31. Perform calculations of the volume.
32. Demonstrate injection of tracer.
33. Explain how peak width, retention time, and resolution are measures of column efficiency and packing.
34. Describe the acceptance criteria for column qualifications.
35. Perform HETP calculations using two methods.
36. Interpret HETP values.

Background

Definition	***Chromatography*** is the process of separating complex mixtures by percolation through a selectively adsorbing medium, as through a column of magnesia, gelatin, or starch, yielding stratified, sometimes chromatically distinct, constituent layers.
Use of Chromoto-graphy in Regulatory Approval	Chromatography is used when obtaining regulatory approval for protein drugs. Regulatory approval requires that the downstream process has at least one chromatography step and in many cases it is common to have three chromatography steps.
Purpose of This Document	The theory of chromatography and its application to large-scale protein purification has been the subject of numerous and extensive useful publications.
	This document does not repeat this information. Rather it focuses on a few parameters that are important in developing a scaleable chromatography step.

Fundamental Properties of Proteins

Introduction   Chromatography methods are so powerful that they can often resolve proteins that differ in composition by a single amino acid residue, and sometimes by even a single atom.

Protein Properties   The chromatographic separations that are used most frequently in biotechnology production exploit the fundamental properties that discriminate proteins from each other and other biomolecules. The four properties that are utilized in chromatographic separations are described in the table below.

Property	Description	Application
Electric charge	Basis for ion-exchange chromatography as well as chromatofocusing.	• Particularly useful for separating other classes of molecules, especially nucleic acids, from proteins. • Straightforward because the binding and elution of most components follows the order predicted by their isoelectric points.
Hydrophobicity	Basis for hydrophobic interaction and reversed phase chromatography.	Somewhat more difficult to develop because elution order is dependent on the type of ligand and the substitution density, as well as the backbone of the resin used. Nevertheless, powerful and unique separations are often obtained.

See next page for rest of chart

Continued on next page

Fundamental Properties of Proteins

Property	Description	Application
Affinity	Based on surface topologies or certain amino acid side chains.	Using immobilized: • Protein to isolate an antibody • Antibody to pull a protein out of a solution *Example*: Affinity chromatography of antibodies using immobilized Protein A is the method of choice because it allows one to achieve ≥99 percent purity in a single step. *Example*: Immobilized metal affinity chromatography (IMAC) is also used. This is the binding of proteins to chelated metals through surface histidine residues. *Reference*: For more information on affinity, refer to the topic "Solute Affinity" in this document.
Molecular size	Based on molecular size (i.e., gel permeation chromatography).	• Although the resolving power of this method is not great, it is often used to separate monomeric from dimeric or aggregated forms of the product. • It can also serve to simultaneously carry out buffer exchange (e.g., into the formulation excipients).

Chromatography Process

Chromato-
graphy Process

The table below describes the stages in a typical chromatography.

Stage	Name	Description
1	Packing	Consolidation of media into a uniform bed.
2	Sanitization	Reduction of microbial load to an acceptable level.
3	Equilibration	Conditioning of the resin for the adsorption step.
4	Load	Selective adsorption step of some species while others are not or only weakly bound.
5	Wash	Removal of unbound or weakly bound species.
6	Elution	Desorption of adsorbed species.
7	Regeneration	Desorption of all adsorbed material and conditioning of the resin for the next purification cycle.

Types of
Elution

The table below describes the three types of elution.

Type of Elution	Description
Isocratic elution	Adsorption, wash, and elution steps are carried out without change in mobile phase properties.
Step elution	After adsorption and wash steps, the mobile phase properties are changed abruptly to conditions for the desorption of adsorbed species.
Gradient elution	After adsorption and wash steps, the mobile phase properties are changed gradually for the desorption of adsorbed species.

Analytic-Scale vs. Production-Scale Chromatography

Introduction

Most researchers are familiar with the use of column chromatography:
- For analytical purposes
- To purify small quantities of protein
  - for structural investigations
  - as assay reagents

Differences Between Analytical and Production Purposes

In many aspects, the majority of production-scale chromatographies resemble scaled-up analytical procedures.

The table below describes the two primary differences between using column chromatography for analytical purposes versus production purposes.

Scale	Description

Production	Uses:
	• Higher product loading (i.e., 5 to 20 grams per liter of packed bed versus <0.5 g/L)
	• The selectivity of elution, which attempts to lump all the applied species into the following three groups:
	  – things that fail to bind
	  – the product
	  – things that are stripped off in the regeneration

Analytical	Attempts to get all species to: • Bind • "Display" as many distinct components as possible in the elution chromatogram

Using Elution Mode

Most steps in analytic chromatography are done in what is called *elution mode*, in which the elution is effected using a gradual or step increase of a weakly competing species, such as a salt.

Note: Applications of *displacement* and *frontal* chromatography, in which elution is effected by a strongly competing species or by other feedstock components, are still rarely used.

Designing Scaleable Chromatography Steps

Introduction	This topic explains the guidelines for designing scaleable chromatography by engineering a column operation to produce kilograms instead of milligrams per run.

Principles in Designing Scaleable Chromatography	Consider the following principles when designing chromatography: • Running analytical columns with the same bed height as that anticipated for the preparative column • Running the analytical column at the same linear flow rate as anticipated for the preparative column • Ensuring that the preparative column should have the same number of "theoretical plates" as the small scale column The rationale for each design consideration is described below.

Rationale for Using the Same Bed Height	There is a rationale for running analytical columns with the same height as that anticipated for the preparative column. Although a taller bed can be seen as a better choice since resolution increases with bed height, because pressure drop increases with bed height, a taller bed will either force the use of more expensive pressure-compatible equipment or it will force the operation to be slowed down. This is often due to the inability of the resin itself to withstand a large pressure drop without collapsing rather than to limitations imposed by the plumbing. A bed height of 20-30 cm is optimal for most applications. *Exception*: Resolution does not increase with bed height in cases where elution is done with a very steep gradient.

Rationale for Using the Same Linear Flow Rate	The rationale for running the analytical column at the same linear flow rate as anticipated for the preparative column is that if the bed height and linear flow rate are preserved upon scale-up, the fluid residence time will also be maintained.

Continued on next page

Designing Scaleable Chromatography Steps

Choosing the Linear Flow Rate

In order to choose a linear flow rate that can be maintained on scale-up, the pressure versus flow behavior for each particular chromatography resin in a large (greater than about 20 cm diameter) column needs to be known.

Notes:
- For some rigid resins such as silica, this dependence can simply be predicted from analytical-scale tests and therefore scale-up is easy.
- For other compressible resins like agarose, which is probably still the most widely used support matrix, this dependence can only be determined by large-scale tests.

Rationale for Having the Same Number of "Theoretical Plates"

"Theoretical plates" is a concept that has been adapted from the petroleum industry in which distillation columns contained plates that aided in the separation. Even though chromatography columns do not contain plates, the concept is still useful in assessing a column's resolving power.

If the scaled up column actually has ...	Then ...
more theoretical plates	you may be surprised by particular increases in purity or yield as the process scales-up, even though small-scale tests will not always fully predict what will happen at large-scale.
fewer theoretical plates	the process may fail to meet specifications when it is scaled-up.

Note: The number of theoretical plates in a column is determined experimentally by loading a very small volume of a non-interacting solute onto the column and observing the width and symmetry of the eluted peak.

Use of HETP in the Design

HETP stands for the "height equivalent to a theoretical plate." It is calculated by dividing the packed bed height of a column by the total number of theoretical plates. Knowing the value of HETP gives a feel for how well a column has been packed and set up, and how it will perform.

Continued on next page

Designing Scaleable Chromatography Steps

Values of HETP

The value of HETP is strongly influenced by:
- The particle size of the medium
- The fluid distribution system of the column
- How well the bed was packed

The smaller the value of HETP, the more plates the column has and the better it will perform. In theory, the smallest possible value for HETP is about twice the particle diameter. With experience and well designed columns, it is possible to get an HETP close to the theoretical limit, when packing rigid media with very narrow particle size distributions.

For very large columns of compressible media, an HETP of about five particle diameters is acceptable. An ongoing awareness of column packing quality as judged by HETP measurements is highly useful in the development process.

Discarding Resins

In the laboratory, researchers often discard a resin after a single use. This practice is highly undesirable at production-scale for the following reasons:
- Packing and unpacking operations are time consuming and laborious
- Buying and disposing of chromatography media is expensive

Unless the media are regenerated and reused, they are often the largest contributors to process material cost. Significant development time is therefore devoted to lifetime studies proving that a packed bed gives consistent performance over many cycles, and to cleaning studies to show that there is no carry-over from one batch to the next.

Solute Affinity

Introduction   This topic describes how solute affinity affects chromatography.

Description   In chromatography, a liquid mixture is passed through a column of packed sorbent particles. Because solutes in the mixture have different affinities for the sorbent, they partition differently in the stationary sorbent phase and in the mobile liquid phase.

Solute bands migrate along the column as the solutes continuously adsorb onto and desorb from the stationary phase. Solutes with higher affinity partition more in the sorbent phase than in the liquid phase and migrate more slowly along the column. Consequently, the solutes will be eluted in the order of the magnitude of their distribution coefficients.

Solute Affinity   The differences in solutes' affinity are due to the differences in:
- Molecular sizes or shapes
- Charge distributions
- Electrostatic field strengths or charged groups
- Hydrophobicities
- Hydrogen bonds

Protein Affinity   The unique three-dimensional structure and charge distributions of proteins cause them to bind with distinctly different affinity.

Example: Replacement of two charged amino acid residues on beta-lactoglobulin can result in different retention time.

Contaminants Removed by Chromatography

Introduction Chromatography is one of the primary means of achieving purification. This topic describes the contaminants that are removed in the purification process.

Contaminants Removed by Purification The contaminants which are typically removed in the chromatography process are described in the table below.

Contaminant	Separation Process	Quantification/ Qualification
Product variant	Variant forms of the product (i.e., misfolds, aggregates, dimers, amino acid substituted species, glycosylated forms, clips, etc.) may have different sizes, charge distributions, or hydrophobicities which allow them to be separated by various types of chromatography.	Purity of the column eluate is typically: • Qualified by SDS/PAGE gels • Quantified by product specific HPLC methods
Host cell related contaminants	Host cell related contaminants can be separated from the product of interest by various types of chromatography.	Quantified by gels and immunoassays.

See next page for rest of chart

Continued on next page

Contaminants Removed by Chromatography

Contaminants Removed by Purification

Nucleic acids	• Nucleic acid content can be reduced by ion-exchange chromatography • Highly charged nucleic acids can bind to anion-exchangers at ionic strengths at which proteins do not usually bind ***Note***: Alternatively, the product can be bound to a cation-exchanger and nucleic acids be allowed to flow through.	Quantified by slot blots
Bioburden/ Endotoxin	• Bioburden is typically removed with a pre-column filter or in the flow-through • Endotoxin is typically removed by ion-exchange chromatography	• Growth on agar plates are the primary means for quantifying bioburden • *Limulus* amoebocyte lysate (LAL) assays and spectrophotometric methods are the primary means for quantifying endotoxin reduction
Process Reagents/ Additives	Reagents and process additives can be reduced during chromatography by flowing through during the load step (i.e., not binding) or binding more tightly during the elution step.	Quantified by reagent specific assays

Chromatography Techniques

Chromoto-graphy Techniques

The table below contains a description of typical chromatography techniques.

Type of Chromatography	Description
Ion-Exchange Chromatography (IEC)	Adsorptive technique in which molecules are separated based on differences in surface charge.
Hydrophobic Interaction Chromatography (HIC)	Adsorptive technique in which molecules are separated based on differences in surface hydrophobicities.
Steric Exclusion Chromatography (SEC)	Diffusive technique in which molecules are separated based on differences in size and shape.
Reversed Phase Chromatography (RPC)	Adsorptive technique in which molecules are separated based on differences in surface hydrophobicities. The mobile phase is more polar than the stationary phase.
Hydroxyapatite Chromatography (HAC)	Adsorptive technique based on electrostatic interaction and complexion of carboxyl groups with calcium ions and positively charged amino acids with phosphate groups. The combinations are cooperative.
Immobilized Metal Affinity Chromatography (IMAC)	Adsorptive technique based on coordinative binding of histidine, cysteine, and tryptophan residues to immobilized transition metal ions.

Chromatography System Components

Introduction   The system components of a basic chromatography are the same whether they are used for analytical, small-scale preparative, or manufacturing use. This topic describes the basic components of a chromatography system.

Flow Diagram   The flow diagram below depicts a basic chromatography system.

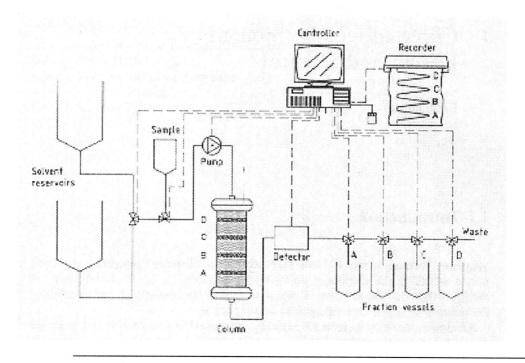

Chromatography System Components

Parts and Functions

The table below describes the parts and functions of the diagram of the chromatography system shown above.

Part	Function
Column	Contains media.
Pump(s)	Pushes load and mobile phase(s) through the column.
Solvent reservoirs	Means for selecting different mobile phases for wash, elution, and regeneration steps.
Detector	Monitors the performance of pressure, UV, pH, conductivity at column inlet and/or outlet.
Fraction vessels	Means for diverting column effluent to waste or product collection (i.e., fractions or bulk).
Controller/ Recorder (e.g., chart recorder or computer with controller)	Collects data for: • Solvent selection • Pump speed • Detector data (pressure, UV, pH, condition) • Fractionation

Affinity Chromatography

Laboratory

Introduction

The purification steps of the antibody produced during cell culture will begin with an affinity chromatography column. Students will prepare resin, pack the column, and purify their antibody for further analysis during the QC laboratories. In addition, the antibody will be submitted to a second chromatography run using ion-exchange resins.

Equipment

Ring stands
Chart recorders
XK50 columns
Peristaltic pumps
UV monitors
Spectrophotometer (UV/visible)

Materials and Supplies

Tubing
Stop watch
Rulers
1X PBS
2.0 N HCl
DMEM
Collection vessels
Graduated cylinders
Protein G Sepharose (resin 9105 Gamma Part AQ1306)
Antibody (Sigma Catalog #I8640, 100 mg)
0.1 N Glycine, pH 3.0
Calf serum

Solutions

1 X PBS

Elution Buffer
    0.1 N Glycine, pH 3.0

Laboratory

Activities at a Glance

Students will purify their antibody using two different chromatography columns. The first step will be an affinity chromatography run using a Protein A column.

DAY 1
1. Make buffers needed for affinity chromatography.
2. If cell culture media is unavailable, students can use DMEM with 10% calf serum and spike it with antibody.
   Filter sterilize. Each group will use approximately 1.6 liters for their column.
3. Perform calculations to determine concentration of load material, column bed height, load capacity of column, and flow rate.
4. Calibrate peristaltic pumps.
5. Pack columns.
6. Wash and equilibrate with columns.
7. Begin column loading and verify flow rate for an overnight run.

DAY 2
1. Wash columns with 1X PBS.
2. Elute antibody using 0.1 N glycine, pH 3.0.
3. Measure A_{280} of fractions. Save aliquots for SDS-PAGE and Westerns.
4. Perform calculations:

	Volume	Protein Conc.	Protein Amt.	Antibody Conc.	Antibody Amt.	Purity %	Purification factor
Load							
Flow though							
Elute after nuetralizing							

Ion-Exchange Chromatography

Laboratory

Introduction

This laboratory is the second step in the purification of the antibody and is designed to provide a working knowledge of the concepts, techniques, and applications of ion-exchange chromatography. Students will gain further experience in the operation and use of the chromatography equipment.

Equipment

Ring stands
UV monitors
Chart recorders
Spectrophotometer
XK50 columns
Peristalic pumps

Materials and Supplies

Tubing
Stop watch
Rulers
1X PBS
2.0 N HCl
0.1 N NaOH
0.01 M sodium acetate, pH 5
50 mL Falcon tubes
Collection vessels
Graduated cylinders
S-Sepharose Fast Flow, Pharmacia
Eluate from affinity columns
Hemostats
Plastic pipettes
pH paper

Laboratory

Activities at a Glance

Students will utilize the same equipment that was used in the affinity chromatography lab using S-Sepharose for the ion-exchange resin.

DAY 1
1. Begin by making all the necessary buffers for the ion-exchange chromatography lab. Filter all of the solutions.
2. Verify the previous calibration of the peristaltic pumps.
3. Each group should make the determination of the necessary column size based on determinations of protein amounts.
4. Pack and equilibrate (0.01 M sodium acetate) S-Sepharose columns using Pharmacia XK50 columns.
5. Determine flow rate for loading column on Day 2.

DAY 2
1. Wash columns with 0.01 M sodium acetate.
2. Load.
3. Elute with 1X PBS.
4. Perform calculations of percent recovery.

Large-Scale Column Packing

Laboratory

Introduction

The previous chromatography laboratories have given students experience in the principles and techniques used in chromatography purification procedures. In this laboratory, students will learn how these procedures are scaled-up to manufacturing levels. A large, 35 centimeter column will be packed and an integrity test run to make determinations on the quality of the packing procedures.

Equipment

35 cm chromatography column
Chart recorder
100 liter Nalgene tank
Pressure gauge
Flow meter
4 way valve
Peristaltic pumps: large volume (121 mL/min) and small (21 mL/min)
UV monitor/detector

Materials and Supplies

25 liters of S-Sepharose, Fast Flow
Acetone
Tygun wraps
Hose barbs
Tubing
Clamps
20% ethanol (20 liters)
DI water
Syringe
Paddles

Laboratory

Activities at a Glance

Students will pack a 35 cm Amicon column and run an integrity test. Students will assemble the column, pumps, chart recorder, and other necessary equipment. Following assembly, the column will be packed following an SOP. The basic steps are given below.

1. Make calculations for column volume on work sheet.
2. Slurry resin.
3. Inspect and assemble column parts.
4. Connect to UV monitor, chart recorder, pumps, pressure gauge, and flow meter.
5. Remove air bubbles/pockets from frits and flow adapters.
6. Equilibrate in packing buffer.
7. Reslurry resin.
8. Pack column.
9. Make measurements of column height.
10. Perform integrity test.

Protein Formulation-Fill-Finish Operations

Overview

Introduction   The advent of recombinant DNA technology in the late 1970's was a significant breakthrough in the history of biotechnology. Prior to that, protein pharmaceuticals were developed from biological tissues or fluids (e.g., insulin derived from porcine and bovine pancreatic tissue). However, this method of protein production was limited by the availability of the source. In addition, there were concerns that minor variations in the protein sequence from one species to another species (e.g., bovine/porcine insulin to human insulin) could potentially lead to immunogenic responses in the user population upon administration of the drug (Fineberg *et al,* 1983). The birth of recombinant DNA technology has largely eliminated these concerns. The ability to precisely alter the genetic code to construct the protein of choice has provided a platform to transform protein synthesis into a large-scale, commercially viable process.

Although recombinant DNA technology enabled protein production at large-scales, the highly unstable nature of the protein molecules has posed several unique challenges for large-scale protein manufacturing for therapeutic purposes. One of the most important of those challenges is the requirement to maintain the stability and efficacy (activity) of the drug throughout the desired fill-finish process, shelf-life, transportation and until the time of administration. This is accomplished by a process called "Formulation". During the formulation process, the protein of interest at the appropriate concentration is mixed with certain ingredients called *excipients* at a selected pH and ionic strength. The excipients and the solution conditions are carefully chosen to protect the drug from any degradations during the shelf-life and until administration. While the science of drug formulation design is better understood for the more traditional and low molecular weight drugs, formulation design for more complex and biologically-derived molecules, such as protein therapeutics, is relatively more esoteric. In this chapter the basic principles and practices related to protein formulation will be introduced. A brief description of subsequent "fill-finish" operations will also be provided for the sake of completion.

Overview

Table of Contents

This document contains the following sections:

Protein Formulation-Fill-Finish Operations

Objectives

1. Explain the levels of protein structure.
2. Explain how protein stability relates to structure.
3. Explain the problem of protein aggregation and its impact on pharmaceutical processing.
4. Explain how chemical degradation of proteins occurs.
5. Explain the role of excipients in formulation.
6. Discuss the different types of formulation excipients.
7. Describe how excipients as "cosolvents" can impact protein stability.
8. Explain why surfactants, cryoprotectants, and lyoprotectants are useful as excipients.
9. Explain the basic goal of formulation.
10. Describe a typical formulation-fill-finish unit operation.
11. Describe the detrimental effects of bulk freeze-thawing.
12. Identify several critical parameters for a large-scale freeze-thaw process.
13. Identify issues that would influence container selection for a freeze-thaw.
14. Explain the role of buffers in formulation.
15. Explain the concerns in the filtration of buffers used in formulation.
16. Explain the critical parameters involved in product filtration following formulation.
17. Describe how vials are prepared for filling.
18. Describe the filling process of protein pharmaceuticals.
19. Explain the purpose of lyophilization.
20. Describe the stages of the lyophilization process.
21. Describe the equipment used in lyophilization.
22. Explain the phenomena of "collapse" and "meltback" and why they need to be avoided during a lyophilization process.
23. State the critical parameters given consideration during lyophilization cycle development.
24. Explain each of these lyophilization process stages: freezing, presublimation annealing, primary drying, primary to secondary drying transition and secondary drying.

Section 1
Protein Structure, Stability, and Function

Overview

Introduction   A brief discussion about protein structure is presented below. For more details, please refer to any standard protein biochemistry textbook. Proteins are made up of amino acids. There are 20 naturally occurring amino acids. Depending on the structure of the amino acid, the nature of the amino acid can be hydrophobic, polar, charged, aromatic, or sulfur-containing. The number and the identity of amino acids in a protein's sequence determine the protein structure (or *conformation*). Since the number of amino acids in a protein's structure can typically vary from hundreds to thousands, and the identity of the amino acid at each position can also vary depending on its nature, the theoretical number of possible protein structures is astronomically large. Of course, the structures that naturally exist and those which are of practical relevance are far fewer in number, and are believed to be the result of natural selection.

Table of   This section contains the following topics:
Contents

Protein Structure

Levels of Protein Structure

Protein structure can be understood at several levels:

- *Primary Structure* is a simple description of the sequence of amino acids that make up the protein.
- *Secondary Structure* refers to elements (or *motifs*) of protein folding such as alpha-helix, beta-sheets and random coils.
- *Tertiary Structure* is a higher level of structural description referring to the three-dimensional structure of the protein, which is the result of a delicate balance between various forces such as electrostatic, hydrogen-bonding and hydrophobic interactions that dictate protein folding.
- Some proteins have multiple subunits, which make up the whole protein, and the arrangement of these subunits relative to each other in space is often referred as *Quaternary Structure.*
- For a few proteins, there may be additional groups called *prosthetic groups* that are required for protein function. An example is the blood protein hemoglobin, which contains the "heme group" - a porphyrin ring with four iron atoms attached to it.

Protein Stability

Protein Stability

It is important to understand that (a) proteins are not optimized for stability, and (b) protein stability is related to their structure. Protein structures are specifically screened via natural selection to perform a specific function in the body. However, a selection based on *in vivo* biological functions does not necessarily ensure that the molecule can withstand *in vitro* process damage. Despite the complexity of protein structures and a large number of possible configurations, it is a well-known fact that proteins are only *marginally stable* (Dill, 1990). Given this marginal stability of proteins, and that protein stability is linked to their structure, it is easy to destabilize a protein molecule by disrupting or altering protein structure physically and/or chemically, during *in vitro* processing operations (Lanfear *et al.,* 1999) as well as during the drug storage and administration. In the remaining portion of this subsection, protein structure related instabilities will be briefly discussed. Protein structural changes/modifications can be physical and/or chemical, leading to *physical instabilities* as well as *chemical instabilities.*

Physical Degradation of Proteins

Aggregation   Aggregation is the most prevalent means by which a physical instability in protein structure is manifested. Causes of protein aggregation are many. Since the protein's native structure (or the structure required for activity) is the result of a delicate balance of multiple forces and interactions, changes in the external environment of the proteins can often disrupt this balance, leading to structural changes, which in turn can lead to protein aggregation. Some of the common examples of such structure detrimental factors that are encountered during protein drug manufacturing include adverse solution changes (pH, ionic strength, additives), temperature, shear, and exposure to hydrophobic surfaces and air-water interfaces. In unfavorable solution environments, the protein conformation may be distinctly different from its native state as the protein assumes the most thermodynamically favorable state in a given solvent environment. The non-native state (*a molten-globule state* or a *denatured state*) can offer an increased number of hydrophobic interactions, which play a pivotal role in denaturation-mediated aggregation. Although there may be exceptions, in most cases, aggregation is preceded by conformational changes that result in a non-native configuration. At elevated temperatures, protein structure becomes more flexible, increasing protein-protein interactions, which in turn increase the propensity to form aggregates. hearing the protein can similarly lead to aggregate formation by resulting in possible conformational changes. Exposure to hydrophobic surfaces during pharmaceutical processing can lead to interactions between the surface and the hydrophobic regions of the protein, resulting in altered states of protein, which can lead to aggregate formation.

Continued on next page

Physical Degradation of Proteins

Pharmaceutical Impact of Protein Aggregation

Aggregates can adversely impact drug activity and half-life. Recombinant human insulin is an exception to this common observation. Zinc-containing hexamers of insulin are not only active, but they dissociate slowly over time compared to dimers or monomers of insulin, allowing a sustained delivery of the drug (Brange *et al.,* 1990). Aggregates are typically insoluble, leading to visible precipitation or particulate formation. Barring exceptions such as the insulin hexamer, the impact of protein aggregation can vary from reduced drug potency to generation of an immune response by the patient's body (Moore and Leppert, 1980). Protein aggregation can occasionally be used advantageously to increase process yields in operations upstream to formulation i.e., during protein expression or purification stages where some or part of the observed aggregation can be reversed during subsequent processing. Other examples of desirable aggregation may include crystallization, isoelectric precipitation, and salt-induced precipitation, where it is possible to maintain protein native structure in the aggregate form as well. However, aggregate formation is undesirable during formulation operations (exceptions include formulation slurries and crystallization for sustained delivery options) because at this stage the drug is typically at the end of its processing, and any aggregation is very likely irreversible at this time.

Conformational Changes

As explained above, adverse processing conditions can sometimes lead to protein conformational changes, which may over time make the protein more susceptible to physical and/or chemical degradations. Conformational changes can be precursors to many of the degradation pathways discussed in this section.

Chemical Degradation of Proteins

Introduction   Chemical degradation of proteins can occur via multiple mechanisms. Some of the most common are h*ydrolysis, oxidation,* and *deamidation.* There exist other degradation mechanisms (such as *disulfide exchange, racemization,* and *beta-elimination),* which are not discussed here.

Hydrolysis   Amino acids that make up the proteins are linked via peptide bonds. Under favorable conditions these peptide bonds can be easily hydrolyzed to yield constituent amino acids, thus disrupting the protein structure. The primary impact of hydrolysis is loss in potency/activity of the drug.

Oxidation   Protein oxidation is one of the major chemical degradation pathways. There are several amino acids that can undergo oxidation with varying chemistries. Examples include methionine, cysteine, cystine, histidine, tryptophan, and tyrosine. Some of the oxidizing agents include peroxides, light, free radicals, and metal ions (Swallow, 1960; Hiller *et al.,* 1981; and Stadman, 1990). Methionine oxidation is commonly observed, and can be induced by hydrogen peroxide, periodate, iodine, dimethylsulfoxide, chloramine-T, N-chlorosuccinimide, or light. The oxidative potential is dependent on the oxidizing agent as well as the location of the methionine residue in the protein structure. Methionine residues that are more accessible to the solvent are usually more reactive than those that are buried in the hydrophobic regions of the protein. The mechanism of oxidation can also vary depending on the conditions. More details about methionine oxidation are found in the following references by Harris and Hill (1969), Teh *et al.* (1987), and Brot and Weissbach (1991). Cysteine can be oxidized to cystine disulfide. Histidine oxidation (in the presence of metals, for instance) is dependent on the amino acids proximal to the reactive histidine as well as the protein conformation (Foote, 1968; Matheson and Lee, 1979; Farber and Levine, 1986).

Pharmaceutical consequences of oxidation can include loss in bioactivity (Cleland et al., 1993), reduced half-lives, and concomitant changes in pharmacokinetics due to increased susceptibility to proteases (McCay and Bond, 1985; and Davies *et al.,* 1987) and changes in antigenicity presumably due to conformational changes (Shima *et al.,* 1975).

Continued on next page

Chemical Degradation of Proteins

Deamidation

Deamidation can occur in proteins when asparagine and glutamine residues undergo deamidation leading to the formation of aspartic acid and glutamic acid, respectively. This protein degradation pathway is of particular interest because this is believed to serve as a biological regulator of protein clearance mechanisms *in vivo*. The susceptibility to undergo deamidation is greater for asparagine than for glutamine. However, the reaction rates are also dependent on the location of the reactive residue and the proximal residues. For more details about deamidation, refer to the review by Wright (1991).

Although deamidation had no detectable impact on the activity of some proteins [e.g. human growth hormone (Skottner *et al.,* 1988) and insulin (Brange *et al.,* 1987)], certain other proteins [e.g., lysozyme (Ahern and Klibanov, 1985) and cytochrome C (Flatmark, 1967)] have shown reduced activity upon deamidation. Deamidated proteins may be more susceptible to protease digestion - an observation that helps link deamidation with natural clearance mechanisms *in vivo* (Cleland et al. 1993). By altering the charge on the protein surface, deamidation can disrupt the delicate balance of forces that hold the protein together, leading to protein conformational changes (Kauzmann, 1959) that can in turn be damaging to protein's function. Although there are exceptions such as insulin for which the immunogenicity was unaltered between the native and the deamidated molecules (Schlichtkrull, 1974), potential immunogenicity is a concern with deamidated proteins as well (Lukash *et al.,* 1987).

Protein Function

Protein Function

In summary, a specific structure or configuration of the protein molecule is necessary to perform its function, and changes in protein structure (depending on the magnitude and location) can often render the protein drug unstable, inactive and/or harmful to patients. Therefore, protein structure, stability, and activity (or drug efficacy) are intricately linked. This is an important concept the reader should be familiar with.

Section 2
Formulation Excipients and Protein Protection Mechanisms

Overview

Introduction

The optimization of the formulation excipients is outside the scope of this discussion. However, a brief discussion of the primary mechanisms through which excipients offer protein protection will be presented.

Various excipients are included in the formulation to protect the drug against multiple degradation pathways. Common attributes of desirable excipients are aqueous solubility, nontoxicity, nonreactivity, rapid clearance from the body, and the absence of immunogenicity. In addition, the excipients should be capable of stabilizing the native conformation of the protein so as to maintain the efficacy and safety of the drug during processing, storage, and administration to the patient. A list of excipients that are used in approved pharmaceuticals with relevant routes of administration provides a good starting point to the formulation scientist to evaluate various excipients against the protein of interest. Interested readers can refer to an exhaustive list of formulation excipients for parenteral formulations that was compiled by Powell *et al.* (1998).

Table of Contents

This section contains the following topics:

Formulation Excipients

Excipients as Cosolvents

Excipients are also referred to as "cosolvents" since they affect the solvation of the protein. Cosolvents typically include salts, sugars, and amino acids. Cosolvent interaction with proteins has been studied extensively (Timasheff, 1992; Schellman, 1990; Carpenter *et al.,* 1990; Timasheff and Arakawa 1988; Arakawa and Timasheff, 1984, 1985a, 1985b). To summarize briefly, excipients impact protein physical stability by two mechanisms.

- *Cosolvent Exclusion*:
  The cosolvent is excluded from the protein surface (for a variety of reasons) thus leaving the protein molecule to be hydrated with water, away from the cosolvent. This mechanism is also referred to as "*preferential hydration*" (of protein). The addition of cosolvent increases the free energy of the system. The system compensates for this by trying to reduce the solvent accessible surface area of the protein. As a result, the native state of the protein (which has lower solvent accessible surface area than the denatured states) is stabilized with respect to the denatured states. The second mechanism is termed

- *Cosolvent Binding*:
  The cosolvent binds to the protein molecule and imparts stability. Mathematically, the interactions between cosolvents and proteins can be measured as a "preferential interaction" terms which are negative for Cosolvent Exclusion, and positive for Cosolvent Binding. In the review by Cleand *et al.* (1993), a summary of cosolvent effects based on cosolvent nature is provided.

It should be noted that multiple conditions impact cosolvent behavior, and it is difficult to classify cosolvents categorically into one of the two classifications. Sometimes both the above mentioned mechanisms may be operative to different extents. The literature in this area is quite extensive and the formulation scientist needs to be familiar with the various excipient effects that have been documented.

Continued on next page

Formulation Excipients

Surfactants

Surfactants are also used as excipients. Commonly used surfactants include polysorbate (Tween), polyethylene glycol (PEG), and block copolymers of polyethylene oxide-polypropylene oxide (Pluronics). In addition to reducing surface tension, which reduces the system free energy as well as protein-surface and protein-protein interactions, surfactants can bind to hydrophobic surfaces and reduce hydrophobic interactions between proteins and other processing surfaces such as hydrophobic container surfaces (Lougheed, 1983), ice-water interfaces (Chang *et al.*, 1996a), and air-liquid interfaces (Donaldson *et al.*, 1980). These effects lead to protein stabilization.

Cryoprotectants and Lyoprotectants

Some excipients are also used to protect against stresses during freezing (cryoprotectants) and freeze-drying (lyoprotectants). PEG is a cryoprotectant, while many sugars can act as lyoprotectants. Lyoprotectants are believed to stabilize the protein by the "water-substitution" mechanism (Pikal, 1990; Carpenter *et al.*, 1990; Levine and Slade, 1992) and by immobilizing the protein in an amorphous phase. In the water substitution mechanism, the lyoprotectant acts as a water substitute for hydrogen bonding, and allows further moisture reduction. Since water can catalyze many degradation reactions, reducing the moisture content can increase protein stability. By forming an amorphous "glassy" phase with the protein, the lyoprotectant increases the "glass transition temperature." Glass transition temperature is the temperature below which the amorphous material is in a glass-like state with negligible mobility on practical time-scales. Therefore, elevating the glass transition temperature to above the storage temperature of the protein reduces the mobility of the protein molecule and consequently increases its stability.

Protein Protection Mechanisms

Introduction

Formulation strategies to stabilize proteins against chemical degradation pathways include optimizing solution conditions.

Continued on next page

Protein Protection Mechanisms

Protection Against Oxidation

Formulation approaches to minimize oxidation include freezing, freeze-drying, and appropriate excipient selection. In general, freezing reduces oxidation although the temperature sensitivity of oxidation reaction rates is rather low because of the low activation energies involved (Johnson and Gu, 1988). Moreover, freezing is not always a viable solution since it can pose logistic/operational challenges. Use of antioxidants (such as vitamin E and propyl gallate) and reducing agents (such as methionine, sodium sulfite, and ascorbic acid) as excipients often helps in minimizing oxidation effects (Johnson and Gu, 1988). If oxidation is primarily mediated by trace metal ions, addition of chelating agents such as EDTA can help deplete the metal ions. Sometimes the protection against oxidation could also be based on cosolvent-induced conformational changes as opposed to solely by scavenging of the metal ions (Hovorka *et al.* (2001). Since trace contaminants present in various excipients can also impact oxidation, excipient screening and selection process based on the drug stability data is critical for minimizing oxidation.

Protection Against Deamidation

The strategies to reduce deamidation in proteins include optimizing solution conditions (excipients, pH, ionic strength, and temperature), freeze-drying of the protein, and protein engineering to eliminate reactive residues. The anion present in the buffer solution can have significant impact on deamidation rates (Gilbert *et al.,* 1949). Typically phosphate ion can lead to increased deamidation rates. Knowledge of the deamidation mechanism can help find an optimum solution pH from deamidation standpoint. For instance, a base-catalyzed deamidation reaction can be hindered by lowering the solution pH. Similarly, increase in ionic strength often enhances the deamidation reaction rates (Scotchler, 1974). Although lower temperatures can mitigate deamidation reactions, since temperature changes can also affect protein stability, temperature provides only a narrow window for formulation optimization. Freeze-drying can also reduce protein deamidation with an appropriate excipient choice (Pikal *et al.,* 1991).

It should be noted that the individual degradations mentioned above could initiate other degradation pathways discussed earlier, leading to a complex degradation profile. Therefore, recommending a formulation that optimizes the protein against all degradation pathways is a true challenge that the formulation scientist constantly encounters. Moreover, the difficulties associated with extrapolating data from accelerated stability studies over the drug shelf-life, and the need for ever-compressing developmental timelines make the formulation recommendation task even more challenging.

Section 3

Formulation-Fill-Finish Processes

Overview

Introduction

In the previous sections we learned the various possible degradation pathways for proteins, and briefly discussed some of the excipient-based approaches to minimize the degradation. In this section, the formulation process and subsequent fill-finish operations (such as filling and freeze-drying) as well as the critical process considerations in each unit operation will be discussed.

After purification, the protein has to be formulated into the recommended formulation (excipients, ionic strength, and pH). Figure 1 shows a schematic of the sequence of formulation operations that typically occur during protein commercial manufacturing. If the formulation is a sustained-delivery formulation, or if a drug delivery device (e.g., insulin pen) is used for more convenient delivery of the drug, the operations involved will vary from those described here.

Table of Contents

This section contains the following topics:

Formulation-Fill-Finish Unit Operation

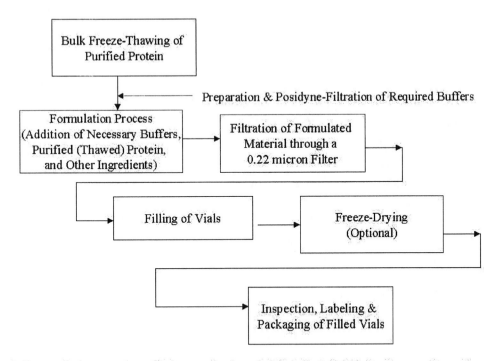

Fig 1. Schematic of Formulation-Fill-Finish Unit Operation Sequence

(The unit operation train will be different for a sustained-delivery formulation or a formulation that requires the use of a delivery device)

Bulk Freeze-Thawing

Introduction   Purified protein is often frozen prior to formulation operations to facilitate inventory buildup, transportation ease and to enable formulation in a campaign mode for different products in a multiproduct facility. Under such conditions, thawing the frozen bulk often constitutes the first step in formulation operations, as shown in Figure 1. Since freezing and thawing are linked together, both steps will be discussed.

Continued on next page

Bulk Freeze-Thawing

Detrimental Effects

Although one of the primary objectives of freezing the purified protein bulk is to extend its stability, the freezing process itself can be detrimental to proteins in several ways:

- All water-soluble species in the formulation can concentrate during freezing, and the increased concentrations can lead to enhanced degradation reaction rates (Franks, 1991; Hatley *et al.*, 1986).
- Buffer components can selectively crystallize causing solution pH shifts that can potentially denature the protein (van den Berg and Rose, 1959).
- Protein-stabilizing excipients in the formulation can crystallize during freezing, leaving the protein unprotected.
- Protein adsorption onto the ice surface can lead to protein denaturation (Chang *et al.*, 1996a).
- Sometimes protein denaturation can be due to the low temperatures achieved during the freezing process. This phenomenon, often termed cold denaturation, is believed to be due to a decrease in the hydrophobic interaction with reduced temperature (Fields, *et al.*, 1992; Privalov, 1990; Bock and Freiden, 1978).
- Freezing can also lead to potential conformational changes, which can subsequently lead to protein denaturation (Ondrias *et al.*, 1981).

Possible sources for product degradation during large-scale thawing include the following:

- Excessive agitation can shear the protein
- Excessive agitation can cause foaming, which can lead to protein degradation at the air-water interface
- While thawing from the freeze-concentrated state, the protein may precipitate.

Bulk Freeze-Thawing: General Guidelines

Critical Parameters

Based on the foregoing discussion, the following parameters are critical for a large-scale freeze-thaw process.

- *Freezing temperature.* Freezing temperature influences product stability in two ways; (i) It dictates the thermodynamic state of the protein. Although *in general* colder temperatures impart better stability to proteins, there are exceptions. (ii) It also controls the availability of formulation excipients to the protein. If the product is frozen to a temperature below the eutectic temperature of a crystalline additive (such as salt), the additive crystallizes and is no longer available to the protein.

- *Freezing rate.* Since freezing can be detrimental to protein stability, it may be advisable to freeze as quickly as possible so that the time of protein exposure to freezing-induced adverse conditions is minimized. However, proteins can have an optimum freezing rate since very high freezing-rates can be detrimental to proteins because of the excessively large ice-surface that results under fast-freezing conditions.

- *Freezing time.* Ensures the completion of the freezing process.

- *Thawing temperature.* Dictates thawing time and the rate of re-solubilization of freeze-concentrated protein back into solution.

- *Thawing rate and agitation.* Similar to freezing rates, faster thawing rates are, *in general,* better for product stability up to an optimum. Although faster thawing rates help reduce processing times, very high thawing-rates may cause foaming, and lead to shear-induced and surface-mediated protein denaturation.

Guidelines for Bulk Freeze-Thaw Process Development

The development approach for a large-scale protein freeze-thaw process can vary with the batch size, production demand, and the drug value. Therefore, only general guidelines and considerations are presented here. The literature in this area is quite extensive. For a review of large-scale protein freeze-thawing, refer to the following: Wisniewski, 1999a; Wisniewski, 1999b; Wisniewski and Wu, 1996. Methods may vary from using readily available containers such as freezing bags, carboys, and the like in a variety of freezers to using custom-designed vessels with stand alone freeze-thaw capabilities (Wisniewski, 1999b). In all cases, the success of a freeze-thaw process is determined by testing the product before freezing and after thawing, and comparing the results.

Continued on next page

Bulk Freeze-Thawing: General Guidelines

Freeze-Thaw Container Selection

The size, material of construction, and configuration of the container are determined based on the process/product requirements. The volume of the production batch, frequency of production, and related logistics dictate the container size. Options for container configuration can be between readily available containers (such as bags and carboys) and custom-designed freeze-thaw vessels such as stainless-steel vessels (Wisniewski and Wu, 1996). Product stability and the batch volume typically play a role in deciding which configuration to choose from. For off-the-shelf containers such as carboys and bags, some of the issues that influence container selection are the following:

- The lot size
- Temperature range of the application
- Container sterilization method
- Ease of use and transportation
- Durability
- Container size availability
- Clarity
- Chemical resistance
- Container closure
- Tamper evidence
- Compendial requirements

The selected container is validated prior to experimentation.

Freezing Temperature Determination

Thermal analysis studies performed via Differential Scanning Calorimetry (DSC) can help delineate the various phase transitions for the different components present in the formulation. Target freezing temperature range is determined based on this data and the available freezing facilities. Usually, the highest temperature at which the product is stable over the desired frozen period is chosen as the target temperature to reduce freezing costs.

Continued on next page

Bulk Freeze-Thawing: General Guidelines

Other Process Parameter Selections

A process designed around readily available containers like bags, carboys, or bottles offers limited control over the achievable freezing and thawing rates and the desirable freeze-thaw times. A common approach is to test if the product can withstand the freezing and thawing rates achievable with available facilities.

(a) Use of readily available containers such as carboys, bags, and bottles:

- *Freezing time and rates*
  Temperature-time profiles can be obtained experimentally by freezing the bulk (or placebo since protein is usually limited) in the selected container and freezer, and positioning temperature recorders at different places in the solution. Freezing rates and times can vary with the size and the number of containers used in the experiment. Placebo experiments at the maximum intended bulk-load can provide information about the longest freezing times and slowest freezing rates. After obtaining freeze-thaw profiles at full-scale, the impact of those freeze-thaw rates on protein integrity is tested by subjecting the protein to the worstcase freeze-thaw profiles. This can be done either at full-scale conditions, or in a controlled rate freezer at small-scale if protein bulk is limited. As mentioned earlier, there is limited choice in altering freezing rates by using different types of freezers, a different freezing set-point, or a different container.

- *Thawing temperature, method, and time*
  To expedite the thawing process, it is usually advisable to choose the thawing temperature reasonably high, based on available stability data. The thawing method may or may not involve some type of agitation. Thawing in a cold room with or without agitation or thawing at room temperature with agitation are some common choices. Agitation helps maintain uniform temperature if thawing temperature is different from storage temperature. On the other hand, a process without agitation is logistically simpler than one with agitation. Thawing time is determined by performing a full-scale experiment with the protein, or placebo if protein is limited. Thawing times are determined based on the temperature-time profiles and confirmed by visually ensuring that there are no residual ice pieces in solution.

Continued on next page

Bulk Freeze-Thawing: General Guidelines

Other Process Parameter Selection

(b) Use of custom-made vessels such as stainless steel vessels specifically designed for large-scale freeze-thawing

While the readily available containers may offer an inexpensive choice (at least during early part of product development), as the scale of operation gets larger, the freeze-thawing process with these containers can be logistically daunting. In addition, product samples taken from multiple containers can add up to significant product loss. Under these conditions, or if the product stability warrants a more controlled freeze-thawing method, custom-designed freeze-thaw vessels can be considered (Wisniewski and Wu, 1996; Wisniewski, 1999b). Standalone freeze-thaw systems (20 L to upward of 300 L) with dedicated refrigeration are commercially available. The vessels have a jacket and a central core, with a heat transfer fluid circulating through both to allow rapid heating and cooling of the vessel contents. The vessel is also symmetrically divided from the center with the help of stainless steel fins, which act as extended heat-transfer surfaces. If the scale of operation and the cost are appropriate, these freeze-thaw systems can offer a robust freeze-thaw process, with several fold higher heat transfer coefficients compared with a freeze-thaw process utilizing traditional freezers.

Preliminary experiments can be performed with commercially available scale-down tools called "cryo-wedges", which are a pie-section of the larger vessel. The cryo-wedges are designed to subject the protein at small scales (~ 0.5L) to the same freeze-thaw profile as those that would be observed at large-scales so that large-scale freeze-thaw impact on proteins could be assessed with a limited amount of protein. The validity of extrapolating small-scale results to large-scales and the logistics involved with transportation of the frozen vessels needs to be worked out on a case by case basis.

In all cases, the product must be analyzed biophysically and biochemically via a battery of tests to ensure that protein integrity is not affected by the recommended freeze-thaw method.

Formulation Process: Excipient Addition

Introduction

The purified form of the protein is usually stored in a buffer, that may or may not have all the ingredients specified in the formulation. The protein concentration at the end of the purification step can also be different (usually higher) from what is required for dosing the patient. Therefore, after the frozen, purified material is thawed, its concentration is adjusted and the recommended excipients are added to it. Addition of the recommended excipients at the right concentrations, and the adjustment of protein concentration, pH, and ionic strength constitute the process of formulation. Excipients are usually prepared in the form of one or more buffer solutions. If the formulation process involves only a protein concentration adjustment, then the required buffer (dilution buffer, in this case) will be identical to the recommended formulation buffer. However, if there are additional ingredients that need to be added, they can be prepared in a dilute buffer at the recommended concentration or at a higher concentration, which will subsequently be diluted.

General Considerations

Although the process of formulation in a manufacturing scenario may appear to be the simple addition of different ingredients, the labile nature of proteins, the large scale of the operation, and the very high purity of the product at this stage, warrant careful consideration of this step. The formulation process should be carefully designed by taking into account all possible concentrations (present and future) of the purified bulk and the formulated bulk, as well as process consistency and ease of operation at multiple manufacturing sites based on the site capabilities. Constituent buffers should be carefully determined so that the operation is manufacturing-friendly and logistically simple. Buffers should also be characterized so that appropriate tolerances are in place for their specifications. Buffer tolerances are established such that the process is practically feasible, while yielding a product that is within established specifications for purity, safety, and efficacy. Purity of each of the ingredients is ensured by carefully choosing the excipient supplier. Trace impurities such as peroxides in polysorbate can lead to protein oxidation. Bovine-derived polysorbate or other excipients with a mammalian tissue source are currently under scrutiny by regulatory agencies because of the potential concerns for Transmissible Spongiform Encephalopathies (TSE). Therefore, the choice of raw material supplier can be critical. The order of addition of excipients can also impact product quality, as in some cases interim interactions between excipients may occur at concentrations higher than their equilibrium concentrations in the postmixed, formulated bulk.

Continued on next page

Formulation Process: Excipient Addition

Buffer Filtration

Buffers that are used in formulation operations are typically filtered using depyrogenation membranes (e.g., posidyne filters) so that the buffers are pyrogen free. It may be necessary to flush the depyrogenation membranes to minimize filter extractables leaching into the filtered solutions. The size of filter membranes and the flushing procedures, including the allowable flow rate, are established up front. Prior to their use in formulation, the buffers are tested for endotoxin levels to ensure that the levels are below the preset specification limits.

Mixing

Mixing speeds and times are critical during the mixing of purified protein bulk and the formulation buffers. Inadequate mixing can leave the solution heterogeneous while excessive mixing can shear the protein; both scenarios could lead to product failing specifications. Mixing studies are performed with solutions whose solution and flow properties match those of the actual product. Full-scale experiments can be performed or small-scale experimental results can be scaled-up using modeling or empirical correlations (Klein, 1999) with appropriate equipment.

Additional Parameters

Other parameters to be considered in formulation operations include acid/base volumes required for pH adjustment, processing temperatures, the amount of time active product can be held at each stage, method of liquid transfer within the plant and product compatibility with product contacting equipment, pumps, and tubing.

Sterile Filtration

Filtration

Following formulation, the active product is sterile-filtered (using 0.22-micron pore size membrane) to ensure a product that is free of bioburden. PVDF membranes are commonly used for this purpose. Product compatibility with the specific filter membrane material is tested by validation studies, prior to using the filter at a commercial manufacturing site. Filter size recommendation is critical, and it can be product specific. Too small a filter could prolong the filtration times (and also lead to filter clogging), while too large a filter could have a large holdup volume, which in turn leads to greater product loss during filtration. Other critical parameters that require careful consideration include:

- Allowable pressure drop across the filter
- The duration over which filtered formulated product can be held
- Temperature of operation
- The mode of liquid transfer during filtration.

To meet European regulatory requirements, sterile filtration in most cases is performed at point-of-use (in-line) just before filling. All filters are integrity-tested prior to and after use, per established procedures.

Filling

Overview

Prior to filling, the vials are washed, depyrogenated, and then cooled to room temperature. Stoppers are washed, siliconized, and sterilized. Prewashed and presiliconized stoppers that are ready for sterilization are also commercially available. Some of the critical attributes are: the type of silicone used, extent of siliconization, the stopper composition, the residual moisture of the stoppers, and moisture permissibility of the stoppers. Use of a lower viscosity silicone can sometimes lead to more particulation compared with the use of a higher viscosity silicone. Adequate siliconization ensures proper machinability of the stoppers on the fill equipment. Based on some recent findings of allergic reactions, there is an increased trend to use latex-free stoppers for pharmaceutical purposes (PDA Annual Conference 2000). Knowledge of the residual moisture content of the stoppers and the moisture-vapor transmissibility are critical for lyophilized formulations where moisture transfer from and through the stopper to the product can be a concern (Pikal and Shah, 1991). Also, the possibility of any deleterious interactions between the product and any leachables from the vials/stoppers is investigated.

Filling of protein pharmaceuticals is performed in a clean room of appropriate classification (Class 100). Most manufacturing facilities use automatic fill machines with multiple needles. Studies are conducted with the product to determine the fill-accuracy capabilities of the fill equipment, and the amount of unrecoverable product (i.e., holdup volume) from vials and disposable syringes. Based on these values, a target fill-weigh, and tolerances around that target, are established. Automatic fill machines typically have the capabilities to periodically test fill-weights on-line.

The filling device's materials of construction must be compatible with the product. While it is necessary to keep the filling speeds as high as practically achievable to maintain high throughput, very high filling speeds can lead to foaming, which can lead to protein denaturation. The maximum time the product can be held at room temperature during filling is specified based on product stability data, and recorded for ensuring product stability For some liquid dose products, the vial headspace is overlayed with nitrogen gas to prevent product oxidation by the headspace oxygen.

Lyophilization

Introduction   The process of freeze-drying or lyophilization is very well documented in literature. The interested readers are referred to the following references for more advanced concepts than those introduced here. Rey and May (1999); Carpenter *et al.* (1997); Cameron (1997); Carpenter and Chang (1996); Pikal (1996); Chang and Fischer (1995); Pikal (1994); Nail and Gatlin (1993); Pikal (1990a); Pikal (1990b).

If the product shelf-life stability is not adequate under liquid conditions, a freeze-dried formulation may be an alternative. Lyophilization is the process by which the moisture content of the product is reduced by freezing and subsequent sublimation under vacuum. Freeze-drying improves product stability by:

- Maintaining the protein in an amorphous phase with its stabilizers
- Immobilizing the protein in a glassy phase below the glass transition temperature (Tg') of the formulation
- Reducing the residual moisture content to a low, desirable value.

Maintaining the protein in an amorphous phase with its stabilizers helps in protecting the protein. Keeping the dried protein below its glass transition temperature minimizes protein immobility on all practical time scales and therefore prevents degradation. Reducing the amount of residual water minimizes all water catalyzed degradations. Although lyophilization is an energy intensive (i.e., expensive) process, the improved product stability often makes this the process of choice.

Process Stages   The lyophilization process primarily consists of three stages:

- The first stage involves freezing the product and creating a frozen matrix suitable for drying. This step impacts the drying characteristics in the next two stages.
- The second stage is primary drying. Primary drying involves the removal of the ice by sublimation by reducing the pressure (to typically around 50-500 µm Hg) of the product's environment while maintaining the product temperature at a low, desirable level.
- The third stage in the process is called secondary drying where the bound water is removed until the residual moisture content reaches below the target level.

Continued on next page

Lyophilization

Equipment   A freeze dryer consists of a chamber with shelves on which the filled vials are loaded for lyophilization, a condenser for capturing the product's sublimed water vapor as ice, a refrigeration system that facilitates temperature control, and a vacuum pump which can reduce the chamber pressure to sub-atmospheric values. The chamber pressure is maintained at its set-point by introducing, in a controlled manner, an inert, dry bleed gas (such as nitrogen) at the front of the chamber. In most cases, the chamber is separated from the condenser via a main valve. The product is loaded onto the stainless steel shelves, whose temperature is controlled via a heat transfer fluid (silicone oil) circulating through the shelves. Temperature of the heat transfer fluid is controlled via the refrigeration system. The freezing stage is initiated by cooling the shelves to the desired freezing temperature and holding the temperature constant for equilibration. The cooled shelves help freeze the product to the desired temperature. Following freezing, the chamber pressure (measured by a capacitance manometer) is reduced to below the saturated vapor pressure of ice at the frozen temperature. This initiates primary drying. Since ambient pressure is below the saturated vapor pressure at that temperature, part of the frozen product instantaneously sublimes (the difference between the vapor pressure of ice and the chamber pressure provides the driving force for sublimation). Sublimation leads to pressure equilibration. However, since the chamber pressure is constantly maintained below the saturated vapor pressure of ice (at that temperature), sublimation continues. The sublimed vapors are trapped at the condenser as ice. Typically, the condenser coil or plates remain at about -50 to -70°C during the drying process. When all the bulk water is removed via sublimation, primary drying is complete. At this point, there is still some bound water remaining in the product which can be removed by desorption at higher temperatures experienced during secondary drying. So, typically the shelf temperature is raised at this stage and held, until the desired residual moisture is achieved. At that point, secondary drying is also complete, and the vials are stoppered in the chamber. The chamber is aerated prior to the unloading of the vials. Note that the above description is generic, and some equipment design variations are available.

Continued on next page

Lyophilization

Collapse and Meltback

The objective of a lyophilization process is to achieve a freeze-dried protein cake with acceptable appearance, biological potency, ease of reconstitution and long-term storage stability. There are two phenomena that should be avoided during a lyophilization process; they are *collapse* and *meltback*.

- *Collapse:* Collapse is described as the loss of microscopic and macroscopic structure of the freeze-dried product. Collapse usually occurs when the product temperature exceeds a characteristic temperature called collapse temperature. When this occurs, the matrix collapses under its own weight. In addition to losing pharmaceutical elegance, collapsed product may lead to increased residual moisture content, uneven distribution of moisture, longer reconstitution times and possible protein conformational changes. Collapse temperature is unique to a given formulation and correlates well with the glass transition temperature (Tg') of the formulation; collapse temperatures are usually slightly above Tg'. Therefore, as a general rule of thumb, the product temperature during primary drying is usually maintained about 2 to 5°C below the collapse temperature of the formulation to avoid collapse.

- *Meltback:* Most formulations have crystalline components such as mannitol or glycine as bulking agents. Eutectic melting of these crystalline components leads to meltback. To avoid meltback, the product needs to be below the eutectic melting temperature of the crystalline components of the formulation. Eutectic melting temperature is the crystalline analogue of glass transition temperature. Since the eutectic melting temperatures of commonly used bulking agents are usually higher than the Tg' of the amorphous phase, meltback is usually prevented by keeping the product below the Tg' of the formulation.

Lyophilization Cycle Development

A prudently designed lyophilization cycle is one that is robust, consumes little time and energy and maintains product quality. Both formulation-related and cycle-related factors contribute to achieving this goal.

Lyophilization Cycle Development

Formulation Impact on Process

Only the impact of formulation on freeze-drying cycle will be discussed, rather than all aspects of formulation optimization. For freeze-dried products, the formulation and the lyophilization process are intricately interrelated. As mentioned earlier, to maintain product stability, the product temperature needs to be below its glass transition temperature (Tg') both during drying and storage. Therefore, a formulation with a higher Tg' allows drying at a higher temperature compared with a lower Tg' formulation and subsequently expedites the freeze-drying time. Since Tg' of the formulation is approximately the mass average of Tg' values of all the amorphous components in the formulation, the Tg' of the formulation can be raised by increasing the weight fraction of high Tg' components of the formulation and/or by decreasing the weight fraction of low Tg' components. Of course, it is necessary that the chosen excipients regardless of their Tg' values, protect the protein from possible degradations.

While better pH control is achieved by choosing amorphous buffer components, amorphous components generally tend to depress the formulation Tg' compared with crystalline components. Therefore, the amount of buffer salts in the formulation should be kept to a minimum. It is usual practice to crystallize the bulking agent (the agent that provides "bulk" to the lyophilized cake) in the formulation.

The concentrations of the bulking agent and other excipients can also impact the fragility of the lyophilized cakes.

Continued on next page

Lyophilization Cycle Development

Preliminary Studies

Measurement of Tg' & eutectic melting temperature. Although the Tg' values and the eutectic temperatures of most commonly used excipients are well documented in literature (Chang *et al.*, 1996b; Chang and Randall, 1992), Tg' of a given formulation is experimentally determined before developing a lyophilization cycle. This can be done by several different methods [e.g., Differential Scanning Calorimetry (DSC)] (Her and Nail, 1994).

Measurement of Collapse Temperature. Collapse temperature can be determined using a freeze-drying microscope by freezing the material and raising the temperature to observe the onset of collapse (Nail *et al.*, 1994).

Stability Studies. Product stability as a function of residual moisture content needs to be determined. Although lower moisture contents generally lead to greater stability, an optimum residual moisture content has been observed in some cases. In addition, obtaining driedproduct stability data at temperatures higher than ambient can significantly help in scale-up and design of secondary drying conditions.

Lyophilization Cycle Development: Process Parameter Considerations

Introduction

Some of the critical parameters to be considered during cycle development are:
- Shelf-temperature in each step
- Chamber pressure, hold times at each step
- Ramp rates during heating and cooling.

Continued on next page

Lyophilization Cycle Development: Process Parameter Considerations

Freezing

As explained in the "Bulk Freeze-Thawing" section, the process of freezing and freezing rates have a significant influence on the quality and stability of the product. In addition to the effects discussed earlier, freeze-induced concentration of the salts and proteins can significantly increase degradation reaction rates. Therefore, faster freezing rates are in general preferred. However, another issue to be considered here is the size of the ice crystals formed during freezing and the size of the pores left behind after their sublimation. Very fast freezing rates lead to the formation of many small ice crystals, which in turn, provide a large surface area. This large surface area decreases secondary drying time, but reduces the sublimation rate during primary drying. A slower freezing rate, on the other hand, produces fewer, larger ice crystals with all the above mentioned effects being reversed. Therefore, there is an optimum freezing rate (range) for every product based on product stability, process time requirements, and equipment capabilities.

Pre-Sublimation Annealing

Some of the crystalline additives such as mannitol and glycine may not crystallize completely during freezing. These excipients have low Tg' values, and if not crystallized fully, they contribute to the overall Tg' of the formulation and reduce the overall Tg'. [As mentioned earlier, a low Tg' necessitates drying at lower temperatures, which prolongs the cycle time.] This can be avoided by presublimation annealing, which helps to crystallize these additives. In an annealing protocol, the frozen product is usually heated to a temperature above the collapse temperature of the formulation. This increased temperature allows enough thermal motion to the excipients so that they devitrify and crystallize. The enhanced thermal motion also promotes formation of larger ice crystals from smaller ones. [The formation of larger crystals from smaller ones is thermodynamically favorable due to the reduced area of larger ice crystals. However, this process is kinetically inhibited at low temperatures. Annealing helps provide the necessary thermal motion to overcome the kinetic inhibition. A word of caution - annealing is not suitable for products that degrade very quickly above their collapse temperature.]

After annealing, the shelf temperature is decreased to the desired operating temperature in primary drying, and then drying is initiated by establishing vacuum in the chamber.

Continued on next page

Lyophilization Cycle Development: Process Parameter Considerations

Primary Drying

Optimization of primary drying involves the appropriate selection of shelf temperature, chamber pressure, and drying time. The shelf temperature determines the heat transfer to the product and controls the product temperature. The chamber pressure also influences the product temperature by controlling the heat transfer between the vial and the shelf.

The objective of primary drying is to dry the product below its collapse temperature. Therefore, based on the collapse temperature of the given formulation, the target product temperature can be established to be a few degrees below the collapse temperature. There are multiple combinations of shelf temperature and chamber pressure that can lead to the target product temperature, and the key in developing a lyophilization cycle lies in knowing which combination to choose. Typically, a combination with higher shelf temperature and lower chamber pressure is better because it leads to higher sublimation rate than a combination of lower shelf temperature and higher chamber pressure. As a general rule, chamber pressure should be chosen such that it is about 10 to 30% of the vapor pressure of ice at the target product temperature. To avoid vial-to-vial inconsistencies in heat transfer, chamber pressures in the range of 100 to 200 mTorr are preferred. After fixing the chamber pressure, an appropriate value of shelf temperature is chosen so that the combination of chamber pressure and shelf temperature leads to the desired product temperature. It is important to ensure that the resulting sublimation rates are not too high to overload the condenser. Therefore, knowledge of sublimation rates and product temperatures associated with multiple combinations of shelf temperature and chamber pressure is critical for the selection of appropriate process parameters. A manuscript by Chang and Fischer (1995) has an excellent analysis of this situation.

Continued on next page

Lyophilization Cycle Development: Process Parameter Considerations

Primary to Secondary Drying Transition

This step is critical because a premature transition to secondary drying conditions (higher shelf temperatures) can lead to product collapse. End of the primary drying (or end of the sublimation) can be detected by temperature or pressure measurement.

Since sublimation takes the latent heat for phase change from the product, the product is maintained colder than the shelf temperature during sublimation, and at the end of sublimation, the vial contents approach the shelf temperature. Therefore, by having temperature sensors (such as thermocouples) in some vials, the end of sublimation (for that vial) can be detected when the vial temperature reaches the shelf temperature. However, we should be aware that the majority of the vials in the batch do not contain thermocouples in them, and as such they are not representative of the vials containing thermocouples. The nonthermocouple-containing vials freeze later, have smaller pores, have greater product resistance to vapor flow, dry at a higher temperature and take longer to dry compared with the thermocouple-containing vials. Therefore, with this method of detection, usually a delay time of 10 to 15% of the primary drying time is used as "soak time" before secondary drying can be initiated.

Transition detected by pressure measurement is more accurate. The chamber pressure is controlled by the capacitance manometer reading. Some lyophilizers have an additional device such as the pirani gauge, which is sensitive to gas composition. During primary drying, most of the chamber is filled with water vapor. On the other hand, the chamber is essentially filled with the nitrogen gas at the end of the primary drying Therefore, during the primary drying, the pirani gauge reads a different pressure reading (because of the water vapor presence) compared with the capacitance manometer, but towards the end of primary drying, the pirani gauge reading converges with that of the capacitance manometer. This is an accurate indication of the completion of primary drying.

Continued on next page

Lyophilization Cycle Development: Process Parameter Considerations

Secondary Drying

After the completion of primary drying, the shelf temperature is raised. Knowledge of the residual moisture levels in the product as a function of shelf temperature and hold time is critical for successful secondary drying. The allowable level of residual moisture content has to be predetermined during formulation development based on stability data. A common starting point for shelf temperature during secondary frying is about 25 to 30°C for proteins. A lower shelf temperature requires longer drying times, but will improve the uniformity of moisture level in the product batch. On the other hand, some products may not dry to the required moisture levels without using a high shelftemperature. Drying rate during secondary drying is independent of chamber pressure up to pressures of at least 200 mTorr (Pikal, 1990).

Secondary drying is complete when the residual moisture levels in the product reach the desired, low level. At that point, the vials are stoppered inside the chamber (typically under a partial vacuum). The chamber is aerated and the shelf temperature is raised to around 4°C until the vials are unloaded.

Final Product Characterization

Since the lyophilization process may lead to measurable conformational changes in the product, often accompanied by aggregation and other product-degradation pathways, pre and postlyophilization characterization of the product is essential to ensure drug potency and stability. Lyophilized protein products are usually analyzed for their moisture content and signs of any aggregation, chemical degradation, and/or conformational changes.

Crimping, Inspection, Labeling, and Packaging

Overview

Unloaded vials are crimped and inspected. Appropriate inspection criteria need to be in place for liquid and solid dose forms. Liquid dose forms should be inspected for particulate matter. Inspection methods can vary from visual inspection to automated machines. An allowable reject rate for inspection should be established. Following inspection, the vials are labeled and packaged.

Section 4
Summary

Key Concepts   The following are the key concepts that were discussed:

- Proteins are complex molecules made up of amino acids. Protein structure is linked to the stability of the molecule, and protein stability in turn, is necessary for ensuring the efficacy of the protein molecule as a therapeutic agent.

- Proteins are only marginally stable. They can undergo both physical and chemical degradation based on a variety of factors such as changes in temperature, pH, ionic strength and the constituents of the solution environment.

- Therapeutic protein formulations contain excipients that are carefully selected to protect the protein against both physical and chemical degradation. Excipients can render protection via different mechanisms, and the nature of the excipient often dictates the mechanism by which it offers protection against a specific stress.

- Formulation-Fill-Finish activities typically include freeze-thawing of the bulk, addition and blending of the various excipients in the appropriate order, sterile filtering the formulated bulk, filling the formulated bulk in vials, freeze-drying (sometimes), crimping of the vials, inspection, labeling, and packaging. The highly unstable nature of the protein molecules require that each of these operations is carefully designed to ensure the safety and efficacy of the protein drug.

References

Ahern, T. J. and Klibanov, A. M., "The Mechanism of Irreversible Enzyme Inactivation at 100°C", *Science,* **228**, 1280, 1985.

Arakawa, T. and Timasheff, S. N., "Mechanism of Salting In and Out by Divalent Cation Salts: Balance Between Hydration and Salt Binding", *Biochemistry,* **23**, 5912, 1984.

Arakawa, T. and Timasheff, S. N., "The Stabilization of Proteins by Osmolytes", *Biophys. J.,* **47**, 411, 1985a.

Arakawa, T. and Timasheff, S. N., "Mechanism of Poly(Ethylene Glycol) Interactions with Proteins", *Biochemistry,* **24**, 6756, 1985b.

Arakawa, T., Kita, Y., and Carpenter, J. F., "Protein-Solvent Interactions in Pharmaceutical Formulations", *Pharm. Res.,* **8**, 285-291, 1991.

Bock, P. E., and Frieden, C., "Another Look at the Cold Lability of Enzymes", *TIBS,* **May**, 100-103, 1978.

Brange, J., Owesn, D. R., Kang, S., and Volund, A., "Monomeric Insulins and their Experimental and Clinical Implications", *Diabetes Care.,* **13**, 923, 1990.

Brange, J., Skelbaek-Pedersen, B., Langkjaer, L., Damgaard, U., Ege, H., Havelund, S., Heding, L. G., Jorgensen, K. H., Lykkeberg, J., Markussen, J., Pingel, M., and Rasmussen, E., *Galenics of Insulin: The Physicochemical and Pharmaceutical Aspects of Insulin and Insulin Preparations*", Springer-Verlag, Berlin, 1987.

Brot, N. and Weissbach, H., "Biochemistry of Methionine Sulfoxide Residues in Proteins", *Biofactors,* **3**, 91, 1991.

Cameron, P. (Editor), "Good Pharmaceutical Freeze-Drying Practice", Interpharm Press, Inc., Buffalo Grove, IL., 1997.

Carpenter, J.F., Pikal, M.J., Chang, B.S. and Randolph, T.W. "Rational Design of Stable Lyophilized Protein Formulations: Some Practical Advice", *Pharm. Res.,* **14**(8), 969-975, 1997.

Carpenter, J. F., Arakawa, T. and Crowe, J. H., "Interactions of Stabilizing Additives with Proteins During Freeze-Thawing and Freeze-Drying", *Dev. Biol. Stand.,* **74**, 225, 1990.

Carpenter, J. F. and Chang, B. S., "Lyophilization of Protein Pharmaceuticals", in *Biotechnology Issues in Pharmaceutical Process Engineering,* Aois, K. E. and Wu, V. L., Eds., Interpharm Press, Buffalo Grove, IL, 1996.

Chang, B. S. and Fischer, N. L., "Development of an Efficient Single-Step Freeze-Drying Cycle for Protein Formulations", *Pharm. Res.,* 12, 831-837, 1995.

Chang, B. S. and Randall, C. S., "Use of Subambient Thermal Analysis to Optimize Protein Lyophilization", *Cryobiology,* **29**, 632-656, 1992.

References

Chang, B. S., Kendrick, B. S., and Carpenter, J. F., "Surface-Induced Denaturation of Proteins During Freezing and Its Inhibition by Surfactants", *J. Pharm. Sci.,* **85**(12), 1325-1330, 1996a.

Chang, B. S., Beauvais, R. M., Dong, A. and Carpenter, J. F., "Physical Factors Affecting the Storage Stability of Freeze-Dried Interleukin-1 Receptor Antagonist: Glass Transition and Protein Conformation", *Arch. Biochem. Biophys.,* **331**(2), 249-258, 1996b.

Cleland, J.L., Powell, M.F. and Shire, S.J., "The Development of Stable Protein Formulations: A Close Look at Protein Aggregation, Deamidation, and Oxidation," Critical Reviews in Therapeutic Drug Carrier Systems, 10(4), 307-377, 1993.

Davies, K. J. A., Lin, S. W., and Pacifici, R. E., "Protein Damage and Degradation by Oxygen Radicals", *J. Biol. Chem.,* **262**, 9914, 1987.

Dill, K. A., "Dominant Forces in Protein Folding", *Biochemistry,* **29**(31), 7133-7155, 1990.

Donaldson, T. T., Boonstra, E. F., and Hammond, J. M., "Kinetics of Protein Denaturation at Gas-Liquid Interfaces", *J. Colloid Interface Sci.,* **74**, 441, 1980.

Eckhardt, B. M., Oeswein, J. Q., and Bewley, T. A., "Effect of Freezing on the Aggregation of Human Growth Hormone", *Pharm. Res.,* **8**, 1360-1364, 1991.

Farber, J. M. and Levine, R. L., "Sequence of a Peptide Susceptible to Mixed Function Oxidation: Probable Cation Binding Site in Glutamine Synthetase", *J. Biol. Chem.,* **261**, 4574, 1986.

Fields, G. B., Alonso, D. O. V., Stigter, D. and Dill, K. A., "Theory for the Aggregation of Proteins and Copolymers", *J. Phys. Chem.,* **96**, 3974-3981, 1992.

Fineberg, S. E., Galloway, J. A., Fineberg, N. S., and Goldman, J., "Effects of Species of Origin, Purification Levels, and Formulation on Insulin Immunogenicity", *Diabetes,* **32**, 592, 1983.

Flatmark, T., "Multiple Forms of Bovine Heart Cytochrome C: A Comparative Study of their Physicochemical Properties and their Reactions in Biological Systems", *J. Biol. Chem.,* **242**, 2454, 1967.

Foote, C. S., "Mechanisms of Photosensitized Oxidation", *Science,* **162**, 963, 1968.

Franks, F., "Freeze-Drying: From Empiricism to Predictability. The Significance of Glass Transitions", *Develop. biol. Standard.,* **74**, 9-19, 1991.

Gilbert, J. B., Price, V. E., and Greenstein, J. P., "Effect of Anions on the Non-Enzymatic Deamidation of Glutamine", *J. Biol. Chem.,* **180**, 209, 1949.

Hatley, R. H. M., Franks, F. and Day, H., "The Effect on the Oxidation of Ascorbic Acid of Freeze-Concentration and Cooling", *Biophys. Chem.,* **24**, 187-192, 1986.

Harris, C. M. and Hill, R. L., "The Carboxymethylation of Human Metmyoglobin", *J. Biol. Chem.,* **244**, 2195, 1969.

Her, L-M. and Nail, S. L., "Measurement of Glass Transition Temperature of Freeze-Concentrated Solutes by Differential Scanning Calorimetry", *Pharm. Res.,* **11**(1), 54-59, 1994.

References

Hiller, K. O., Masloch, B., Gobl, M., and Asmus, K.-D., "Mechanism of the OH-radical Induced Oxidation of Methionine in Aqueous Solution", *J. Am. Chem. Soc.,* **103**, 2734, 1981.

Hovorka, S. W, Hong, J. Y., Cleland, J. L. and Schoneich, C., "Metal-Catalyzed Oxidation of Human Growth Hormone: Modulation by Solvent-Induced Changes of Protein Conformation, *J. Pharm. Sci.,* **90(1)**, 58-69, 2001.

Johnson, D. M. and Gu, L. C., "Autooxidation and Antioxidants" in *Encyclopedia of Pharmaceutical Technology, Volume 1. Absorption of Drugs to Bioavailability and Bioequivalence",* Swarbick, J. and Boylan, J. C., Eds., Marcel Dekker Inc., New York, 1988.

Kauzmann, W., "Some Factors in the Interpretation of Protein Denaturation", *Adv. Protein Chem.,* **14**, 1, 1959.

Klein, G. F., "A New Approach to the Scale-Up of Liquid Pharmaceuticals", *Pharmaceutical Technology,* 136-144, March 1999.

Lanfear, D., Hassler, R., Sitney, K., Curless, C., Patro, S., Tsai, L., and Ogez, J., "Protein Drug Manufacturing", In *Biopharmaceutical Drug Design and Development*, Eds., Wu-Pong, S., and Rojanasakul, Y., Humana Press Inc., Totowa NJ, 275-327, 1999.

Lougheed, W. D., Albisser, A. M., Martindale, H. M., Chow, J. C., and Clement, J. R., "Physical Stability of Insulin Formulations", *Diabetes,* **32**, 424, 1983.

Lukash, A. M., Pushkina, N. V., and Tsibulsky, I. E., "Autoantigenic Properties of Deamidated Serum Albumin", *Immunologiya,* **68**, 89, 1987

Matheson, I. B. C. and Lee, J., "Chemical Reaction Rates of Amino Acids with Singlet Oxygen", *Photochem. Photobiol.,* **29**, 879, 1979.

McKay, M. J. and Bond, J. S., "Oxidation of Protein Sulfhydryl Groups as an Initial Event in Protein Degradation", in *Intracellular Protein Catabolism,* Alan R. Liss, Inc., New York, 351, 1985.

Moore, W. V. and Leppert, P., "Role of Aggregated Human Growth Hormone (hGH) in Development of Antibodies to hGH", *J. Clin. Ensocrin. Metabol.,* **51**, 691, 1980.

Nail, S. L. and Gatlin, L. A., "Freeze Drying: Principles and Practice", in *Pharmaceutical Dosage Forms,* Avis, K. E., Lieberman, H. A. and Lachman, L., Eds., Marcel Dekker, Inc., New York, 163-233, 1993.

Nail, S. L., Her, L-M., Proffitt, C. P. B. and Nail, L. L., "An Improved Microscopic Stage for Direct Observation of Freezing and Freeze-Drying", *Pharm. Res.,* **11**(8), 1098-1100, 1994.

Ondrias, M. R., Rousseau, D. L., and Simon, S. R., "Structural Changes at the Heme Induced by Freezing", *Science,* **213**, 657-659, 1981.

Pikal, M. J., "Freeze-Drying of Proteins", In *Peptide and Protein Delivery, Ed.* V. H. L. Lee, Marcel Dekker, Inc., New York, 1996.

References

Pikal, M. J., "Freeze-Drying of Proteins. Part I: Process Design", *BioPharm*, 18-27, September 1990.

Pikal, M. J., "Freeze-Drying of Proteins. Part II: Formulation Selection", *Biopharmaceutics*, **3**, 26-30, 1990.

Pika, M. J., Dellerman, K., and Roy, M. L. and Riggins, R. M., "The Effects of Formulation Variables on the Stability of Freeze-Dried Human Growth Hormone, *Pharm. Res.*, **8**, 427, 1991.

Pikal, M. J. and Shah, S., "Moisture Transfer from Stopper to Product and Resulting Stability Implications", *Develop. Biol. Standard,* **74**, 165-179, 1991.

Powell, M. F., Nguyen, T. and Baloian, L., "Compendium of Excipients for Parenteral Formulations", *PDA Journal of Pharmaceutical Science & Technology,* **52**(5), 238-311, 1998.

Privalov, P. L., "Cold Denaturation of Proteins", *Crit. Rev. Biochem. Mol. Biol.,* **25**, 281-306, 1990.

Rey, L. (Editor) and May, J. C (Editor)., "Freeze-Drying/Lyophilization of Pharmaceutical and Biological Products", Marcel Dekker, Inc., New York, NY, 1999.

Schellman, J. A., "A Simple Model for Solvation in Mixed Solvents. Applications to the Stabilization and Destabilization of Macromolecular Structures", *Biophys. Chem.,* **37**, 121, 1990.

Schlichtkrull, JU., Brange, J., Christiansen, A. H., Hallund, O., Heding, L. G., Jorgensen, K. H., Rasmussen, S. M., Sorensen, E., and Volund, A., "Monocomponent Insulin and its Clinical Implications", *Horm. Metab. Res. (Suppl. Ser.),* **5**, 134, 1974.

Scotchler, J. W. and Robinson, A. B., "Deamidation of Glutaminyl Residues: Dependence on pH, Temperature and Ionic Strength", *Anal. Biochem.,* **59**, 319, 1974.

Shima, K., Sawazaki, N., Tanaka, R., Tarui, S., and Nishikawa, M., "Effect of an Exposure to Chloramine-T on the Immunoreactivity of Glucagon", *Endocrinology,* **96**, 1254, 1975.

Skottner, A., Forsman, A., Skoog, B., Kostyo, J. L., Cameron, C. M., Adamfio, N. A., Thorngren, K. G., and Hagerman, M., "Biological Characterization of Charge Isomers of Human Growth Hormone", *Acta Endocrinol.,* **118**, 14, 1988.

Stadman, E. R., "Metal Ion Catalyzed Oxidation of Proteins: Biochemical Mechanism and Biological Consequences", *Free Radical Biol. Med.,* **9**, 315, 1990.

Swallow, A. J., "Effect of Ionizing Radiation on Proteins, RCO Groups, Peptide Bond Cleavage, Inactivation - SH Oxidation" in *Radiation Chemistry of Organic Compounds,* Swallow, A. J., Ed., Pergamon Press, New York, 211, 1960.

References

Teh, L. C., Murphy, L. J., Huq, N. L., Surus, A. S., Friesen, H. G., Lazarus, L., and Chapman, G. E., "Methionine Oxidation in Human Growth Hormone and Human Chorionic Somatomammotropin", *J. Biol. Chem.,* **262**, 6472, 1987.

Timasheff, S. N. and Arakawa, T., "Mechanism of Protein Precipitation and Stabilization by Co-solvents", *J. Cryst. Growth,* **90**, 39, 1988.

Timasheff, S. N., "Solvent Effects on Protein Stability", *Curr. Opin. Struct. Biol,* **2**, 35, 1992.

van den Berg, L., and Rose, D., "Effect of Freezing on the pH and Composition of Sodium and Potassium Phosphate Solutions: The Reciprocal System KH-2PO4-Na2HPO4-H2O", *Arch. Biochem. Biophys.,* **81**, 319-329, 1959

Wisniewski, R., and Wu, V., "Large-Scale Freezing and Thawing of Biopharmaceutical Products", In *Biotechnology and Biopharmaceutical Manufacturing, Processing, and Preservation*, Avis, K. E., and Wu, V. L., Eds., Interpharm Press, Buffalo Grove, IL, 1996.

Wisniewski, R., "Principles of Large-Scale Cryopreservation of Cells, Microorganisms, Protein Solutions, and Biological Products", In *Cryopreservation: Applications in Pharmaceuticals and Biotechnology,* Edited by Avis, K. E. and Wagner, C. M., 11-179, Interpharm Press, Denver, CO, 1999a.

Wisniewski, R., "Large-Scale Cryopreservation: Process Development for Freezing and Thawing of Large Volume of Cell Suspensions, Protein Solutions, and Biological Products", In *Cryopreservation: Applications in Pharmaceuticals and Biotechnology,* Edited by Avis, K. E. and Wagner, C. M., 181-313, Interpharm Press, Denver, CO, 1999b.

Wright, H. T., "Nonenzymatic Deamidation of Asparaginyl and Glutaminyl Residues in Proteins", *CRC Crit. Rev. Biochem. Mol. Biol.,* **26**, 1, 1991.

Acknowledgements

I wish to thank Dr. Byeong Chang for his valuable comments and insights on this manuscript.

Investigations

Overview

Introduction

The basis for a successful biotechnology business is that the facilities, equipment, systems, processes, and personnel are maintained in a steady state of control. Procedures are established to ensure that the processes are executed consistently. Monitoring of critical process parameters and in-process testing are performed throughout the process. Facility cleanliness and environmental conditions such as temperature, humidity, and differential air pressures are monitored. Final drug product is inspected and assayed. Although firms endeavor to design facilities, equipment, systems, and processes with adequate controls built-in, unexpected or undesirable results may still occur. Generally referred to as "deviations", "exceptions," or "excursions", these occurrences must be investigated for both regulatory and business reasons.

It is extremely important for the firm to conduct thorough and systematic investigations that accurately identify the root cause or causes for the "deviation", "exception," or "excursion". The goal is to determine the root cause or causes so that measures can be taken to eliminate, or at least reduce the chance, for recurrence.

Tools have been developed and are used in the industry to establish a systematic approach to investigations and root cause determination. One such tool is commonly known as the "fishbone analysis". Once the root cause or causes have been determined, corrective and preventive actions are implemented. Corrective/preventive measures must address root cause elimination. The effectiveness of the actions taken needs to be monitored, measured, and evaluated to confirm root cause elimination.

The documentation of investigations and their conclusions is of critical importance. When regulatory agencies perform inspections, they frequently focus on documentation of investigations. Investigators will evaluate the information and draw conclusions regarding the firm, their status of compliance, and whether or not the firm has placed public health at risk.

Overview

Table of Contents

This document contains the following topics:

Excursion Investigation

Objectives

1. Explain what an investigation is.
2. Explain why investigations are performed.
3. Explain why an investigation is documented.
4. Explain when investigations are performed.
5. Describe the objectives of an investigation.
6. Distinguish between an isolated incident and a trend.
7. Describe the points to consider in an investigation.
8. Discuss the areas for evaluation in making a determination of probable root cause.
9. When considering microbial excursions, list at least six areas to investigate.
10. When considering failure of product against specifications, list at least six areas to investigate.
11. Describe how to "narrow the list" in an investigation.
12. Describe the ongoing role of documentation in the investigation.
13. Describe the role of corrective actions.
14. Explain the evaluation of product disposition.
15. Describe the role of preventive actions.
16. Describe how the effectiveness of preventive measures will be determined.
17. Identify items to include in the report and the significance of the report.
18. Demonstrate/explain the use of a Fishbone Diagram during investigations.

Background

What is an Investigation?	An investigation is a systematic inquiry that is conducted to determine the cause and/or conclusion for a failure, discrepancy, or out-of-specification result. Investigations are performed for a number of reasons including, but not limited to:

- When there has been a deviation from a procedure
- A process failure, sterility test failure
- Environmental monitoring data has reached "action-level limits"
- Product complaints
- The actual yield and theoretical yield do not reconcile
- Assay results are out-of-specification
- Stability testing failure

Why Perform investigations?	Performing investigations is required by the Good Manufacturing Practices defined in 21.CFR.211 in a few sections such as (211.192) for: "the failure of any batch or any of its components to meet any of its specifications, whether or not the batch has already been distributed. The investigation shall extend to other batches…that may have been associated with the specific failure…" Investigations, root cause determination, and the implementation of effective corrective and preventive actions makes good business sense, in that rejected batches are costly.

Why Document Investigations?	It is critical to document the investigation because the FDA and other regulatory agencies will tell you, if you did not document it, you did not do it. Efficient documentation of investigations makes sense from a business standpoint, as they provide a history from which other employees can learn and benefit. The knowledge gained can be applied in novel situations or if the situation should reappear (indicating that not all root causes were eliminated).

Background

When Do We Perform Investigations?
The following are examples of situations where an investigation would be deemed necessary:
- In-process testing failures
- Final container QC testing failures
- Theoretical yield failures
- Process failures
- System failures
- Environmental monitoring excursions
- Raw materials which fail release testing
- Stability failures

Performing Investigations

What Are the Objectives?
When a situation has arisen that requires an investigation, it is critical that the objectives of the investigation are clearly defined. The objectives of a typical investigation would be:
- Define the problem
- Identify the probable root cause
- Investigate each probable cause
- Analyze the information and determine root cause or conclusion,
- Evaluate the effect on batches
- Determine actions to correct the problem (if possible) and prevent a recurrence

Performing Investigations

Points to Consider

Investigations usually involve cross-functional teams. It is effective to bring together many different types of expertise. The following provides several different levels for consideration in undertaking an investigation:

- Is this an isolated incident or trend?
- Has anything changed?
- Do any regulatory or compliance commitments exist?
- Are there effects on purity, safety, efficacy, stability, or quality?
- Could other lots have been affected?
- Can timeliness of the investigation and closure be achieved?
- NEVER ASSUME ANYTHING!!! Frequently, there is more than one contributing factor to a failure. Too frequently there is a focus on a single aspect or there is a rush to judgement.

Evaluation of Effect on Product or System

The evaluation of the effect on the product or system is critical. The firm must establish sufficient data or evidence to demonstrate that there was no adverse effect or that the effect is acceptable and the reasons why (scientific rationale). If there is an adverse effect, or potential for adverse effect, the product shall be rejected (withheld from the public).

If the product is involved:

- Is the safety, purity, sterility, efficacy, or stability compromised?
- Are there compliance issues?
- Will this affect customer perceptions?
- Is there a potential for complaints?

If a system is involved:

- Can the system have an effect on the product or the process?
- Are there compliance issues?

If an assay is involved:

- Consider the validity of the results. Was the assay performed properly? Were the instruments performing properly?
- What is the effect of inaccurate or misrepresented data?

In considering these factors, the approach should be to think about the effect as if your child's life was at risk.

Performing Investigations

Determination of Probable Root Cause

The root cause is simply what is actually responsible for causing the problem or incident. It is important not to confuse the root cause with the symptoms. For example, if acquiring the common cold during winter months is considered the problem, then the symptoms would be a runny nose, sneezing, sore throat, and cough. These are symptoms, not the cause. The root cause is a virus. Finding the root cause for many incidents is not as straightforward as this. First, the actual problem must be defined. Using a process flow chart to define the process will help establish the scope of the problem and assist in the root cause analysis. Such an analysis is also greatly facilitated by the use of a Fishbone Diagram. With the use of the Fishbone Diagram, the following areas should be evaluated when trying to determine the root cause:

- Methods (SOPs, CTPs, Run Sheets, etc.)
- Measurement (instruments, calibration)
- Machines (equipment)
- Materials (chemicals, components, supplier)
- Man (personnel, training)
- Environment (HVAC classification, activity)
- Microorganism Identification (habitat, source)

Performing Investigations

Fishbone Diagram

Figure 29.1 shows a sample Fishbone Diagram. The 'bones' coming off the central horizontal line are identified with possible causes for the excursion. Typically a cluster of 'bones' are considered together for a given area (e.g., methods, measurement, machines, etc.). Thus, each of the 'bones' coming off the central horizontal line are divided further to give a more detailed analysis of possible causes for the excursion in the area under consideration.

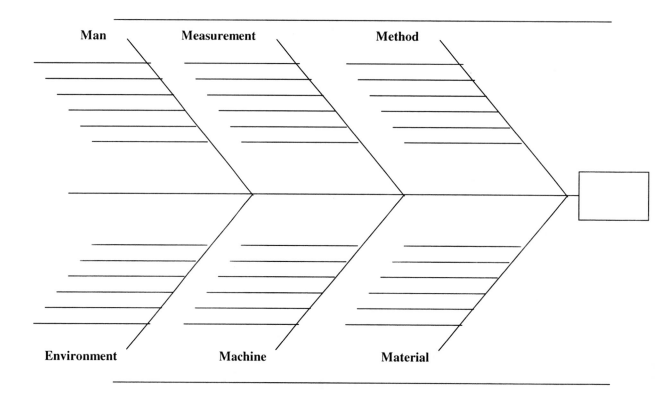

Figure 29.1 Fishbone Diagram

Performing Investigations

Narrow the List

Once a list of probable causes has been developed the task of segregating the possibilities begins. This process is defined here.

- Investigate each probable cause using interviews, audits of areas and activities, record/procedure review, additional testing, or other methods. During this process, it is critical to assign actions, responsibilities, and due dates.
- Document the activities and supply data.
- Separate what is certain from the uncertain.
- Look for positive correlations.
- Document which probable causes may be involved and which can be eliminated from the list. State the reasons and rationale for each of these actions.

Corrective Actions

When the root cause has been identified, it is important to determine corrective actions. Corrective actions are a remedy that may help support the release of a batch or correct the specific discrepancy. This may not always be possible. If not, it is critical to state the reasons why corrective actions were not taken. Corrective actions must be allowed by license.

Product Disposition

When the effect of a "deviation," "exception," "excursion," or "nonconformance" on a product has been evaluated, a conclusion regarding the suitability of the product for human use is made and the disposition of the product determined. Possible dispositions include:

- Reject the lot or batch (usually destroyed)
- Rework (subjecting the product to a step that is not part of the normal process). Must be validated and allowed by license.
- Reprocess (repeating a step in the process). Must be validated and allowed by license.
- Release (only if data substantiates that the lot is safe)
- Research and development (lot or batch is rejected as considered not safe for human use, but may be of value in the research lab, especially since biotechnology products are relatively expensive)

Performing Investigations

Preventive Actions

Preventive actions are implemented to help ensure the same incident does not reoccur. Implementation of preventive actions should be done through the appropriate change control process and may involve such things as:

- Implementing modifications to systems, procedures, equipment, or the environment (think in broad terms)
- Retraining or counseling personnel (rarely a direct cause, issues attributed to "operator error" are usually indicative of another system failure)
- Rewriting procedures

Following the implementation of preventive measures, it is necessary to continue to monitor the situation and/or data. This can involve a long or short term follow-up depending on the problem. Any data or information obtained should be reviewed regularly until there is satisfaction that the preventive measures are effective.

Areas to Investigate

Introduction

The best approach is to develop investigation plans for specific types of failures or "excursions." This approach helps to ensure a thorough, consistent approach to the investigation. One should always look for what has changed, or is different, as this may point to a potential root cause.

Areas to Investigate

Microbial Excursions

Tests are performed to detect the presence or confirm the absence of microorganisms throughout the facility and process. Samples of the air, surfaces, raw materials, and the product itself are taken. Acceptable limits of microorganisms are established for each type of monitoring. The drug product itself is tested to confirm sterility. When these limits are exceeded, the "excursion" must be investigated. Product is considered to be nonconforming in the case of a sterility test failure and is not suitable for distribution.

The following is a list of subjects to consider investigating in the case where limits of microorganisms have been exceeded:

- Employee training records, new employees
- Disinfection and sterilization practices and records
- HEPA filter testing and certification records
- Smoke studies, HVAC trends (differential pressures, temperature, and humidity)
- Gowning methods and practices
- Aseptic practices
- Room cleaning practices and records
- Test instruments, sampling methods and practices
- Identification of the organism and its habitat

Areas to Investigate

Failure of Product Against Specifications

Product specifications are established by license. These cover a broad range of quality attributes including purity, safety and strength. A sampling plan, based on a statistical rationale or regulatory requirements, is established for each assay. Assays are validated. Laboratory personnel are trained and qualified to perform the assays.

So when an assay result fails to meet specifications, an investigation needs to be conducted. This investigation covers both laboratory, and if the assay is deemed valid, manufacturing operations. The following is a list of subjects to consider investigating when product fails to meet specifications:

- Laboratory investigation performed
- Review batch records and QA inspection logs for unusual occurrences deviations, and process parameters
- Review manufacturing procedures and practices
- Review raw materials and components
- Review personnel training records and look for patterns
- Check change control records, critical systems, hardware/software and documentation for any recent changes
- Review equipment logs for cleaning, use, repairs and preventive maintenance

Areas to Investigate

Label Errors: In-house Controls

Packaging and labeling operations are extremely critical in the pharmaceutical/biotechnology industry. There are strict, minimum standards established in the Good Manufacturing Practices. This is because a mislabeled or misbranded product can have the potential to cause great harm to the consumer. Great care must be taken to ensure that labeling is accurate. One mechanism to ensure that no mix-ups occur is to count roll labels before and after use, that is, to "reconcile the label count". If the variation exceeds the tight, preestablished limit, an investigation to determine the source of the error must be performed. The following practices and documents, minimally, should be reviewed:

- Receiving inspection
- Label control issuance
- Label storage
- Line clearance
- Housekeeping
- Area access and security
- Staging
- Packaging operation
- Shift changes and breaks
- Packaging equipment
- Training and use of temporary employees
- Handling of returns
- Destruction of labels
- Review the records of the affected lot and the lots before and after

The Report

Writing the Report

The report is what will stand as the record for the FDA and other regulatory agencies. The importance of this report and its contents cannot be understated. The report may have an impact on future inspections. The following considerations should be foremost when writing a report:

- The report reflects the quality of the investigation.

- It must be well-organized, logical, and have a flow sequence. Clarity is a must.

- The report should include appropriate and sufficient details and information. The report should be complete and as "standalone" as possible.

- The report may be read by the FDA or other regulatory agency and should facilitate the reviewer's evaluation.

- It is critical that data be included to provide background and support any and all conclusions. Be sure that the data really supports the conclusions. Assure the data has been verified for accuracy.

The Report

Items to Include in the Report

It is important to ensure the report contains all pertinent information regarding each aspect of the investigation. The items that should be included in the report are:

- All batch related information, such as affected lot numbers and lot numbers of lots investigated as potentially implicated but determined not to be (reasons should be given for this).
- Description of the process using a flow chart if possible
- Applicable procedures that are viewed as part of the investigation - include document number and revision or issue date
- Equipment used for manufacturing or testing
- A description of how the problem was discovered (routine testing, customer complaint, stability test, etc.)
- How the problem was confirmed (retesting, inspection, etc.),
- The applicable specifications and results - take care to consider the presentation of the data
- Dates of manufacture, testing, retesting, interviews, audits, inspections, etc.
- All probable causes investigated
- The results for each probable cause investigated with a list of all findings
- How the suspect cause was identified and confirmed,
- A discussion as to the extent, impact, significance, and scope of the problem
- Support the evaluation with reference (scientific, compliance, industry publications)
- Remedial or corrective actions taken to save the batch and a justification
- Conclusion and recommendation regarding disposition of the batch, including supportive data
- Preventive actions implemented, dates and data which demonstrates their effectiveness
- All reports must bear the approval signatures of the appropriate reviewers
- Reports must be retrievable
- Failures must be trended

Excursion Investigations

Laboratory

Introduction

This exercise is designed to give students experience and familiarity with the use of investigations during manufacturing of a product. Brainstorming with Fishbone Diagrams, preventive and correction actions, documentation and reports are all included in exercises addressing these investigations.

Materials and Supplies

Fishbone diagrams

Excursion investigations:
1. High endotoxin in water purified by reverse osmosis
2. Molds in the purification suite
3. RCS excursion in Bulk Formulation Room

Activities at a Glance

1. Students will work in groups of 3-4 on excursion investigations.

2. Each group will be given a scenario. The information is incomplete. Students will need to ask questions of the instructor.

3. Each group will brainstorm using Fishbone Diagrams. Focus should be on history of the area, not the small details.

4. Upon completion of the Fishbone Diagrams, an action plan will be developed. Students should determine a root cause (pick one they like) and generate a list of what will be implemented for future prevention.

Mycoplasma Detection

Overview

Introduction   Mycoplasma are a diverse group of parasitic organisms that have until recently been difficult for the average microbiology laboratory to isolate and identify. The mycoplasma cell contains the smallest known genome and least number of genes for a self-replicating cell. Some mycoplasma are obligate parasites of humans. Although some species can be considered normal flora, as a whole, they have a great potential for causing disease. Contamination of human and animal tissue cultures with mycoplasma is a potentially costly and dangerous occurrence in the contemporary laboratory and industrial biomanufacturing facility.

Table of Contents   This document contains the following topics:

Mycoplasma Detection

Objectives

_____

1. Identify the three domains under which all of life can be grouped.
2. Explain in what grouping mycoplasma are placed.
3. Describe the size of mycoplasma.
4. Explain why mycoplasma are a concern to the biotechnology industry.
5. Describe where mycoplasma may be found.
6. Explain the effects of mycoplasma on cell culture.
7. Describe the methods for detection of mycoplasma.
8. Describe the polymerase chain reaction and the use of this technique in mycoplasma detection.
9. Explain how/why PCR can be used for identification of mycoplasma species.

Background

Introduction
Mycoplasma can be introduced into cell cultures or bioreactors via untested tissue culture reagents, uncertified microbiological filters, or by breath aerosols produced by infected humans. Standard microbiological methods, including microscopy and staining, cannot discern the mycoplasma infected tissue culture because the organisms grow directly on the eukaryotic cell membrane. Traditionally, suspected mycoplasma samples are cultured on rich agars [pleuro-pneumonia-like organisms (PPLO) agar for example] which support their complex nutritional requirements and are examined microscopically for the presence of pleiomorphic, cone or fried-egg shaped colonies that appear on the culture media. These organisms divide by binary fission to form coccoid cells. No flagella seem to be present, even though individual cells of some species are capable of movement by gliding. The mycoplasmas are extremely fastidious, require cholesterol and are typically cultured in the absence of oxygen. Until recently, identification facilities have been specialized diagnostic laboratories, universities, and departments of public health. Cost effective, regular testing of cultures and personnel is now possible in a biomanufacturing environment. Genetic methods can detect mycoplasma using the polymerase chain reaction (PCR) as is described in the following pages.

Examples

Example: Validated Sterile Technique
The production and isolation of proteins that are used as pharmaceuticals from eukaryotic cell cultures require that the culture environment be kept free of all contaminants. This is a stated goal of a good manufacturing practice (GMP) document which is submitted to the Food and Drug Administration (FDA). Mycoplasmas are a serious challenge to the most diligent laboratory standard operating procedures (SOP) that support the GMP. One example of the application of this technology is the ability to test the personnel who might contaminate a production facility or the product itself. Inoculation of eukaryotic cell cultures by humans can occur when manipulations such as cell passaging, media transfers, direct microscopy, and rescaling of cultures takes place.

Continued on next page

Examples

Example: Association with Humans

The mycoplasma have been consistently identified with certain human illnesses including pneumonia, postpartum sepsis, arthritis, pelvic inflammatory disease, urethritis, and neurological abnormalities. Recent discussions of the progression of HIV to AIDS include a significant association with particular mycoplasma species. It is equally important to recognize that some mycoplasma species are components of the microbial flora of the mouth and genital tract of certain healthy humans. Using genetic methods, mycoplasma can be demonstrated to be present in healthy humans and cell cultures with seemingly normal characteristics. These identifications are safe to perform since the organisms are not themselves cultivated.

Example: Concepts of Cell Biology and Antibiotic Treatment Strategy

Studying the mycoplasma can reveal evolutionary insights as to the minimal set of genetic instructions for a living cell. The small size of some mycoplasma genomes (600 to 2,000 kilobases) made them an early target for the sequencing of a complete genome of a single organism. The complete sequencing of the genomes of the species *Mycoplasma genitalium* and *Mycoplasma pneumonia* in the mid-1990s by the Celera company revealed that these organisms contained fewer than 500 genes each. Efforts to identify the functioning of these genes may reveal the minimal set of instructions required to produce a self-replicating cell (estimated to be as few as 200 genes).

One popularly held view of the evolutionary origin of the mycoplasma places them as rapidly mutating descendants of certain gram-positive bacteria including *Bacillus, Lactobacillus,* and *Clostridia.* The contemporary view of mycoplasma origins favors the evolutionary loss of genes for the synthesis of peptidoglycan for the cell wall. Mycoplasma infection can be resolved with antibiotics which target their specific prokaryotic elements. Antibiotics of the penicillin family (beta-lactams) will not resolve the mycoplasma infection since these antibiotics generally target the transpeptidase which links peptidoglycan together. Erythromycin and tetracycline are antibiotics currently favored to treat mycoplasma as these target the prokaryotic ribosome. Understanding the diversity of microbial contaminants in the manufacturing environment and how to eliminate them requires studying their basic biology.

Detection Strategy

Overview of the DNA structure

In this exercise, Polymerase Chain Reaction (PCR) technology is used to amplify a sequence of DNA using a pair of oligonucleotide primers that are oriented towards each other and span a segment of DNA known as the "target region." Within the context of a biotechnology course, this module typically requires a review of basic genetics with an emphasis on the particular features of the amplification of DNA from mycoplasma. In this exercise, the target region to be amplified is typically between 100 and 500 nucleotide base pairs. This owes to the fact that the detection of the target DNA as bands on an agarose electrophoresis gel can be resolved within certain limits for the average procedure.

A quick review of the structure of DNA reminds us that when it is double stranded (dsDNA), its two strands are "antiparallel" and thus are oriented in opposing directions. Each strand's "backbone" consists of repeats of sugar-phosphate molecules. Ringed structures termed "bases," because of their nitrogen rich chemical character, occupy the interior space between the strands in a planar arrangement perpendicular to the axis of the DNA backbones. Typically DNA is illustrated with the backbones wound around an axis in a right-handed helix. This form most accurately represents the DNA in eukaryotic chromosomes.

A deoxynucleotide consists of a deoxyribose with a base and phosphate attached appropriately. Knowledge of the atomic nomenclature of the deoxyribose sugar moiety in DNA, facilitates an understanding of the structure and orientation of the molecule. One of four bases [guanine, adenine, cytosine or thymine (abbreviated G, A, T, C)] are attached to a single 2'-deoxyribose at position 1' carbon. The phosphate atoms are attached to the 5' carbon atom The two strands of a double stranded DNA molecule are held together by two hydrogen bonds between the pairs of A-T and three hydrogen bonds between G-C. The two paired strands are termed termed "complementary." The relative attraction of the two strands of DNA in any region is thus dependent upon the relative percentages of A/T and G/C base pairs in a sequence of DNA. All DNA polymerase enzymes (which replicate DNA) known to date amplify by adding nucleotides to the 3' hydroxyl of the deoxyribose moiety of the nucleotide, thus connecting the 5' phosphate with the 3' hydroxyl. Deoxynucleotide triphosphates are provided to the DNA polymerase enzyme during DNA replication. The energy provided by the removal of two phosphates drives the reaction.

Detection Strategy

The PCR Reaction

The PCR reaction requires that DNA amplification proceed from both strands flanking a target region. This is accomplished by using two primers with 3' ends facing each other. The target region is typically between a hundred and a thousand base pairs. The hybridization properties of DNA have demonstrated that relatively short primers (15 to 30 bases) can be used to exactly identify a target region from billions of base pairs. Primer design involves calculating not only the uniqueness of the sequence to be matched but also the melting "temperature" of the primer-template pair. Melting temperatures are dependent on the ratio of A/T and G/C base pairs and influence the actual reaction temperatures at which DNA primers and templates bond and separate (crucial features to PCR reactions). Accurate "hybridization" of DNA primers to a region to be amplified occurs when DNA is heated in a slightly salty aqueous solution which is properly buffered.

The PCR reaction is an adaptation of normal DNA replication that occurs in every cell. The reaction starts in a single tube and occupies a volume of 10 to50 microliters. It typically requires an overlay of mineral oil to prevent evaporation. The reaction components consist of: double stranded DNA template, two primers specific for the target region, a DNA polymerase buffer, magnesium chloride, and the four deoxynucleotides (dGTP, dATP, dTTP, dCTP). The DNA polymerase specific to PCR is isolated from a thermophilic (heat-loving) organism found in a hot spring or deep oceanic thermal vent. The DNA polymerase of the organism *Thermus aquaticus* (Taq pol) was used in the first classical demonstrations of PCR in the mid-1980s and is still popular today. The organism was isolated from a 72 degree Celsius hot spring pool in Yellowstone National Park. The polymerase requires a primer matched to the template by hybridization in order to proceed. DNA "melts" or denatures to become single stranded in solution simply by heating to 90 degrees Celsius. The DNA is cooled in the presence of an excess of primer to between 37 and 55 degrees Celsius. In this way, it is possible to match every template with a primer. The PCR polymerase becomes active at 72 degrees and then replicates the DNA.

Using a polymerase whose activity can be stably modulated with temperature and an excess of primers and free nucleotides, it is possible to run successive cycles of DNA amplification. Theoretically, 30 cycles are required to amplify the DNA in binary fashion from 1 copy to billions.

Detection Strategy

Ribosomal RNA Sequences

Prokaryotic (bacterial and archaeal) ribosomes are isolated directly from bacterial extracts as a 70S entity, which consists of 50S and 30S subunits. The S refers to Svedberg, a unit describing the sedimentation rate in a standardized centrifugation gradient (the larger the number, the larger the RNA). The discrepancies in size are due to the associations of rRNA with proteins that constitute the final structure. Cytoplasmic eukaryotic ribosomes are 80S and dissociate readily to 60S and 40S subunits. Eukaryotic organelles (mitochondria and chloroplasts) contain 70S ribosomes that are indistinguishable from prokaryotic ribosomes and support an endosymbionic theory of acquisition of these organelles.

The 23S RNA contains approximately 2,900 nucleotides and the 16S contains 1,540 nucleotides. Because of its central role in binding messenger RNA and charged transfer RNAs to produce proteins from amino acids and accomplish translation, certain distinct parts of the ribosome function the same in all species. The exact nucleotide sequences of the ribosome genes differ between the life's three domains: within the groups Bacteria and Archaea, there appears to be unique permutations of the 16S and 23S genes in each species examined. The same is true for the 25 to 28S, 18S and 5S rRNA of eukaryotes.

The use of ribosome nucleotide sequences to distinguish the taxonomy of the three domains of life, the Eukarya, Bacteria, and Archaea, is now largely credited to the pioneering work Carl Woese performed in the early 1970s. Woese's RNA sequencing of rRNA genes from many organisms, and more recently the complete DNA sequencing of many microorganisms, has revealed the taxonomic value of the intragene (spacer) region between the 16S and 23S rRNA genes. It is this spacer region that will be utilized to detect and identify mycoplasma species.

Detection Strategy

Mycoplasma Detection

In the case of the American Type Culture Collection (ATCC) mycoplasma detection, a spacer region of the DNA between the large and small RNA subunit genes is used as the target for determining differences between bacterial species. The spacer region was not subject to the strict evolutionary constraints of the intact ribosome and was found to be of different sizes in various mycoplasma species. Using several DNA oligonucleotide primers in a two stage PCR reaction, it is possible to identify as few as two dozen contaminant mycoplasma cells and classify them as any one of 20 species. The research and production applications of this technology can be applied to detecting mycoplasma in eukaryotic cell supernatants, cell monolayers, and cell suspensions. In addition, for the purpose of demonstration, it is also possible to extract DNA from the scrapings of cheek cell extracts that may potentially harbor Mycoplasma. Performing the PCR analysis on parallel sets of samples from both humans and cell cultures underscores the fact that humans are often the vectors for contamination in industrial settings. This technology serves as an excellent introduction to the power and sensitivity of genetic testing, using polymerase chain reaction (PCR) methods. In the near future, new technologies such as the microarray and DNA on silicon chips will vastly improve the sensitivity and specificity of these testing methods. However, the PCR method for mycoplasma identification is likely to be used for some time to come due to its cost effectiveness, simplicity, and malleability.

Mycoplasma Detection

Laboratory

Introduction *Mycoplasma* testing will be performed on the cell cultures students have been carrying throughout the semester. Several different methods are available for detecting the presence of *Mycoplasma*. Students will use a PCR based method to analyze their cultures.

Equipment

LAF hood
Power supplies
Microfuge
Gel boxes
Thermal cycler
UV transilluminator
Micropipettors
Polaroid camera
Ice buckets
Automatic pipettors

Materials and Supplies

Mycoplasma Detection Kit: ATCC #90-1001K
TAQ polymerase
dNTPs
Buffer
Cell culture samples
Cell scrapers (sterile)
Microfuge tubes: 1.5 ml and 0.5 ml for the thermal cycler
Sterile 15 ml conical tubes
Pipette tips
Agarose
10X TBE
DNA markers
Ethidium bromide
Polaroid film

Laboratory

Activities at a Glance

1. Distribute to each student 2 microfuge tubes containing Chelex (200ul/student). Typically the Chelex resin (looks like beads) occupies about half the volume of the solution.

2. Samples from a student's cell culture from the biotechnology lab and from the student's mouth are acquired. A separate sterile pipette is required for each sample. Only a fractional amount of material is required from a scraping of the inside of the mouth for example. Cell cultures can be aspirated and then scraped. A volume of material (roughly 50 ul) is mixed with the Chelex resin.

3. A cap is placed on the microfuge tube and the tubes are boiled for 10 minutes in a floating rack.

4. The samples are centrifuged for 2 minutes at high speed and 5uL of supernatant of each sample is extracted into a PCR tube.

5. The PCR reactions are then prepared according to the Mycoplasma Test Kit.

6. Two sequential PCR reactions are required to obtain results (allow time).

7. The DNA is loaded onto 2% agarose DNA gels.

8. After electrophoresis, the DNA is visualized and recorded (photographed).

9. Interpretation with students will reveal the possible presence of mycoplasma. Students should be reminded that these results are of no diagnostic value and are strictly for demonstration purposes.

Enzyme-Linked-Immunosorbent-Assay

Overview

Introduction

With the advancement of science in the twentieth century, doctors and scientists throughout the world saw the development of the Enzyme-Linked Immunosorbent-Assay known as ELISA. ELISA is a bioanalytical technique used in biotechnology to detect, discriminate, quantitate or identify trace amounts of impurities or analytes of interest within many matrices. The ELISA technique employs two main formats:

- Competitive or "inhibition" format
- Noncompetitive or "double antibody sandwich" format. The sandwich format can be either direct or in-direct.

Table of Contents

This document contains the following topics:

Enzyme-Linked-Immunosorbent-Assay

Objectives

1. Explain the use of the ELISA technique.
2. Describe the two main formats for the ELISA.
3. Describe the requirements for the ELISA technique.
4. Describe the structure of an antibody.
5. Distinguish between monoclonal and polyclonal antibodies.
6. Explain how polyclonal antibodies are produced.
7. Explain the production of monoclonal antibodies.
8. Define the terms epitope and paratope.
9. Explain monoclonal antibody specificity.
10. Describe the competitive ELISA or "inhibition assay."
11. Describe the role of primary antibody, secondary antibody, substrate, and the blocking step in this assay.
12. Explain how color development occurs in the ELISA.
13. Give examples of common substrates used.
14. Describe how a standard curve is generated and used.
15. Discuss the limitations of the competitive ELISA.
16. Describe the noncompetitive or "sandwich" assay.
17. Describe the role of primary antibody, secondary antibody, substrate, and the blocking step in this assay.
18. Explain the differences between the direct and indirect noncompetitive ELISA.
19. Describe the use of a standard curve for the noncompetitive ELISA.
20. Demonstrate use of the multichannel pipettor.
21. Demonstrate ability to set up an ELISA.
22. Demonstrate use of the ELISA plate reader.
23. Demonstrate ability to generate a standard curve.
24. Demonstrate ability to perform data analysis and interpret results.

Background

Techniques   The underlying science of the ELISA technique is based on chemistry, immunology, and the fact that specific antibodies can be produced against a desired protein. ELISA testing can be used to detect antibodies and/or analytes (i.e., proteins) in a sample, depending on what the scientist is trying to capture. This testing technique is facilitated by availability of the following:

- A large sample plate (microtiter plates)
- The use of multichannel pipettes
- Test volumes that range from 50 to 100 microliters in size
- Specific binding and low cross-reactivity (nonspecific binding)

The ELISA testing technique is usually performed in microtiter plates where analytes, enzymes, antibodies, and aberrant proteins are non-specifically adsorbed to the plastic through noncovalent bonding. Other types of support used in these procedures are polystyrene beads (of different sizes) and nitrocellulose membranes. In this chapter we will only be looking at assays that are used to detect proteins in microtiter plates. The ELISA technique uses a primary (or capture) antibody, a secondary (detector) antibody that is labeled, a substrate which produces a color change, and a wash buffer to separate bound from unbound material. A comparative reading of colored product will allow us to generate a quantitative value when the unknown's data is interpolated against a curve of known values.

Basic Immunology

Introduction An antibody is a protein in a group known as immunoglobulins. Antibodies have the ability to bind specifically to a target molecule or antigen. There are different classes of antibodies (IgG, IgM, IgD, and IgE) which are differentiated by the number of Y-shaped basic subunits. Each subunit is comprised of two heavy chains and two light chains. A disulfide bond covalently links the heavy and light chains. Figure 31.1 is a diagram of an immunoglobulin G (IgG) molecule which has one Y-shaped subunit:

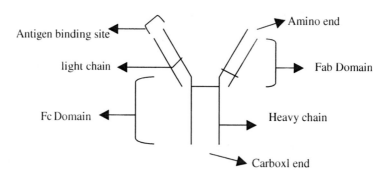

Figure 31.1: Antibody Structure

Each Y-shaped subunit consists of four polypeptide (a polymer of amino acids) chains, two light chains, and two heavy chains. Disulfide bonds hold the light and heavy chains together. The antigen binding sites are at the amino ends and have a positive charge. The other end is known as the carboxyl end and has a negative charge. The area where the heavy chains bend is known as the hinge region. In the Fab domain, the light and heavy chains are split into two regions. The top half is the variable region and the lower half is known as the constant region. This constant region extends down to the carboxyl end in the heavy chain. The variable region is the area that makes one antibody different from another. The antibodies are produced during an the immune response by B lymphocytes, upon stimulation from a foreign antigen. The antibodies can be of two types: monoclonal or polyclonal. The antigen binds to the antibody at the antigenic binding site through noncovalent bonding such as hydrogen bonding and Van der Waals forces.

Monoclonal and Polyclonal Antibodies

Key Features
The two key features of a monoclonal antibody are:
- Highly specific
- Indefinite supply of identical population can be produced

The three key features of a polyclonal antibody are:
- Multipopulation
- Strong reactivity
- Easy to produce

A feature shared by both polyclonal and monoclonal antibodies is:
- Can be labeled with many different substances

Monoclonal Antibodies

Specificity
The monoclonal antibody is highly specific (high affinity) to a particular epitope (antigenic determinant) because it is produced within a single population, thus giving the antibody a single antigenic specificity. The antigenic determinant is the portion of the antigen (i.e, protein) to which the antibody binds. The paratope is the portion of the antibody that is also known as the antigen binding site. With this high specificity there is a low chance for crossreactivity with other proteins in the sample that have similar epitopes thus leading to low nonspecific binding. The two problems with high specificity are that monoclonal antibodies have a weaker overall reactivity and are also more difficult to produce. The weaker reactivity comes from the fact that one epitope binds to one paratope, and therefore the overall number of binding sites is smaller.

Indefinite Supply
Identical antibodies are difficult and costly to produce. However, a large indefinite supply of this specific population can be generated through tissue culture techniques and the production of hybridomas. An immune response is generated in an animal to a particular antigen. Individual B cells from the animal are used to form hybridomas which provide an unlimited supply of a single antibody.

Polyclonal Antibodies

Multi-Population

A polyclonal antibody is produced in the classic model when an animal is injected with an antigen resulting in an immune response. This response produces antibodies with multiple paratopes and different subclasses. These antibodies will have the capacity to make both low and high affinity contacts to a particular antigen. The one problem with the use of these antibodies is that because they are a mixed population, they can have a high level of crossreactivity. This is a result of the numerous epitopes to which they can bind.

Strong Reactivity

A distinctive feature of polyclonal antibodies is their strong reactivity. This is due to the fact that the antibodies will bind to many sites (epitopes) on the antigen making the binding very strong.

Ease of Production

Polyclonal antibodies are easy to produce and are not as costly as the monoclonal. However, reproduction of identical populations is not possible. Each time an antigen is injected into an animal, the immune response will be different. The ease of production is due to the fact that you only have to inject an animal, allow the animal time to generate the immune response, bleed the animal at different time intervals to maximize its dose effect, and purify the antiserum. This is an easier and less expensive method for making antibodies compared to the production of hybridomas.

Labeling

Both monoclonal and polyclonal antibodies can be labeled with many different kinds of compounds for use in the ELISA. Enzymes can be conjugated to the antibody through a variety of techniques. When the enzyme encounters its substrate (added in the detection steps of the technique), a colorimetric reaction occurs and can be quantitated. Examples of some of the molecules used in these conjugates are alkaline phophatase, horseradish peroxidase, extravidin peroxidase, urease, and biotin. Radioisotopes and fluorometric, and chemiluminescent labels can also be attached to the antibody. Examples of these are Flourescein, I^{125}, Eu^{3+}, and acridinium esters.

Competitive ELISA

Key Features

The key elements of the Competitive ELISA technique are:
- The primary antibody (capture antibody)
- The secondary antibody (detection antibody)
- The substrate
- The blocking step

Primary Antibody

The primary antibody in this assay type can be either polyclonal or monoclonal. The antibody used must be against the analyte (protein) that is being targeted. If the antibody is omitted, then there will be no binding and no color development. During assay development, the concentration of the antibody will need to be optimized in the overall matrix. In this assay, the primary antibody is the limiting reagent with a restrictive number of binding sites available for the analytes. This causes competition to occur between the analyte adsorbed to the plate and the free analyte within the sample.

Secondary Antibody

The secondary antibody is the antibody that has the label attached to it and will be involved in providing the light or color source, depending on what type of label is being used. The labels can be of different types and this must also be optimized upon assay development within the matrix of the assay. If secondary antibody is omitted, then no color development will occur since the label will not be part of the complex.

Substrate

The substrate is needed for detection. An enzyme reaction may occur producing a color change or light may be emitted. This depends on the type of assay and labels being used, and may involve such things as chemical oxidation, pH changes, etc. Examples of substrates are: para-nitrophenyl phosphate (pnpp), hydrogen peroxide (H_2O_2), and urea. Examples of dyes that are used to generate the color are pnpp, OPD, and bromcresol. It must be noted that a buffer must be selected that would work with the type of substrate being used. Examples of these are diethanolamine, citrate phosphate, and normal saline.

Continued on next page

Competitive ELISA

Blocking Step   The blocking step occurs after the adsorption of either antibody or analyte to the solid matrix (microtiter plate). This is done with a blocking buffer that contains blocking agents like gelatin or bovine serum albumin (BSA). If a blocking buffer is not used, then you would see very high background caused by nonspecific binding.

Method   The method for the ELISA technique is summarized below.

- In the competitive ELISA or "inhibition" assay, antigen is adsorbed to the wells of the microtiter plate. This is known as coating the plate. After this step the plate is treated with a blocking solution that will block any nonspecific areas of the plate not taken up by the antigen.

- The next step would be to add the controls, sample to be tested, standards (which includes known values to make up the standard curve) and a primary antibody. This step is allowed to proceed to equilibrium. Competition for the antibody occurs between the antigen adsorbed to the plate and the antigen in the standard, control, and samples. The antibody is called the limiting reagent, because it is in a lower concentration than the antigen. Competition for the limited amounts of available binding sites takes place.

- The plate is washed to remove any unbound antigen and free antigen-antibody complexes. An enzyme labeled secondary (detection) antibody is then added to the complex and allowed to bind. The plate is again washed to remove any unbound labeled secondary antibody.

Continued on next page

Competitive ELISA

Method

- Substrate is now added, resulting in color development. The amount of color is directly proportional to the amount of antibody that has bound to the antigen coated well and is inversely proportional to the amount of analyte (protein) in the samples.

- In this assay a curve with known amounts of analyte would be generated. The curve in this example will be linear. (There are also other types of curves: 4-parameter, log, power-fit, etc.) From this curve the data points from all the unknowns and controls will be plotted and data values will be interpolated. In this way we can quantitate a numerical amount of the analyte in a given sample. Figure 31.2 shows an example of this type of curve.

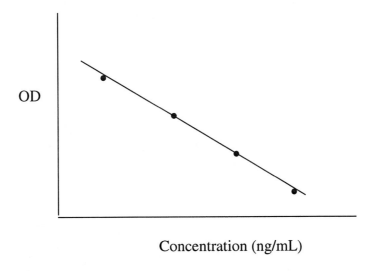

Figure 31.2: Standard Curve for Competitive ELISA

Limitations

The competitive assay is not the format of choice due to its many limitations. This type of assay usually has limited sensitivity, a limited working range, slow reaction kinetics, and increased imprecision.

Noncompetitive ELISA

Key Features
The key elements of the noncompetitive ELISA technique are:
- The primary antibody (capture antibody)
- The secondary antibody (detection antibody)
- The substrate
- The blocking step

Primary Antibody
The primary antibody in this assay type can be either polyclonal or monoclonal. The antibody should be against the analyte (protein) that is being targeted. This antibody is the capture antibody that will be bound to the surface of the microtiter plate. If the antibody is omitted then there will be no binding and no color development. During assay development, the concentration of the antibody will need to be optimized in the overall matrix.

Secondary Antibody
The secondary antibody is also against the analyte. In this type of non-competitive assay, this antibody is needed because there is no labeled antibody made that can bind to the analyte species directly. Since this is true, the secondary antibody acts like a bridge, allowing the labeled antibody to bind.

Labeled (Detection) Antibody
The detection antibody recognizes and binds to the secondary antibody. The detection antibody is the antibody that has the label attached to it and is involved in producing the light or color, depending on the type of label being used. The labels can be of different types and this must also be optimized upon assay development within the matrix of the assay. If this is not added, then color development will not occur since the label will not be in the complex.

Continued on next page

Noncompetitive ELISA

Substrate

The substrate is needed with the labeled detection antibody so that a color change occurs or light gets emitted. This can be done through chemical oxidation, pH changes, etc. Examples of substrates are: para-nitrophenyl phosphate (pnpp), hydrogen peroxide, and urea. Examples of dyes that are used with these to generate the color are pnpp, OPD, and bromcresol. It must be noted that a buffer must be selected that will work with the substrate being used. Examples of these are diethanolamine, citrate phosphate, and normal saline.

Blocking Step

The blocking step occurs after the adsorption of either antibody or analyte to the solid matrix (microtiter plate). This is done with a blocking buffer that contains blocking agents like gelatin or bovine serum albumin (BSA). If a blocking buffer is not used then you would see very high background caused by nonspecific binding.

Continued on next page

Noncompetitive ELISA

Method

There are two types of non-competitive ELISA assays: the direct and the indirect. These differ slightly in the procedure. The differences are given below.

- The noncompetitive ELISA is also referred to as the two antibody "sandwich" assay. A capture (primary) antibody is adsorbed to the wells of the microtiter plate. After this step, the wells are washed to remove any excess unbound material.
- The plate now needs to be blocked with a blocking reagent buffer. After this point there are differences between the direct and indirect methods.

Direct:

- Add the controls, the sample, and the standards (which are your known values that make up the curve). These are allowed to incubate and react with the primary antibody bound to the well. When the samples, controls, and standards are diluted down to workable ranges, the buffer used in the dilution step must be made of reagents that helps prevent nonspecific binding.
- The plate is washed to remove any unbound antigen. A secondary antibody (detection antibody) is added to the plate and allowed to incubate with the previous complex. After binding, this complex is again washed to clean out any unbound conjugate.
- Subsequent addition of a substrate results in color development, which is directly proportional to the amount of the protein (analyte) in the sample. In this noncompetitive assay, all the steps are brought to equilibrium before washing separates any unbound material.

Indirect:

- Add the controls, the sample, and the standard (which are your known values that make up the curve). These are allowed to incubate with the primary antibody.
- The plate is washed to remove any unbound antigen and a secondary antibody (which is the anti-species to the protein being tested) is added and allowed to incubate and come to equilibrium. The difference between this indirect method and the direct method is that this secondary antibody is not labeled in the indirect. The plate is now washed again with a wash buffer to remove excess secondary antibody.
- After the wash step, a labeled conjugated antibody (which is an anti-species to the secondary antibody) is added and allowed to incubate and reach equilibrium. This is now followed with the wash buffer.
- The next step is to add the substrate to start the reaction, and thus color development. The density of color development is directly proportional to the amount of analyte in the sample. A numerical amount of protein in the sample can now be generated based on the standard curve.

Continued on next page

Noncompetitive ELISA

Method   The noncompetitive method is the preferred choice for doing ELISA testing. The advantages are that it has greater sensitivity, greater precision, and a greater working range than the competitive method. With both direct and indirect noncompetitive assays there is a relationship between the signal (OD) generated and the amount of analyte in the samples. This can be seen in Figure 31.3.

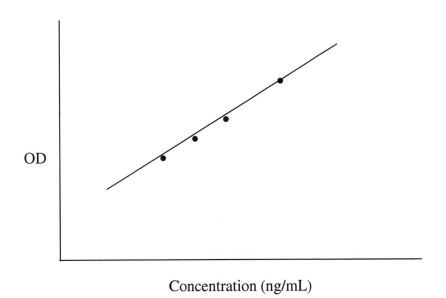

Figure 31.3: Standard Curve for Noncompetitive ELISA

ELISA

Laboratory

Introduction   This laboratory exercise will provide students the opportunity to learn the ELISA technique and gain experience in the operation and applications of the ELISA plate reader.

Equipment   Plate washer
Plate reader
Multichannel pipettors

Materials and Supplies   96 well flat bottom plates
Plate sealer
Microfuge tubes for dilutions
Buffer and reagents for ELISA
Pipet tips and trays

Activities at a Glance   A detailed protocol for the ELISA procedure will be given to each student.

Protocol will be followed as written.

Radial Immunodiffusion

Overview

Introduction   Radial Immunodiffusion (RID) is based on antigen-antibody interactions. While antibodies (Ab) are glycoproteins in serum and tissue fluid which are produced by plasma cells (developed from B lymphocytes), antigens (Ag) are foreign molecules which stimulate the production of antibodies and bind to them.

Antigen-antibody interaction occurs both *in vivo* and *in vitro*, and is followed by a physical change that is easily observable and measurable. This is demonstrated by allowing antigens and antibodies to diffuse towards each other in agar gel. A precipitate forms at points of equivalent proportions of both Ag and Ab.

Table of Contents   This document contains the following topics:

Radial Immunodiffusion

Objectives

1. Explain the difference between an antibody and an antigen.
2. Discuss the specificity of antigen-antibody interactions.
3. Discuss the use of Radial Immunodiffusion (RID).
4. Give a brief overview of the RID technique.
5. Explain the materials needed to perform RID.
6. Explain what an RID plate is and what the components include.
7. Explain the use of calibrators.
8. Explain the formation of a precipitin ring.
9. Demonstrate ability to perform the RID.
10. Demonstrate use of the jeweler's eyepiece for reading results.
11. Demonstrate use of the Microsoft Excel spreadsheet to calculate results.
12. Demonstrate ability to generate a graph using the data from the standards.
13. Demonstrate ability to calculate the correlation coefficient, the slope, and the y-intercept.
14. Demonstrate ability to calculate sample concentration.
15. Demonstrate ability to troubleshoot and investigate possible causes of unanticipated results.

Background

Introduction   Radial Immunodiffusion is used in clinical immunology for the detection and quantitation of immunoglobulins and other serum components. For example, in measuring albumin, antibody to albumin (produced by injecting human albumin into another species) would be mixed in agar, which would then be poured onto a suitable surface for hardening. Circular wells would then be cut into the agar and samples containing known and unknown concentrations of albumin would be pipetted into the wells. This will result in the formation of visible circles of precipitate around the wells. This is the antigen-antibody complex. The area within the precipitin ring, measured as ring diameter squared, is proportional to the antigen concentration. Since a linear relationship exists between antigen concentration and square of the ring diameter, a standard curve can be constructed using samples with known antigen concentrations. This curve is then used to determine antigen concentrations in test samples.

Reagent and Material Requirements

Introduction   Materials are commercially available from The Binding Site, PO Box 4073, Birmingham, B29 6AT, England.

Key Features   RID kits consist of the following:
- RID plates, which contain a monospecific antibody in agarose gel
- Calibrators containing high, medium, and low concentrations of the antigen
- A diluent (for example, sheep albumin) for sample preparation
- A control with the expected antigen concentration labeled on the vial

Additional materials required but not provided in the kit include:
- Sample tubes
- Vortex for mixing sample and diluent
- Pipettes for sample dilution and micropipettes for sample application
- Jeweler's eyepiece to measure precipitin rings

Some of these are described in more detail below.

RID Plates   RID plates should be stored at 2-8 degrees Celsius. Because of preservatives present in the agarose gel, plates should be disposed of in properly labeled biohazard containers.

Calibrators   Calibrators are also stored at 2-8 degrees Celsius. Ring diameters of precipitin rings of the calibrators are later used to construct the standard curve. Calibrators should also be disposed of as hazardous waste.

Diluent   The diluent should only be used for sample and control preparation. Calibrators usually come prediluted in the kit.

Continued on next page

Reagent and Material Requirements

Controls
The control provided in the kit can be substituted with another control as long as the expected concentration of the antigen in the substituted material is known.

Pipettes
Pipettes and micropipettes should be calibrated prior to use. Micropipettes should be able to accurately deliver as small as 5 microliters.

Eyepiece
The jeweler's eyepiece has a built-in scale for accurate measurement of the precipitin ring diameter to 0.1 mm.

Methodology

Procedure
1. Allow the plate to come to room temperature in its unopened pouch.

2. Remove the plate from the pouch and allow it to air dry at room temperature for 5-10 minutes.

3. Dilute the sample to be tested to a value that is between the highest and lowest standard on the curve.
   For example, if the lowest standard = 500mg/L and the highest standard = 5000mg/L, a sample with 39,959 mg/L albumin can be diluted 1/13 (100uL of sample + 1200uL of diluent) to yield 3074mg/L.

4. When adding the calibrators (standards) and samples to the wells, make sure there are no air bubbles in the pipette tips.
   Lightly touch the tip onto the bottom of the well and dispense the solution without touching or damaging the gel. Make sure all of the solution is dispensed.
   To wells 1 and 2 add 5 uL of the 5000mg/L standard.
   To wells 3 and 4 add 5 uL of the 3000mg/L standard.
   To wells 5 and 6 add 5 uL of the 500mg/L standard.
   To wells 7 and 8 add 5 uL of the diluted sample.

5. Snap on the plate lid when the solutions have diffused into the gel.

6. Incubate plate at room temperature, preferably in a moisture chamber, for a minimum of 18 hours.

7. After incubation is complete, measure the diameter of each ring both vertically and horizontally using the jeweler's eyepiece, which can be held against the bottom of the plate. Holding the plate up to a light source will make the reading process easier.

Calculation of Results

Method 1　　　The fastest and easiest approach is to use a Microsoft Excel spreadsheet or equivalent.

Method 2　　　An alternate method would be to use a calculator and/or a graph paper:
- Construct a line by linear regression using the average of each standard ring diameter squared.
- Plot the concentration of the standard on the x axis and the diameter squared on the y axis.
- Calculate the correlation coefficient, the slope, and the y-intercept.
- Calculate sample concentration using the following formula:

Concentration =[(Diameter squared - y intercept) / (slope)] * dilution factor

Assay Criteria
- Duplicate ring diameter readings should be within 20% of each other.
- Horizontal vs. vertical ring diameters should be within 10% of each other.

Radial Immunodiffusion

Laboratory

Introduction A variety of immunoassays are utilized in the analysis of therapeutic proteins. Students will gain experience in performing Radial Immunodiffusion, as well as learn the principles of the technique. Each student will be given an unknown sample and will determine its concentration using RID. Students will utilize Microsoft Excel for their data analysis as well as generate their own calibration curve.

Equipment Micropipettors
Vortex
Jeweler's eyepiece

Materials and Supplies RID Kit from The Binding Site, England
Sample tubes
Pipettes
Pipette tips
Unknowns

Activities at a Glance
1. Each student will perform the RID following the manufacturer's protocol.
2. Each student will be given an unknown for determination of its concentration.
3. Following incubation, each student will measure the diameter of the rings using the jeweler's eyepiece.
4. Each student will perform data analysis with an Excel spreadsheet.

SDS-Polyacrylamide Gel Electrophoresis

Overview

Introduction

The inherent complexity of proteins has allowed scientists the opportunity to invent many methods for the separation of proteins. These may involve exploiting certain native feature of the proteins such as its surface charge, size, hydrophobicity/hydrophilicity, or their ability to associate with other proteins. Classically, polyacrylamide gel electrophoresis (PAGE) is a method which reliably separates proteins by molecular weight. The applications of PAGE as a first separation also allow one to prepare proteins for amino acid sequencing or Western blotting. It is also the method used as the first dimension in 2-dimensional gel electrophoresis.

Table of Contents

This document contains the following topics:

SDS-Polyacrylamide Gel Electrophoresis

Objectives

1. Explain the concept of electrophoresis.
2. Describe the applications of SDS-PAGE.
3. Describe the general structure of a protein.
4. Define isoelectric point.
5. Explain the function/use of the following reagents in this procedure:
    SDS
    Coomassie blue
    Mark 12 standards
    Acetic acid
    PBS
    2-Mercaptoethanol or dithiothreitol
    Glycine
    Methanol
    Sample buffer
    Acrylamide
    bis-Acrylamide
6. Explain discontinuous electrophoresis.
7. Distinguish between a stacking gel and a separating gel.
8. Distinguish between a linear gel and a gradient gel.
9. Describe the methods of detection of proteins used with SDS-PAGE.
10. Perform buffer/reagent preparations.
11. Demonstrate use of spectrophotometer for protein concentration determinations.
12. Perform assembly of Novex electrophoresis apparatus.
13. Perform loading of a gel.
14. Demonstrate use of power supplies.
15. Perform staining/destaining of gel.
16. Demonstrate ability to make molecular weight determinations of unknown proteins.

Fundamentals of SDS-PAGE

Polyacrylamide Gels

The gel is a polymer, which acts as a porous mesh to accomplish the separation of protein molecules in an electric field. The polymer starts as a liquid solution of polyacrylamide (a dangerous neurotoxin). The gel is cast into a set of matched glass plates separated by spacers several millimeters thick. The polyacrylamide is poured into this mold which roughly resembles the shape of a cereal box. A gel "comb" is placed in the solution before it hardens and its "teeth" become the "wells" or indentations where samples are loaded. Specialty suppliers exist for all the accessories one might need to cast gels, though this document specifies a precast gel supplier which is commonly used in industry. Precast gels have the advantage of providing standardization and consistency.

Electrophoresis Conditions

Most commonly, proteins are run on Tris-glycine gels in running buffer containing a detergent, sodium dodecyl sulfate (SDS). Tris is a common, biologically compatible buffering molecule. Classically, the gel consists of two parts: a stacking gel that is cast directly on top of a running gel. The two parts of the gel differ in buffer and acrylamide concentration. The stacking gel is designed to focus all the proteins of the samples in the wells of the gel (with samples typically occupying a few millimeters) into a sharp band (occupying a fraction of a millimeter). When the stacked sample encounters the running gel, it separates the proteins (over a distance of several to tens of centimeters). This procedure is called SDS-PAGE, and was successfully described by Laemmli (Nature, 227, pg 680-685, 1970). The presence of SDS causes denaturing conditions, under which the tertiary structures of the proteins are destroyed. Complete denaturation is accomplished by exposing the protein to reducing conditions. These are achieved by adding mercaptoethanol or dithiothreitol (DTT) to the protein sample buffer prior to loading the gel. The reducing conditions cause cleavage of disulfide bonds and breakup of multimeric protein complexes.

Continued on next page

Fundamentals of SDS-PAGE

Separation of Proteins

Once protein samples are loaded onto a gel, and electric current is applied, proteins are separated by molecular weight and migrate in the electric field from the cathode (-) to anode (+). The proteins migrating in the gel have a uniform random coil shape and constant charge to mass ratio (1.4g SDS/g protein). Low molecular weight proteins migrate in the gel front and reach the bottom of the gel first, whereas higher molecular weight proteins trail behind.

Gels consisting of a polyacrylamide matrix are generally applied to the task of separating proteins that range in size from several kilodaltons to hundreds of kilodaltons. Lower molecular weight proteins can generally be separated at finer resolution than larger molecular weight proteins with SDS-PAGE. Polyacrylamide concentrations in the gel can be varied to preferentially resolve proteins in a specific molecular weight range to a resolution of several kilodaltons.

Visualization of Proteins

When the gel run is finished, individual protein bands can be visualized by staining with coomassie blue or by silver staining. Alternatively, the proteins can be transferred to membranes by Western blotting. If the protein samples were prelabeled with radioactivity such as ^{35}S, acrylamide gels are further processed by fixation in a methanol/acetic acid containing buffer and dried in a gel dryer or a drying cassette. Radioactive protein bands are visible after exposure to autoradiographic (X-ray type) film.

Applications

Examples

Polyacylamide gel electrophoresis is used in a wide array of applications:

- **Protein Chemistry**
  A very common use for PAGE is in protein chemistry, where it can be used to determine the quality of protein preparations after purification. Fractions of protein samples taken off a chromatography column can be placed side by side in a gel to determine if the chromatography step was successful.

- **Cell Extracts**
  Cell extracts can also be analyzed by SDS-PAGE for the presence or absence of certain protein complexes.

- **Immunoprecipitation**
  A method for enriching a sample prior to gel electrophoresis is immunoprecipitation whereby antibodies specific to a protein of interest are used in conjunction with protein A and precipitated by centrifugation. This yields information about what proteins are bound to the antibody complex under certain conditions, such as when a signal is being transduced by changes in protein complexes in the cytoplasm.

- **Isoelectric Focusing**
  Isoelectric focusing (IEF) separates proteins in an electric field on the basis of their isoelectric points (pI). The pI is the point in a pH gradient of an electrophoretic gel where the external amino acid charges of a protein have no net charge and thus migration of the protein ceases.

- **Two-dimensional Gel Electrophoresis**
  IEF is also used as the first dimension in a two dimensional gel (2-D gel). A gel slice containing a single lane of a IEF is laid at the origin of a second SDS-PAGE gel. The resulting separation by size and charge yields spots which represent unique proteins at positions along two axis. Efforts to catalog the reproducible location of these proteins on 2-D gels into databases is at the heart of some current efforts in proteomics. Such efforts, when applied to the inner workings of the cell, can yield information about the presence or absence of a protein, which supercedes gene activity and RNA expression studies.

Methodology

Introduction A major advantage to using contemporary integrated electrophoresis systems is that several types of analysis can be performed using interchangeable components and standard equipment. One high quality system of this type is available from Invitrogen. Standardized precast gels, which vary by buffer system, thickness, acrylamide percentage, and/or gradient are available. Many different ways of analysis are possible. The objective of this example of SDS-PAGE is to generate a gel, which can either be directly stained using coomassie blue or placed into the electrophoretic transfer apparatus for Western blotting. A standard Tris-glycine buffered gel is used to resolve the proteins in this example.

Sample Preparation Prior to protein electrophoresis protein samples are prepared. For denaturing conditions, protein samples, such as purified proteins or cell extracts, are mixed with 2X SDS sample buffer and boiled in a heat block for 2-3 minutes. If reducing conditions are required, the sample buffer should contain a 1:20 dilution of mercaptoethanol.

Equipment Set-up and Gel Run A summary of the steps required to perform SDS-PAGE is given below:

- Precast gels are removed from their protective pouch and inserted in the gel apparatus.
- The gel box is assembled according to manufacturer's instructions.
- Buffer chambers are filled with the appropriate amount of running buffer. Confirm that the chambers are sealed tight, and no buffer leaks out of the upper chamber.
- Once the gel apparatus is fully assembled, the comb is pulled out of the gel cassette and the wells are rinsed with running buffer for removal of any excess acrylamide and air bubbles.
- Protein samples are loaded with a micropipettor. At least one well should be loaded with a prestained molecular weight marker.
- The lid is placed on the buffer core and the electrode wires are connected to the power supply. Constant voltage (approximately 125 volts) is applied until the gel front reaches the bottom of the gel.
- Once the run is complete, the power is turned off, and the gel cassette is removed from the apparatus. If the gel is going to be stained, then it is transferred to a tray containing coomassie blue stain.
- Alternatively, if the goal is visualization by western blotting, proceed with the transfer of the proteins to a membrane.

Reference

Laemmli, U.K. (1970) *Nature*, 227, pg. 680-685.

SDS-PAGE

Laboratory

Introduction

A protein product purified in the chromatography laboratories will be analyzed using SDS-polyacrylamide gel electrophoresis and a subsequent Western blot. Students will make assessments of the identity and purity of their protein using these methods. Students will perform SDS-PAGE using samples from the affinity and ion-exchange chromatography labs.

Equipment

Novex electrophoresis apparatus
Staining trays
Power supplies
Gel knives
Shaker platform

Materials and Supplies

Mark 12 molecular weight standards (1X), 1ml
Tris-glycine SDS sampler buffer (2X), 20 ml
Tris-glycine SDS running buffer (10X), 1L
4-20% Tris-glycine gel, 1.0 mm X 10 well
2-mercaptoethanol
Ice
PBS
Staining Solution: 1.25 g coomassie, 400 ml methanol, 100 ml glacial acetic acid. QS to one liter.
Destaining Solutions: 75 ml absolute methanol, 100 ml glacial acetic acid. QS to one liter.

Activities at a Glance

Each pair of students will run two gels. Samples will be run under reducing and nonreducing conditions. One gel will be stained with coomassie blue and the other will be used for Western blots.

Samples: (10 micrograms of each)

1. Original protein stock
2. Affinity sample
3. Ion-exchange sample
4. Media sample (load for chromatography runs)
5. Affinity effluent

Western Blots

Overview

Introduction

During the process of therapeutic protein drug development and manufacturing, it is important to determine the quality of the generated protein products. Western blotting is a commonly used procedure in research, process development, and quality control for the evaluation of protein expression levels and protein quality. Western Blotting can determine whether the protein of interest is pure or contaminated with degradation products, whether the protein is in monomeric or multimeric form, and whether it is modified, for example, by glycosylation.

Table of Contents

This document contains the following topics:

Western Blots

Objectives

1. Explain the purpose of Western blotting.
2. Cite specific examples of instances where Western blotting would beused.
3. Explain the purpose of each part of the equipment used in performing a Western blot.
4. Demonstrate the set up of a Western blot.
5. Explain the function of the primary antibody and the secondary antibody.
6. State the function of the horseradish peroxidase.
7. Explain the functions of the various incubations in the Western blot procedure.
8. Explain what can be done to increase the transfer/absorption of very large or very small proteins.
9. Demonstrate proficiency in the reading and interpretation of a Western blot.
10. Compare and contrast Western blotting with SDS-PAGE and ELISA in purpose, methodology, sensitivity, method of detection, and use.

Methodology

Introduction   Western blotting is a standard method for the detection and characterization of proteins which were resolved by SDS-polyacrylamide gel electrophoresis (SDS-PAGE). During electrophoretic transfer, the proteins migrate out of the gel and are immobilized onto a nitrocellulose or nylon membrane. For protein detection, usually two antibodies are required. The primary antibody binds to the protein of interest. The secondary antibody, which is horseradish peroxidase (HRP)-conjugated, binds to the first antibody. When the membrane is incubated with chemoluminescent substrate (ECL-substrate), a light signal is induced by the HRP-conjugate. After exposure of the membrane to autoradiography film, specific protein bands are developed.

Method
- Proteins are separated according to molecular weight by SDS-PAGE using NOVEX precast gels.
- After completion of the electrophoresis run, the gel is lifted out of the gel cassette, and placed on top of the transfer membrane. If a polyvinylidene fluoride (PVDF) membrane is used for transfer, it needs to be prewetted in methanol and rinsed with water and transfer buffer. Gel and membrane are then placed between two sheets of blotting paper and four blotting pads, which were also presoaked in transfer buffer.
- The assembly is then placed into the mini-cell transfer apparatus with the gel facing the cathode (-). Transfer buffer is filled into the transfer chambers covering the gel/membrane sandwich. 100mA electric current are applied for 1 to 2 hours. In the electric field, proteins transfer out of the gel and are absorbed onto the membrane.
- Once the transfer is completed, the transfer apparatus is disassembled and the membrane is placed in a tray containing methanol and rinsed. This is followed by rinses with water and PBS. Prestained molecular weight markers should be visible on the membrane.
- The membrane is incubated in block buffer for one hour, which prevents nonspecific binding of the Western reagents to the membrane.
- The blocked membrane is now ready for incubation with the primary antibody which specifically recognizes the protein of interest. The primary antibody should be diluted in block buffer. Subsequently, the membrane is washed several times with wash buffer, to remove unbound antibody. If the primary antibody is a mouse monoclonal antibody, it is recommended to use a goat anti-mouse HRP-conjugate as a secondary antibody. The secondary antibody is also diluted in block buffer. Again, unbound antibody is removed by washing, and ECL substrate is applied to the membrane. After a short incubation time, the wet membrane is wrapped in Saran wrap and exposed to film. After film developing, specific protein bands should be visible.

Data Analysis

Application
Traditionally, Western blotting results are read manually. More recently, imaging systems have become available for documentation and analysis of the results. By either method, the molecular weights of the proteins of interest are compared to protein standards on the same blots.

This procedure allows for the analysis of the purity of protein preparations. Lower molecular weight bands can indicate contamination of the protein preparations with degradation products. The intensity of the bands can be compared to protein standards. This allows for the estimation of protein concentrations.

Troubleshooting

Trouble-Shooting
The following considerations are important for maximizing the quality of the results:

- Two typical problems which occur during Western blotting are incomplete transfer of large molecular weight proteins (>120KD) and loss of very small proteins due to transfer through the membrane. Low percentage acrylamide gels should be chosen in order to achieve maximum transfer of large proteins. PVDF membranes offer a better retention of adsorbed proteins compared to nitrocellulose membranes and prevent loss of low molecular weight proteins.
- Removal of air bubbles in the gel/membrane assembly is essential, as they can block transfer of proteins.
- High quality antibody reagents are required to assure highly specific, clean Western blot results.

Equipment, Materials, and Reagents

Equipment	Most equipment and materials for Western blotting are commercially available.

- Power supply from Hoefer Scientific Instruments, San Francisco, CA

- Xcell II Mini-Cell and Blot Module from Invitrogen

- Nutator shaker from Beckton Dickinson, Sparks, MD

Reagents

- Methanol, deionized water

- Tris buffered saline (TBS): 10 mM Tris-HCl, 0.15 M NaCl (pH 7.4)

- Blocking Buffer: TBS containing 1% BSA or 3% dry milk

- Wash buffer: TBS containing 0.2% Tween 20

- Primary antibody

- Secondary antibody (HRP-conjugated)

Materials

- Precut blotting membranes (nitrocellulose or PVDF), blotting pads, filter paper, and transfer buffer from Invitrogen

- Shallow tray for equilibration and incubation of membranes

- Previously electrophoresed mini-gels (maximum gel size 9x9 cm)

- ECL substrate (Amersham), Kodak film

Continued on next page

Equipment, Materials, and Reagents

Notes

- As an alternative to the NOVEX wet blotting apparatus, a semi-dry transfer apparatus is available from Amersham/Pharmacia, Piscataway, NJ. This system is equally reliable. It has the advantage of requiring less transfer buffer.

- Both nitrocellulose and PVDF membranes are commonly used for Western blotting. PVDF membranes are hydrophobic and require wetting with methanol directly before use. PVDF membranes have a higher protein binding capacity and durability compared to nitrocellulose, and are therefore preferred.

- Tris-glycine transfer buffer is available from Invitrogen as a 25X stock solution. 1X Tris-glycine transfer buffer contains 12 mM Tris base and 96 mM glycine in deionized water. Addition of methanol to the transfer buffer to a final concentration of 20% will enhance binding of the proteins to nitrocellulose membranes. However, decreasing the concentration of methanol will improve the transfer of proteins out of the gel, resulting in a more complete transfer of high molecular weight proteins.

Western Blotting

Laboratory

Introduction   Students will do a Western blot using one of their gels from the SDS-PAGE run.

Equipment   Trans-blot electronic transfer cell
Gel holder cassette
Power supplies
Shaker
Plastic tubs

Materials and Supplies   Sponge pads
Filter paper
Transfer buffer
Blocking agent
Membrane wash buffer
Detection kit
Tween 20
Pipettes for rolling
Ice
Nitrocellulose or equivalent
Small Tupperware containers
Petri dishes

Activities at a Glance
1. Each student will use one of the gels from their SDS-PAGE laboratory and perform the transfer onto nitrocellulose.
2. Students will wash and block membranes as directed in the appropriate SOP.
3. Incubations with primary antibody, secondary antibody, and substrate will enable the proteins of interest to be detected.
4. Students will interpret and analyze results.

Introduction to Validation

Overview

Introduction

The term Validation describes the inspection and qualification of GMP equipment and systems and the associated documentation to verify that predetermined fabrication, installation and operational specifications are met.

The FDA demanded these activities be part of all GMP manufacturing installation in response to identified failures with the post-manufacturing inspection methods that were in practice at the time.

Validation applies to all equipment and support systems involved in the manufacturing of drug products, as well as to any associated computer systems and automation. For medical devices, this also applied to the device itself.

Validation is required by law and is described in the CFR 21 sections dedication to drug and medical device manufacturing. The European, Canadian and many other regulatory agencies also require validation for the manufacturing of drugs and devices.

Since validation is often a complex operation, the appropriate planning, and strategic implementation can help ensure that the validation activities are performed in a timely and cost-effective manner. This section also describes some strategies for the effective deployment of validation.

Table of Contents

This document contains the following topics:

Introduction to Validation

Objectives

---

1.   Explain the general concept of validation.
2.   Explain the origin of the Food and Drug Act.
3.   Describe the origin of the Food, Drug and Cosmetic Act and the expansion of the FDA.
4.   Describe the role of the FDA in the biotechnology industry.
5.   Explain the origins of cGMPs.
6.   Discuss the role of SOPs and validation in the GMPs.
7.   Explain the origin of validation.
8.   Distinguish between prospective, concurrent and retrospective validation.
9.   Discuss why validation is done.
10.   Explain the role of CFRs in validation.
11.   Explain when it is necessary to validate.
12.   Discuss who is responsible for validation.
13.   Explain the validation life cycle approach.
14.   Distinguish between Installation Qualification, Operation Qualification, and Performance Qualification.
15.   Discuss the role of validation maintenance.

History of Validation

History

Prior to 1978, drug product quality and sterility were based solely on finished product testing. This concept became seriously questioned in the 1960s and 1970s as a result of serious incidents that showed that product testing by itself was not reliable. Examples of this are Thalidomide in 1962 and Septicemia in the 1970's.

The Septicemia outbreaks in the early 1970's had the largest impact on the development of the validation concept. It was caused by sterility problems with large volume parenterals (LVP). Fifty-four deaths and 410 injuries resulted. This prompted the FDA to inspect all LVP manufacturing facilities. This resulted in 600 LVP product recalls and temporary closure of several plants.

The FDA inspections of facilities found severe problems, including inadequate specifications, procedures and test data for production or control systems. There was a lack of environmental monitoring procedures, specifications and test data for water, air and surfaces.

In 1976, the FDA proposed changes to the GMPs detailing how equipment and processes were to be designed, constructed and tested. These changes were primarily aimed at sterilization procedures including Steam and Dry Heat Sterilization, Ethylene Oxide (ETO) Sterilization, Depyrogenation, Steam in Place (SIP) and filtration. Terms such as Validation, Protocol and Qualification began to be used.

The FDA expanded the need for validation of processes and systems outside of sterilization. While these systems were not intended to sterilize they were critical elements in the preparation of parenteral products. The areas affected included Aseptic Processing, Media Fills, Environmental Controls, Sanitization and Water Systems.

The FDA used frequent inspections and the issuance of FD 483s to convince the industry of the seriousness of its intentions. A FD 483 is the official form used to inform a company of the observations identified during an inspection. The desire to comply with the FDA ensured a quick response and implementation of FDA demands.

What Must Be Validated?

General Approach

The cGMPs (1978) state that any facilities or systems used in the manufacturing, processing, packing, or holding of a drug or device shall conform to Current Good Manufacturing Practice Guidelines; to assure the product meets its predetermined quality characteristics. Examples of the types of systems and utilities that are included in this statement are given below.

Examples

The following list provides examples of what must be validated:
- Environmental systems
- HVAC
- Sanitary water systems (WFI, etc.)
- Sanitary utilities
- Sterilization systems
- Sanitization processes
- Solution preparation systems
- Filtration processes
- Aseptic filling
- Labeling systems
- Packaging systems

Examples

Examples of Sterilization and Thermal Processes that must be validated are given below:
- Steam autoclaves
- Dry heat ovens
- Depyrogenation tunnels
- ETO sterilizers
- Freeze dryers
- Form, fill, and seal
- Filling lines (SIP)
- Cold rooms
- Stability chambers
- Incubators
- Warehouses (environmentally controlled)
- Refrigerators
- WFI/Clean steam systems

Why Validate?

Reasons for Validation

Some of the key reasons for validation are the following:

1. Regulatory Requirement
   - 21.CFR 211: 68(b); 84.d (2); 84.d (3); 165.e
   - Section 501 (a)(2)(B) of the Federal Food, Drug and Cosmetic Act
   - FDA Guidelines on General Principles of Process Validation

2. More Economic Process
   - Increase yields
   - Improve efficiency of operations
   - More reliable process

3. Builds Team Confidence
   - Increases confidence of production staff, lab personnel and customers

4. Fewer Rejected or Deviant Lots
   - Reduces cost of production
   - Less reworks
   - Reduces risks (recalls, FDA action, etc.)

Continued on next page

Implementation of Validation

Introduction

The validation of a GMP manufacturing facility is a complex and multi-faceted operation. There are many associated documents that need pre and post validation approval. Qualified staff must perform the inspections and performance tests in the facility. Good planning, resource allocation and test design are required for the successful deployment of validation activities and the timely completion of reports.

Validation Life Cycle

Once the initial validation is concluded, the equipment or system must be monitored to ensure that it remains in a validated state throughout its use.

This is described as the "validation life cycle," which indicates that any changes or modifications to a system must be evaluated for their impact on the validated state. Equipment must be periodically tested to ensure that it is still operating within its pre-determined specifications. Revalidation must be done after modifications to ensure the same.

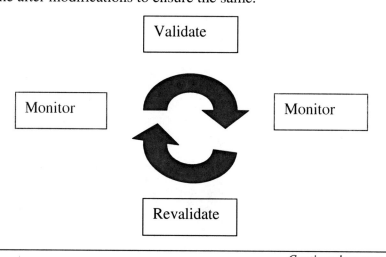

Continued on next page

Implementation of Validation

**Steps of
Validation**

1. System Documentation

2. SOPs (operation, calibration, maintenance, sampling, testing)

3. Write Documentation (IQ/OQ/PQ) with input from:
   - Engineering
   - Facilities
   - Manufacturing
   - QA
   - RA (often as policies)

4. Execution of IQ/OQ/PQ in Facility

5. Review and approvals (by same functions that approved the Protocols)

How Does Validation Get Done?

Introduction
- A validation protocol needs to be developed.
- The validation procedures (IQA, OQ, PQ) need to be performed and documented.
- The Validation Technical Report needs to be singed and issued.

Validation Protocols

A Validation Protocol is an experimental plan intended to produce documented evidence that a system has been validated.

Types of Validation Protocols:
1. Installation Qualification (IQ)
   An IQ is documented verification that all key aspects of the installation adhere to appropriate codes and approved designs, and conform to production department's and the manufacturer'sspecifications.

2. Operational Qualification (OQ)
   An OQ is documented verification that the system or sub-system performs as intended throughout all anticipated operating ranges.

3. Process Qualification (PQ)
   A PQ is documented evidence which provides a high degree of assurance that a specific process will consistently produce a product that meets its predetermined specifications and quality attributes.

Executing the Validation Protocols
- The procedures described in the respective SOP need to be followed carefully and documented fully.
- The validation work continues until the acceptance criteria are met.
- If acceptance criteria cannot be met, the suitability of the facility, equipment, process or of the specified criteria needs to be discussed.

Continued on next page

How Does Validation Get Done?

Technical-Summary Report

- The technical report should summarize the validation study's goals and approach.
- The results should be summarized.
- Deviations from the original acceptance criteria should be explained and justified.
- Approval signatures are required.

Review of IQ Requirements

It is important to understand the rationale for the IQ and OQ in order to understand why certain information is required for them to be satisfactory.

Review of IQ Requirements

The rationale for the Installation Qualification is to document that the equipment installed not only meets the design criteria and specifications, but that the equipment is installed appropriately and connected to the correct services.

Some of the typical information required:

- Original specification documentation
- Purchase orders and Shipping Invoices
- Vendor submittals
- Drawings (PI&Ds, Mechanical: Electrical, Orthometrics)
- Materials documentation (ASTM, Passivation Reports, Bio-compatibility)
- Weld log with boroscope (visual) report and welder certifications
- Slope verifications for self-draining piping
- Industrial code documentation (UL, ASME, NEMA, ASTM, NEC, NFPA)
- Vendor manuals received in-house
- Spare parts list
- Computer hardware documentation and installation
- Copies of software documentation and software

How Does Validation Get Done?

Review of OQ Requirements

The rational for the Operational Qualification is to document that the equipment or system operates according to its predetermined specifications. Some of the typical information required:

- SOP and training verification
- Operators manual
- Start-up and shut down
- Instrumentation calibration
- Alarms test
- Instrumentation operation
- Controls test (including: manual override, local control, safety interlocks)
- Integrity of filters, vessels and seals (e.g. leakage, pressure)
- Emergency recovery (after loss of power, services)

Examples of Typical OQ Testing

Some of the equipment requiring OQ testing include:

- **Pumps**
  Direction of rotation, RPM, Amperage draw, deadhead pressure
- **HEPA filters**
  Particulate reduction (DOP Test), uniformity of air flow across filter, FPM air flow (Federal Standard 209E)
- **Chromatography**
  Meets flow and pressure specifications, valve sequences, gradients, sample injecting and peak detection
- **Fermentors**
  Pressure test, sanitization cycle, sterility hold, valve and pump operation, temperature maintenance, control and monitoring systems

How Does Validation Get Done?

Scoping the Validation Project

- It is critical to correctly identify the scope of the validation project
- A pre-project audit of the existing documentation, the equipment and system,s and the available resources can be helpful in the accurate scoping of the validation work.
- A clear and concise presentation needs to be made to management, showing the true scope of the work and underlining the fact that allocating sufficient funds in advance will save funds in the future. This will also prevent the common "change of scope" request on the third day of execution.

Cost Overruns

What causes cost overruns in validation?
- The scope of work is underestimated, leading to overruns during execution.
- Documentation has not been assembled prior to the start of execution.
- Engineering drawings are incorrect.
- Equipment or facility not designed or built properly.
- Unrealistic or unnecessary acceptance criteria.
- Unrealistic timelines.
- Lack of budgeting to account for the company-wide resources critical for completion of validation.

Cleaning Validation

Overview

Introduction   Cleaning validation is a process that demonstrates a cleaning regime that consistently and reliably removes debris and cleaning agents from a surface. The program involves extensive additional testing for residuals, typically on three consecutive trials. Once the cleaning procedure is validated, the additional testing can be discontinued and replaced by a few, easy to perform tests that are used to ensure the cleaning was performed properly and the equipment is ready for use.

Table of Contents   This document contains the following topics:

Cleaning Validation

Objectives

1. State three methods of cleaning verification.
2. Describe the advantages/limitations of each of the above methods.
3. Explain which method is considered by the FDA to be the most important.
4. Describe what information may be obtained from surface swabbing.
5. Explain how sample sites are chosen for surface swabbing, and once chosen, describe the subsequent steps.
6. Discuss the different approaches to calculating limits.
7. Demonstrate ability to perform acceptance criteria calculations.
8. Explain why identification of material seen in a visible inspection is desirable.
9. Discuss the use/importance/sequence of various cleaning regimes.
10. Explain why testing for material released with each cleaning is essential.
11. Evaluate cleaning data and make determinations of effectiveness.
12. Explain the value/importance of continued monitoring.
13. Discuss the use of control charts in cleaning validation.
14. Describe the three types of impurity classifications.
15. Explain the analytical tools/techniques used to characterize impurities.
16. Perform a visual inspection of specified surfaces.
17. Perform surface swabbing of specified sample sites.
18. Demonstrate ability to follow Cleaning Validation SOP.
19. Identify surface contaminants based on observations.
20. Give suggestions for analytical methods to identify contaminants.

Background

Examples   Cleaning validation is performed by Clean-in-Place (CIP) of surfaces such as piping, vessels, and bioreactors. It also applies to non-CIP systems such as chromatography columns and diafiltration membranes.

CIP Systems

Key Features   This section describes the following elements of cleaning validation:
- Concepts of cleaning validation
- Verification methods
- Setting acceptance criteria
- On-going monitoring and revalidation

Continued on next page

CIP Systems

Concepts of Cleaning Validation

Regulatory Guidance:

- GMP guidelines do not specify what the limits should be, or that they should be zero
- Rather, they should be "reasonable and achievable"
- It is desirable that limits be based on scientific method as opposed to arbitrarily picking a number that might be difficult to defend if challenged by a regulatory agency

Cleaning Process:

- Set up CIP Skid to automatically deliver pulses of:
  Pure water
  Phosphoric acid
  Sodium hydroxide
  Pure water
- Dirty the system and clean per the programmed method
- Analyze final rinse water, swab the surface, and perform visual examination
- If analyses fail, tweek the pulse duration, frequency, or concentration until analyses pass

Validation Process:

- Choose appropriate analytical methods
- Choose acceptance criteria
- Write protocol
- Perform 3 consecutive demonstration (validation) runs
- Analyze data
- Write report
- Celebrate!

Continued on next page

CIP Systems

Verification Methods

Final Rinse Water:

- Purpose: To demonstrate soluble material has been flushed from the system
- Advantage: Easy
- Disadvantage: Does not examine residue remaining on surface
- Analytical methods: Conductivity, pH, TOC, SDS-PAGE, ELISA, RP-HPLC

Swabbing:

- Purpose: Quantitate surface residue
- Advantage: Very sensitive
- Disadvantage: Tedious, can't swab all surfaces, must reclean
- Analytical methods: TOC, SDS-PAGE, ELISA, RIA, RP-HPLC

Visual Inspection:

- Purpose: To look for dirty surface
- Advantage: Very sensitive, the only way to detect insoluble material
- Disadvantage: Can't see all areas, must reclean

Analytical Methods: Organoleptic

Setting Acceptance Criteria

Regulatory Guidance:

- Guidelines do not specify what, how, or that they need to be zero
- Limits should be "reasonable and achievable"
- Should be justifiable based on science

Continued on next page

CIP Systems

Acceptance Criteria The following table provides information on acceptance criteria.

Method	Advantages	Disadvantages	Applications
Just Say Zero	Shows high commitment Easy to calculate	Very, very small number Impossible to prove	None
LOD	Easy to determine Easy to achieve if LOD is high	May fail if LOD is low. LODs get lower as assays are improved.	When LOD is reasonable
Based on Dose	Scientific Easy to calculate	Toxicity may be known in early phases of development	When dose is known
Based on Toxicity	Scientific Easy to calculate	Toxicity may be known	When toxicity is known
Arbitrary	Easy to calculate	Not science-based	When all else fails
Imposed	Easy to calculate	Not always science-based May be too low	When specified by FDA

Continued on next page

CIP Systems

Examples

The approach and numerical value to limits will vary depending on the nature of the assay.

- Easy:

  pH - Somewhere near neutrality; 6.5 to 7.5, is usually adequate. This shows the rinse water flushed out the caustic and acid solutions, and that the next process fluid to be exposed to the surface will not be harmed.

- Difficult:

  Drug product of unknown dose or toxicity

  Estimate the dose and calculate MAC (maximum acceptable carry over)

  $$MAC = \frac{TD \times BS \times SF}{LDD}$$

  MAC = maximum allowable carry over

  TD = a single therapeutic dose

  BS = batch size of the next product

  SF = safety factor (typically 1/1000)

  LDD = largest daily dose of the next product

  This value is then compared with total amount of residue found, which is estimated by:

  $$\frac{\text{(Maximum amount of residue detected by a swab)} \times \text{(Total estimated area of system)}}{\text{Area swabbed}}$$

Continued on next page

CIP Systems

Ongoing Monitoring and Revalidation

When validation is completed, the testing can be reduced, but not eliminated.

Common Programs for Assessing CIP Following Validation

Programs	Element	Assay	Frequency
Ongoing Monitoring	Final Rinse Water	Conductivity, pH	Every cleaning
Revalidation	Final Rinse Water, Swabbing, Visual Inspection	Conductivity TOC, SDS-PAGE, ELISA, RIA Organoleptic	Annual or when a change is made

Non-CIP Systems

Introduction

Non-CIP systems are those not cleanable with direct piped caustic and acid.

Examples

Packed chromatography columns
Diafiltration membranes

Approach

1. Develop a well-characterized cleaning procedure.
2. Run the system several times (typically ten).
3. Clean with the established procedure.
4. Perform a blank run.

Sample and test for product.

Continued on next page

Non-CIP Systems

Acceptance Criteria   These cannot be set by the same approaches available for CIP systems, but the 1/1000 rule can apply.

Example:

Criteria for a blank column run could be less than 1/000 of what would normally be present in the elution pool of a real protein run. Appropriate assays might be UV, SDS-PAGE and ELISA (for the target protein), DNA, and endotoxin. Thus protein, DNA, and endotoxin would be expected to be less than 1/1000 of what would normally be present.

References

PDA Technical Report No. 29, Points to Consider for Cleaning Validation.

Brunkow, Roger, et al., "Cleaning and Cleaning Validation," in *A Biotechnology Perspective*, PDA (1996)

Cleaning Validation

Laboratory

Introduction

Experience and knowledge of cleaning validation will be developed through two exercises. Students will perform a visual inspection lab and also a surface swabbing lab.

Materials and Supplies

12 stainless steel coupons (with known contaminants on them)
50 ml Falcon tubes
Cotton swabs
Squirt bottles with water
15 ml Falcon tubes
Wire cutters (to clip swabs)
Labels

Activities at a Glance

Visual Inspection Exercise
1. Stainless steel coupons are contaminated with a variety of materials that are commonly encountered during the manufacturing process.
2. Students will perform a visual inspection of the stainless steel surfaces.
3. Students should attempt to identify contaminants.

Surface Swabbing Exercise
1. Students will receive instructions on basic surface swabbing techniques.
2. Students will then follow an SOP to practice these techniques.
3. Stainless steel coupons used in the Visual Inspection lab will be used for this exercise.

Process Validation

Overview

Introduction   Process validation of a biotechnology process is a set of activities that document a process is in control and consistently performs to predefined in-process acceptance criteria and final purified bulk specifications. It differs from equipment and utilities validation in that it focuses on the microbiology and biochemistry of the process. It involves extensive sampling, testing, and monitoring of initial large-scale runs to show consistency. Following validation, the sampling is reduced to a few key points that are tracked continually to demonstrate the process remains in a state of statistical process control.

Table of Contents   This document contains the following topics:

Process Validation

Objectives

1. Discuss the various stages of product development.
2. Describe the role of Process Development in these stages.
3. Distinguish between Phase I, Phase II, and Phase III trials.
4. Explain what is meant by an operational variable and give specific examples.
5. Explain performance variables and give specific examples.
6. Explain critical variables and give specific examples.
7. Explain how such variables are addressed in a challenge.
8. Explain in-process testing and its relationship to validation.
9. Define in-process controls and give specific examples.
10. Define acceptance criteria and their significance to production.
11. Explain how in-process controls and acceptance criteria relate to validation.
12. Explain how in-process controls help to ensure batch uniformity and integrity of drug products.
13. Explain how final specifications are determined.
14. Explain the role of conformance lots in production.
15. Identify items from process validation that may be inspected by the FDA.
16. Explain the role of change control in validation.

Concepts of Process Validation

Regulatory Guidance
- GMP guidelines give general guidance.
- It is important to document that the process runs consistently.
- It must be demonstrated on a minimum of three lots, and they must be consecutive.

Validation Process
- Choose appropriate sites in the process to sample or collect data.
- Choose appropriate analytical methods.
- Choose acceptance criteria.
- Write protocol.
- Perform three consecutive demonstration (validation) runs at full-scale.
- Analyze data.
- Write report.
- Write protocols and reports for the ancillary process validation items.

Elements of Process Validation

Stages of Product Development

The table below outlines the stages involved in the development of a biopharmaceutical product.

Phase	Purpose	Scale
Initial Development	Define a workable process	Lab bench
GLP Toxicology Material	Produce material for animal safety studies	Pilot scale
Phase 1	Safety in humans	Small GMP facility
Phase 2	Define dose and show efficacy	Medium GMP facility
Phase 3	Pivotal demonstration trial	Commercial-scale, if possible
Commercial	Manufacturing for sale	Commercial-scale

Continued on next page

Elements of Process Validation

Protocol List

Activity	Purpose	Typical Timing	Scale
Buffer hold times	Show buffer stability	Phase 1	Full
Process pool hold times	Show pool stability	Phase 1, 2	Lab
CPI* stability	Show long-term stability	Phase 1, 2	Lab
Extended cell generations	Show genetic stability after many cell doublings	Phase 3	Lab
In-process impurity profile	Show consistent level of impurities at each step	Phase 3	Full
Resin/membrane reuse	Demonstrate continued performance after many reuses	Phase 3	Lab and full
Monitoring the 3 conformance lots	Demonstrate process consistency	Phase 3	Full
Biocomparability	Show comparability when the process is changed	Throughout	Pilot and full
Sterile filter validation	Show bacterial retention by the final bulk sterilizing filter	Pre-inspection	Lab
Lyophilization	Validate the lyophilizer is effective and consistent	Pre-inspection	Full

* Cell Product Intermediate (inclusion bodies or diafiltered medium)

Notes

- Not all activities apply to every process.
- The timing is suggested. In general, the sooner the better, but everything has to be completed by the time of the Pre-Approval Inspection, which is typically 3 to 6 months after filing.
- Monitoring the three Conformance Lots and extended cell generations are the major activities, which are summarized in the license application.
- The other nine protocols fall into the ancillary class and are reviewed at the time of the inspection.

Setting Acceptance Criteria

Introduction The protocols must define the exact samples to be taken, the tests to be run, and the set limits needed on the expected values.

Approaches There are several different approaches to setting limits on expected values given in the table below.

Method	Advantage	Disadvantage	Preference
$\pm$ 3 SD of historical mean	Most scientifically justified	May have limited data at validation scale	Preferred
Pick a reasonable range	Easy to set	Less justified	Acceptable
Pick a wide range	East to meet	Even less justified	Unacceptable
Claim internal consistency in the 3-5 runs	Consistency is the goal of validation	Need to define consistency	Acceptable, if defined

Continuous Monitoring

Introduction Following validation, the sampling is reduced to a few key points that are tracked continually to demonstrate the process remains in a state of control. These data are used for statistical process control and are monitored by control charts. Upper and lower action limits (typically set by $\pm$ 3 standard deviations from the mean) are assigned. When a control limit is exceeded, a formal investigation is made and corrective action taken. These data also serve as a form of continuous process validation and show that the process continues to perform as it did in the conformance lots.

Continued on next page

Continuous Monitoring

Change Control   At the time of process validation, there should be a mechanism in place to document process or procedural changes. Elements of the change control include:
- Written, signed request for a change
- Data and justification for the change
- QA signed agreement to the change
- Proposal on how the change will be evaluated to:
  - Not effect product quality or safety
  - Not impact other steps in the process
  - Re-validate the step, if the change is significant
- Follow-up report documenting the results of the change

Change control is not intended to prevent process changes, but rather to carefully and clearly document and evaluate the change.

References

Seely, R. and Murphy, R., "Validation of Biotechnology Bulk Pharmacueticals," in *Validation of Bulk Pharmaceutical Chemicals*, Interpharm Press, Ira Berry and Daniel Harpaz, eds., 271-299 (1997).

Process Validation

Laboratory

Introduction   In this laboratory exercise students will gain familiarity with some of the basic concepts in validation, as they apply to process validation.

Materials and Supplies   Process flow diagram

Activities at a Glance

1. Following discussion with the instructor, students will develop a set of performance parameters and identify acceptance criteria for a defined unit operation.

2. Students will be given a process flow diagram and a written description. They are to complete the missing text and data tables in a process validation protocol. There is no strict right or wrong, rather it is degrees of completeness, clearness, and meeting the objective.

3. Don't validate too much or too little.

Metrology and Calibration

Overview

Introduction   Calibration of process instrumentation and a well established metrology program are critical for ensuring GMP compliance and reliable processes. Calibration of instrumentation ensures that the measurements are accurate, and therefore, can be used to control the process. This section gives an overview of what metrology and calibration are, and what the key terms "calibration," "tolerance," and "out of tolerance" mean. Some discussion is given on how to manage a metrology program, including examples of automated metrology management software.

Table of Contents   This document contains the following topics:

Metrology and Calibration

Objectives

1. Define metrology.
2. Give examples of metrology measurements in the industry.
3. Describe several metrology services in the pharmaceutical setting.
4. Give a definition of a metrologist.
5. Define calibration.
6. Using four different instruments, give examples of calibration.
7. Explain what "out of tolerance" (OTT) means.
8. Describe the response to an OOT condition.
9. Explain the purpose of a metrology program within a biotechnology company.
10. Discuss possible activities and functions of a metrology group.
11. Explain why it is necessary to calibrate.
12. Explain when it is necessary to calibrate.
13. Discuss how and why Metrology, Validation, and QA could be integrated.
14. Describe components of a system for controlling and tracking calibrations.
15. Discuss in-house versus contract service calibration.
16. Describe the elements of a compliant metrology program.
17. Distinguish between critical and non-critical devices.
18. Explain what is meant by a reference only device.
19. Explain the use of calibration stickers and where they are placed.

What are Metrology and Calibration?

Metrology

Metrology is the science of measurement.

Examples of metrology measurements in industry are:
- Temperature
- Dimensions (length, width)
- Time
- Pressure
- Frequency (cycles/time)
- Speed (distance/time)
- Chemical measurements (pH, conductivity, etc.)

Purpose of a Metrology Program
The purpose of a Metrology Program within a company is to establish a system for the control and calibration of testing and measurement instrumentation. In addition it establishes uniform procedures (SOPs) for implementation and operation of the Metrology Program.

Responsibilities of Metrology
- Schedule or perform calibrations
- Maintain records of all calibrations
- Maintain records of equipment status
- Maintain and operate test equipment
- Review the equipment and advise on calibration intervals and tolerances
- Work with the users to ensure a high degree of compliance to the Metrology Program

Continued on next page

What are Metrology and Calibration?

Calibration

Calibration is the comparison of a measurement standard of known accuracy with another instrument of similar response with unknown accuracy, to detect, correlate, report, or eliminate by adjustment any variation in the accuracy of the item being compared. This is done in such a way as to certify that the instrument with the unknown accuracy is operating within expected predetermined parameters. This is referred to as "within specifications." Calibration checks whether an instrument or indicator was showing accurate readings (within its tolerances), and then adjusts the indicator for accurate readings, if necessary.

Examples:
- Thermometer accurate to within +/- 1°C
- Pressure gauge accurate to within +/- 3% of full-scale
- Timer accurate to within +/- 2 seconds
- pH meter accurate within 0.1 pH units

Calibration Concepts

Traceability to National Standards

The Standards Hierarchy
- Intrinsic
- NIST
- Calibration
- Reference
- Equipment

All instruments should be calibrated in reference to a traceable standard that itself has been calibrated in reference to a more accurate standard. The instrumentation on the equipment is calibrated against a reference standard in the field or lab. This reference standard is calibrated against a high-accuracy standard found in the corporate lab or from a specialized contract lab. Periodically these high-level standards are calibrated against a national standard at the NIST (National Institute of Standards and Technology, in Boulder, CO). The national standards usually refer to global or intrinsic standards (i.e. speed of light, decay of radioactive Cesium, gravity, etc.). An intrinsic standard is one that is created by a phenomenon of nature, and some are available for use at the site level, such as the triple point of water standard for calibrating temperature at 0.0098°C.

Calibration Concepts

Out of Tolerance

Out of tolerance (OOT) is a condition where the indicator's accuracy at the test point(s) is wider than the specified tolerances. The indicator tolerance should be narrower than the process tolerance.

Responses to an out of tolerance condition:
1. Evaluate calibration data.
2. If OOT result is less than process tolerances, no action may be necessary. Also, in the case of "reference only" indicators, tolerances are not significant.
3. If OOT result is greater than process tolerances, remedial action may be necessary (responsibility of the using department):
   - Review of assay results and standard curves
   - Cross-check controls and standards
   - QA Deviation Report, if the GMP process may be in question

Why Calibrate?

- More accurate results
- More consistent results
- Control over equipment
- Identification of equipment failure
  Ensure preventive maintenance

When to Calibrate?

- Upon installation or receipt of new equipment
- When the scheduled recalibration time is near
- When an instrument is repaired

Any time that the performance of a measurement device is questioned

Critical and Non-critical

Critical devices are devices whose failure would impact the process or product quality and safety. Examples of these are balances and pipettes in QC and manufacturing and pressure gauges that are used to set up manufacturing processes. Non-critical devices are devices whose failure would not impact process or product quality. Examples of these are equipment and utilities that are not utilized by QC or manufacturing.

The Metrology Group

Activities and Functions

The activities and functions of the Metrology Group within a biotechnology company are numerous. These include:

- Provide central measurement control for certification, calibration, test, and inspection for all appropriate instruments and equipment
- Provide and operate specialized test equipment
- Provide necessary maintenance and repair services to support measurement activities
- Assign instrument and equipment numbers
- Assign calibration intervals
- Coordinate the use of outside calibration service contractors
- Perform vendor audits to evaluate calibration vendors
- Maintain metrology documentation system and master equipment/instrument list.

Outside Versus In-House Calibration

Calibration can be managed in two ways, using an in-house calibration lab or by contracting outside calibration services. The required standards of documentation and traceability are the same whether the calibration is done by in-house or outside personnel. Many companies augment in-house staff with outside contract service staff. However, the ultimate responsibility for all documentation and certifications is always with the in-house group in charge of Metrology.

In-House Calibration

Significant resources are needed to set up a comprehensive calibration lab:

- Expensive standards must be purchased and maintained, which includes keeping them regularly calibrated as well.
- Skilled staff must be hired.
- Overhead for administrative work and other support is considerable.

The benefits to in-house calibration are numerous:

- Greater flexibility in scheduling calibrations exists, and load distribution is more likely.
- There is more control over the documentation and the paper trail.
- "Real-time" data for the status of equipment and instruments can be entered into the database.
- Metrology staff can collaborate with validation and engineering personnel when needed.

Continued on next page

The Metrology Group

Integration of Metrology, Validation and Quality Assurance

An effective program must ensure that Metrology, Validation, and QA all work in coordination with each other.

- Every time an engineering change request is submitted, the metrology group must be notified in order to evaluate whether associated instruments need:

  - Recalibration after repair or extensive manipulations

  - Change of calibration interval due to change of usage

  - To be decommissioned or transferred to a new user, if not in place after the change.

- Production should receive clearance from metrology prior to using systems that have been changed, to ensure that all instruments are calibrated. Communications can be via e-mail, forms, work-order sign-off, etc.

- Integration will ensure that newly added instruments are tracked and calibrated prior to use.

- Calibration control ties in directly to the GMP remedial action process. Out of tolerance conditions in process equipment or in critical analytical equipment should trigger a QA investigation:

  - Using out of tolerance equipment in BMP processing is a deviation since control of that instrument, and therefore the process, cannot be assured.

  - Once the investigation is in the hands of QA, metrology may be requested to advise.

Continued on next page

The Metrology Group

Suggestions for Optimal Integration

- Create clear systems of communication and authorization if metrology is separate from QA (e.g., under Facilities)

  - Ensures that QA is notified of failures and OOT results for critical equipment.

  - QA sign-off should be required to close out the calibration remedial actions for critical equipment.

  - It is imperative to get buy-in from metrology management and from senior management for this coordination.

- Operate metrology as part of QA

  This allows the corporate metrology policy to mesh with the corporate QA policies. It will result in improved communication between QA/Metrology and Manufacturing, since the functions are integrated. Integrating Metrology into Validation/Metrology is a logical step since Validation is the most technically oriented "hands-on" group in QA.

Controlling and Tracking Calibrations

Documentation System

In order to manage, track, and verify the calibration status of the instrumentation and standards, a well-designed documentation system is required. This should track all of the relevant information regarding the item, such as its identifying number, due date, calibration data, associated work orders, and comments.

Calibration Stickers

Each instrument that receives calibration will have a sticker indicating:

- ID number
- Date calibrated
- Calibration due date
- Technician's initials

Controlling and Tracking Calibrations

Example of a Calibration Sticker

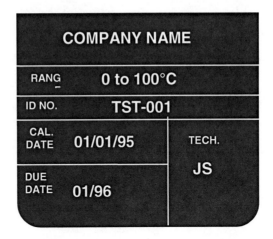

COMPANY NAME	
RANG̲E 0 to 100°C	
ID NO. **TST-001**	
CAL. DATE 01/01/95	TECH.
DUE DATE 01/96	JS

Equipment and Instrument Identification

Each piece of equipment and each calibrated instrument must have a unique identifying number. This will prevent confusion and allow accurate tracking of the status of each item.

- Equipment and instrument tagging

  If both engineering and metrology are managed in-house, it may be possible to integrate the engineering tagging system with the metrology tracking system.

- Numbering system

  An unchanging asset numbering system is crucial for the proper tracking of instruments throughout their life.

- Benefits of computerization

  Scheduling of calibration recall dates is automatic and can compensate for holidays and weekends.

  Data retrieval for a specific item is rapid.

  User notifications and other documentation can be printed out.

  Less paperwork saves time and money.

  It is easier to obtain an up-to-date overview of the status of the equipment.

  Tremendous time saver for groups with limited staffing.

Controlled Temperature Chamber Validation

Overview

Introduction

In-process products, process solutions, bulk products, finished goods, and raw materials may require storage at controlled temperature. Certain manufacturing operations, such as purification steps and incubation of cell cultures, may also require controlled temperatures environments. The validation of controlled temperature chambers is performed to establish documented evidence that provides a high degree of assurance that the proper temperature is maintained during storage and/or manufacturing operations.

Table of Contents

This document contains the following topics:

Controlled Temperature Chamber Validation

Objectives

---

1. Explain what Controlled Temperature Chambers (CTC) are.
2. Give numerous examples of controlled temperature chambers.
3. Explain why controlled temperature chambers require validation.
4. Explain the general approach to validating CTCs.
5. Discuss the system Prequalification.
6. Explain the Installation Qualification.
7. Explain the role of Change Controls in validation.
8. Explain the Operational Qualification.
9. Discuss various system safeguards for CTCs.
10. Give several process operating variables for CTCs.
11. Explain the Performance Qualification.
12. Discuss how to perform an Empty Chamber Study.
13. Discuss the acceptance criteria for a CTC Performance Qualification.
14. Explain the reasons for revalidation.
15. Explain when it is necessary to requalify a system.
16. Explain the use of the Digistrip in validation of CTCs.
17. Discuss the use and placement of thermocouples.
18. Explain the general process for using the Digistrip to validate a CTC.
19. Demonstrate ability to interpret data generated from the Digistrip.

Background

Examples
- The storage of in-process products, process solutions, bulk products, finished goods, and raw materials is often within a freezer or cold room.
- Some stability studies and assays performed in the analytical laboratories are in temperature and humidity controlled incubators.
- Incubation of cell culture is performed in large temperature and humidity controlled warm rooms.
- Sterilization of manufacturing equipment is obtained by sustained heat achieved though a steam line or an autoclave chamber which controls temperature and pressure.
- Bioreactors use controlled temperature in combination with gases and media for enzyme reactions and fermentation.

Design and Specification

Introduction

This section describes the key features to consider when deciding upon which type of controlled temperature chamber to use for a particular application.

Design and Specification

The design and specifications for controlled temperature chambers will be driven by the needs of the user. Controlled temperature chambers can be purchased "off-the-shelf" or custom-built.

Custom-built chambers are typically needed for a larger application where a high volume of items must be stored in like conditions. These large chambers are typically walk-in rooms that are freezers, refrigerators, or warm rooms. The important design characteristics to take into account when generating project specifications are size and the desired temperature and/or humidity range that will need to be maintained whether the chamber is full or empty. Construction is performed on site and will include a turnover package detailing all the specifics of the installation and operation. A good turnover package will include much of the necessary information to complete the validation.

Off-the-shelf units are similar in size to a standard refrigerator or freezer and come with an owner's manual that details the installation and operation procedures. A good manual will contain most of the information needed for validation activities as well.

Installation Qualification

Instruction

This section describes the aspects of the Installation Qualification portion of validation.

Installation Qualification

The Installation Qualification is used to document that the equipment is properly installed per design and/or manufacturer's specifications. If the equipment is custom-built, the Installation Qualification will compare the client specifications with the actual as-built system. Examples of these are material, finish, NEMA rating, UL listing, and isolated ground. Additionally, the Installation Qualification is a survey of all process instrumentation, drawings, and manuals. Any required utilities would be verified at this time including, voltage supply, amperage rating of the supply circuit, fuses, circuit breaker identification, and liquid/gas supply pressures.

Installation Qualification is usually accomplished though the use of a standard template. This ensures that all equipment is qualified in a similar fashion.

Operational Qualification

Introduction

This section describes the aspects of the Operational Qualification portion of validation.

Operational Qualification

The Operational Qualification is documented verification that the system operates as intended through specified ranges, as well as alarm conditions. This documentation should include performance of the following checks on the system:

- Verify that all instruments and recording devices are calibrated.
- Verify proper unit operation for each system component.
- Verify operation of the defrost cycle, if applicable.
- Verify the length of time required for the system to recover from a temperature loss due to a door opening sequence.
- Verify proper humidity control in the chamber, if applicable.
- Verify operation of the back-up system, if applicable, by simulating power failure.
- Verify operation of system as a whole, recording chamber temperature and any other critical operating parameter for at least 24 hours. Verify each operating parameter for at least 24 hours. Verify that each operating parameter is within its specified range during the test period.
- Review associated standard operating procedures for completeness and applicability.

This qualification can also be performed using a standard template.

Temperature Mapping

Introduction

This section details the methods used for assuring acceptable temperature throughout a chamber.

Temperature Mapping

Temperature mapping consists of placing calibrated thermocouples within a chamber and monitoring temperature for a period of at least 24 hours to ensure reliability and consistency. Thermocouples are calibrated prior to use with an NIST traceable standard and can be done automatically using appropriate software. The thermocouples are connected to a Digistrip, which works in conjunction with the software, to collect the raw data and produce temperature distribution reports. The thermocouples are then placed throughout the chamber to cover as many different areas as is practical. A study is then initiated, though the software and the unit should remain untouched throughout the study. At the conclusion of the study, the thermocouples must go through a post-verification study to ensure that they have remained within the calibration limits. Acceptance criteria during the study usually consists of all thermocouples that are recording temperatures remaining within the acceptable range throughout the study.

Monitoring Controlled Temperature Chambers

Laboratory

Introduction   The purpose of this exercise is to instruct students on the use of the Digistrip for monitoring controlled temperature chambers.

Equipment   Kaye Digistrip
Thermocouples
Controlled temperature chamber

Activities at a Glance

1. Students will receive instruction on the function and use of the Digistrip.

2. Students will assist in the set up of the thermocouples. The initial monitoring will be performed with different students holding the thermocouples in their hands.

3. Discuss and analyze results from temperature measurements of students.

4. Select a controlled temperature chamber in the laboratory for monitoring.

Continuous Process Monitoring

Overview

Introduction   Continuous Process Monitoring (CPM) tracks the key output variables (those that indicate the quality of the process), as determined in validation studies, to show that those outputs are stable and by extension, that the process is stable. Validation studies are developed using "characterization" studies, which are based on the original research that developed the production process itself. This interdependence is shown in Figure 40.1 on page 3 of this document.

Table of Contents   This document contains the following topics:

Continuous Process Monitoring
Objectives

1. Define the following acronyms: CPM, EMP, DOE, and SPC.
2. Explain Process Characterization.
3. Explain Process Validation.
4. Explain Process Monitoring.
5. Describe the purpose of continuous process monitoring.
6. Explain why statistical tools are utilized throughout the process development cycle.
7. Define the following statistical tools: EMP, SPC, and DOE.
8. Describe how Process Monitoring uses SPC.
9. Describe the basic elements of Process Monitoring.
10. Define a unit operation.
11. Explain the two types of parameters in a process and their use.
12. Demonstrate the use of a Fishbone Diagram in evaluating a unit operation.
13. Explain what a histogram is and how it can be utilized to examine the process.
14. Explain what histograms indicate.
15. Demonstrate/explain how to build a histogram.
16. Explain normal distribution, standard deviation and average.
17. Explain whether or not histograms can show process stability.
18. Explain what a control chart is and describe its key parts.
19. Describe the use of control limits in control charts.
20. Distinguish between common cause variation and special cause variation.
21. Define run rules and explain which type of variability they are based on.
22. Give examples of the different types of control charts.
23. Describe how to create X Bar and R charts.
24. Explain what the FDA has to say about sampling.
25. Distinguish between average and range charts.
26. Explain the use of a table of control chart constants.
27. Demonstrate/explain how control limit calculations are performed.
28. Demonstrate construction of a control chart.
29. Explain the use of a special cause response matrix.
30. Explain the 6 M's of measurement.
31. Demonstrate ability to interpret control charts.
32. Identify which control rules are violated in a given chart.
33. Propose explanations of what is happening in the Process to cause the rule violation.
34. Distinguish between Preliminary Trending and Finalized Trending.
35. Discuss the questions to ask when considering a reset of control limits.

Role of Continuous Process Monitoring

Overview   The steps to bring a process from research to production include: characterization, validation, and monitoring, with CPM to maintain it and improve it. Figure 40.1 is an overview of the steps to bring a product to market and the statistical tools used to monitor the process at each stage. If root cause investigations (required when a process shows instability on control charts) lead to new knowledge of the process behavior, then changes may be implemented to reduce variation and put the process more "on target." This is process improvement. Root cause investigations may use such problem solving tools as brainstorming, cause and effect diagrams, process flow diagrams, histograms, regression, correlation, and creative use of control charts.

Research	Phase I / II Mfg.	Conformance Lots	Commercial
Process Development & Characterization		Process Validation	Continuous Process Monitoring
EMP, DOE, and SPC		DOE and SPC	SPC, Root Cause Analysis and DOE

Figure 40.1 Characterization, Validation, and Continuous Monitoring Including the Use of Statistical Tools.
EMP: Statistical Evaluation of the Quality of the Measurement Process;
SPC: Statistical Process Control;
DOE: Statistical Design of Experiments

Explanation of Terms

- <u>Process Characterization</u> uses experiments to develop a good understanding of the process variability, its stability, susceptibility to upsets and capabilities.

- <u>Process Validation</u> establishes documented evidence to provide a high degree of assurance that a specific process will consistently produce a product meeting its specifications and quality characteristics.

- <u>Continuous Process Monitoring</u> is the continuous confirmation that a process is stable and producing quality products within the defined control chart limits, as well as within product specifications.

- <u>Design of Experiments (DOE)</u> is the use of statistics to test many factors simultaneously for their simple and complex effects on the responses.

- <u>Statistical Process Control (SPC)</u> is the use of histograms and, especially, control charts to monitor the process data. Signs of instability on control charts represent opportunities to investigate and learn the cause(s), which will then enhance the success of preventive measures.

- <u>Evaluating the Measurement Process (EMP)</u> is the application of control charting to monitor the quality of measurements (precision and accuracy).

- <u>Control Charts</u> are graphs (usually with time-ordered data) used to detect situations showing "out of control" variation as opposed to the usual or "common cause" variation. Control charts may be called Shewhart Charts to recognize their original development by W.A. Shewhart. There are a variety of control charts each designed for specific types of data and process improvement needs. For example, control charts for measurements data (variables data) differ from control charts for counts data (attributes data).

- <u>Quality</u> is being on target with minimum variations

- <u>Stability</u> refers to a process having only common cause variation.

- <u>Capability</u> means that the process makes 99+% of product in specification.

Establishing Continuous Process Monitoring

Major Steps to Establish Continuous Process Monitoring

The following is a series of logical steps to show how a CPM plan can be put into place:

1. Process and Product Quality Indicating Variables. Choose:
   - Key variables that are direct indicators of process and product performance.
   - Troubleshooting parameters that provide insight into the performance of the process for the purpose of investigations.
   - Investigation-support parameters that temporarily require monitoring in order to complete a test or support an investigation.
2. Collect Data for the Above Variables and Set Up Control Charts
   - Choose the best measurement methods for the input and output variables.
   - Establish statistical control limits based on logical subgroups of data (subgroup size of n=1, if necessary, or greater if possible). Control charts for measurement data using n=1 are the least able to detect "out of control" situations.
3. Evaluate Results and Interpret the Control Charts for Patterns
   - Look for evidence of process instability using the control charts.
   - Set up investigation procedures to standardize responses to process out of control or instability. The goal is to learn to prevent process instability.
4. Determine Process Capability
   - Once a process is stable (predictable) based on the control charts, then determine its capability to make product within specification. If it does not have a very low "out of specification" rate, then find the major sources of variation (e.g. measurement variation, inherent process variation, or process drift), determine its root caus,e and correct or improve it.

Control Charts

Control Charts are the only tools that are able to detect process instabilities or out of control situations. If one is concerned about a process drifting or about data trending away from the target, control charts are the right tools to use. Control charts operate on the logic of letting the data show if there is instability. The control limits are based on measurements of common cause variation, usually short-term variation. Thus longer-term variation can be seen on the chart in comparison to the common cause variation, which is represented by the control limits themselves.

Planning and Communication

Introduction   With the broad perspective of a sequence of steps; 1. developing, establishing and characterizing a production process, 2. making conformance lots - documenting the process operation and 3. establishing a continuous monitoring procedure (as seen in Figure 40.1), the place for planning, communication, and data-based tools can be seen. Project management tools, including formalized documentation of the time schedule and the expected milestones, will establish support for the project and help with communications.

Project Management Tools   Understanding many statistical tools and having them ready to use is not sufficient. These tools must be logically and often sequentially used. If there is a team involved, then it is even more important to organize and communicate the process. This makes project management as important as statistical tools for process improvement.

A recommended tool for project management is time planning with identification of the critical path to completion. Determine rate limiting steps and anticipate possible project restrictions (constraints of time, money, resources).

Root Cause Investigations   Process improvement depends not only on knowing when to investigate but knowing how to investigate. Control charts indicate when to investigate by showing an out of control state. The methods of investigation depend on the type of out of control state, be it for "off target" or for "high variation." If off-target a search for an incorrect process setting is done. If the out of control is for excessive variation while still on target, a search for the reasons for short-term deviations or item-to-item problems as opposed to process trends is done. In all cases investigations should simultaneously check for measurement problems and for process problems.

Other investigation tools include fault tree analysis, critical control point failures, anticipated failure modes, and the tools of brainstorming.

Project Tools

Introduction   Popular tools of brainstorming (flow diagrams, cause and effect diagrams and nominal group techniques) greatly enhance communication among team members. The data-based tools (EMP, DOE, SPC, and histograms) tend to be intimidating, largely because they seem to rely on obscure or incomprehensible numerical methods. If the project goals are kept in mind, letting them drive the choice of methods, and if the process itself (be it a measurement or a production process) is allowed to dictate how it is best monitored (what subgroup structure etc.), then the huge number of statistical tools available need not be intimidating.

Brainstorming Tools   Some of the more commonly used tools include:
- Flow Diagrams to help conceptualize the process
- Cause and Effect Diagrams to record ideas in relation to the effect or problem
- Nominal Group Techniques to encourage idea generation and creative thinking

Data-based Tools   The data-based tools include:
- EMP (evaluating measurement systems using control charts)
- DOE (experimentation)
- SPC (control charts)
- Histograms (frequency distributions)

Continuous Process Monitoring Review

Review

Achieving Continuous Process Monitoring is valuable to the organization. CPM will help the company to maintain its processes in a validated condition and help to recognize when the process shows significant changes. The application of brainstorming, problem solving, and process improvement tools will help bring the process back to its validated condition if a change is noted in the control charts. The Quality goal is to minimize variation while keeping the process on target. CPM is a major process to achieve and maintain that goal.

SPC and Continuous Process Validation

Laboratory

Introduction	A variety of exercises will be performed to illustrate the concepts and techniques involved in SPC and continuous process validation. Each of these exercises are integrated into appropriate places of the lecture.

Materials and Supplies	Blank Fishbone Diagrams Samples of histograms Raw data for generating histograms Control Charts

Activities at a Glance	Exercise 1: Fishbone Diagrams 1. Students should be divided into small groups. 2. Students should decide on a unit operation to evaluate. 3. Brainstorm inputs that affect the unit operation and outputs that indicate performance. 4. Create a fishbone diagram based on the brainstorming using one of the outputs-effect. 5. Put asterisks on the parameters that have the biggest effect on the process.

Exercise 1: Fishbone Diagrams
1. Students should be divided into small groups.
2. Students should decide on a unit operation to evaluate.
3. Brainstorm inputs that affect the unit operation and outputs that indicate performance.
4. Create a fishbone diagram based on the brainstorming using one of the outputs-effect.
5. Put asterisks on the parameters that have the biggest effect on the process.

Exercise 2: Histograms Indicate What?
1. Examine the histograms on the sheet provided.
2. Answer the questions for each.

Exercise 3: Build a Histogram
1. Take the data provided and build a histogram
2. Describe the distribution.
3. Compare your histograms to those provided.

Exercise 4: Interpreting Control Charts
1. Students should look at the control chart generated and do the following:
   a. Identify which controls are violated.
   b. Explain what is happening in the Process to cause the rule violation.